MODULAR STUDY GUIDE FOR SECOND SEMESTER GENERAL CHEMISTRY (CHM 1046)

FOURTH EDITION

Marta E. Goicoechea-Pappas
Anthony J. Pappas

XanEdu
Change the course.

This document has been printed directly from the authors' electronic file.

Fourth Edition

For information, contact the authors at Miami Dade College, Chemistry Department, 11011 S.W. 104 St.; Miami, FL 33176.

Printed in the United States of America

10 9 8 7 6 5 4 3 2 1

ISBN 978-1-50669-551-8

XanEdu
530 Great Road
Acton, MA 01720
www.xanedu.com

PREFACE

The study of chemistry will provide you, the student, with the opportunity to study certain abstract concepts and to learn new problem-solving techniques necessary in understanding chemical phenomena.

We created this modular study guide with several purposes in mind:

1. To provide our students with a brief summary of those topics that are emphasized both in lecture and examinations. Each topic covered contains illustrative examples showing detailed set-ups.
2. To provide exercises and multiple choice practice exams similar in format to those used in examinations. The exercises and multiple choice practice exams are also intended to provide you, the student, with an opportunity to master the topics that are covered in each module. The exercises also show the variety of ways in which numerical problems may be asked, and the variety of pertinent definitions, notations, and symbolism that should be mastered.
3. To emphasize the importance of problem solving. No matter what your career goals are, learning how to solve problems is very important; with this in mind, many of the problems provided have been designed to stimulate your intellectual curiosity and to encourage analytical thinking.

We would like to acknowledge the contribution of many of our general chemistry students and colleagues (Larry Bray, Eileen Delgado Johann, Georgina C. Hart, Michael McGauley, and Maria E. Tarafa) who have given us feedback and corrections. We are more than willing to give consideration to any feedback; we thus welcome your comments as to the usefulness of this modular study guide, to any suggestions that you may have, and to any errors or ambiguities that we have inadvertently overlooked.

Marta E. Goicoechea-Pappas
Anthony J. Pappas

May 31, 2010

LIST OF MODULES AND APPENDICES

LIST OF APPENDICES

MODULE 1. *Liquids and Solids*

I. Gases, Liquids, and Solids

State	Volume/Shape	Density	Compressiblity	Motion
Gas	assumes shape & volume of container	Low	very compressible	T, R & V
Liquid	has definite volume but assumes shape of container	High	slightly compressible	T, R & V
Solid	has a definite shape & volume	High	virtually incompressible	V

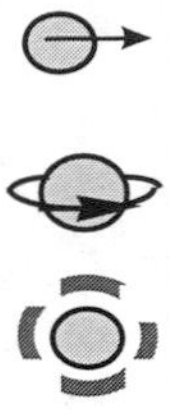

Translational motion involves movement from one place to another

Rotational motion causes a particle to turn or spin

Vibrational motion causes a particle to vibrate about the same point

A. Effect of Temperature and Pressure on Phase Transitions and Terminology

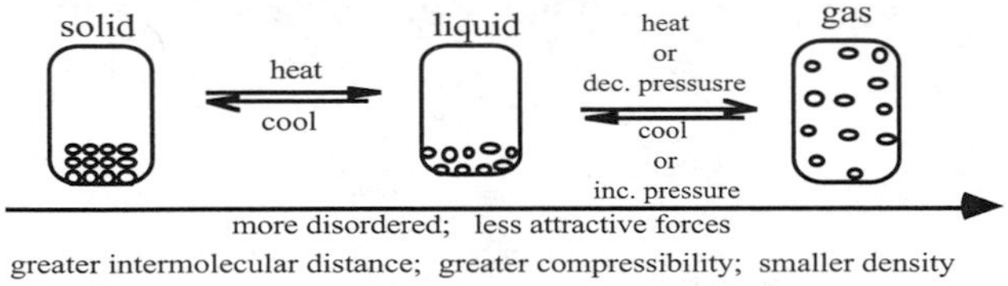

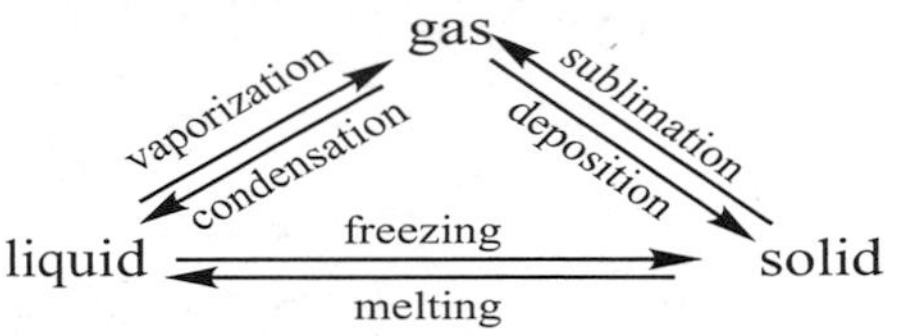

vaporization ~ evaporation ~ boiling   freezing ~ solidification ~ crystallization   melting ~ fusion

solid	liquid	gas
If T < mp/fp	If T is between mp/fp and bp/cp	If T > bp/cp

where, mp (melting point) = fp (freezing point)
bp (boiling point) = cp (condensation point)

II. Intermolecular Forces (IMF) [The word molecule generically applies to molecules, atoms, FUs, and ions]

Intramolecular Forces - Forces holding atoms (or ions) within molecules (or formula units) together -- a chemical bond.

Intermolecular Forces - Attractive force between molecules, atoms, and/or ions. *Intermolecular forces are relatively weak compared to intramolecular forces.*

$$H - \ddot{\underset{..}{O}} - H\ (g) \xrightarrow{920\ kJ/mol} 2\ H\bullet\ (g) + \bullet\ddot{\underset{..}{O}}\bullet (g) \quad \Big| \quad H_2O\ (l) \xrightarrow{41\ kJ/mol} H_2O\ (g)$$

Intramolecular Forces > Intermolecular Forces

For covalent compounds, IMF, as well as, the molar mass (MM) of a compound (or a non-metallic element) to a substantial degree, determines the physical state of a compound (or non-metallic element).

For covalent compounds and elements, the stronger the IMF is [also, the higher the molar mass (MM)], the higher its mp/fp and its bp/cp.

A. Ion-Ion Interactions

Ionic bonding may be thought of as having both intermolecular and intramolecular interactions.

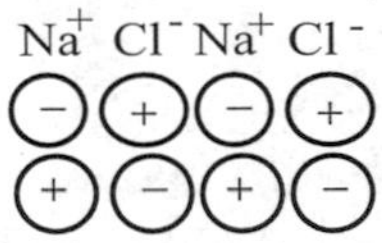

ion-ion interaction

Coulomb's Law gives the force (F → IMF) of attraction that exists between oppositely charged particles (q^+ and q^-) at a certain distance (d).

$$F \propto \frac{q^+ q^-}{d^2}$$

Most ionic bonding is strong, and as a result most ionic compounds are high melting solids.

Ionic substances with multiply charged ions (e.g., Al_2S_3 --- q is larger → IMF is greater) usually have higher mp and bp than those having singly charged ions (e.g., NaCl). When comparing compounds having ions with the same charge (e.g., MgO vs CaO), the compound having the ions with the smallest radii (d is smaller → IMF is greater) will usually have higher mp and bp.

Compound	mp (°C)
NaF	993
NaCl	801
KCl	770

Compound	mp (°C)
MgF_2	1261
Na_2S	1180
K_2S	840

Compound	mp (°C)
MgO	2800
CaO	2580
BaO	1923

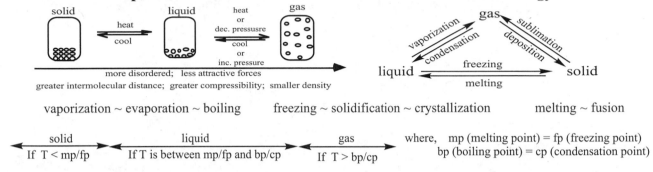

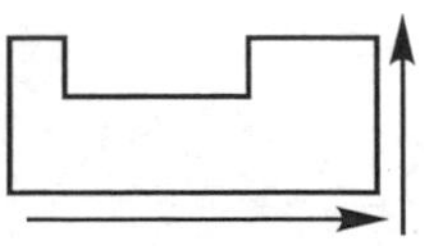

atomic radius (dec)

Example Problem:

1. Which is expected to have the highest mp: K_2S (MM = 110) or CaS (MM = 72.1)?

   CaS - For **ionic compounds** according to Coulomb's Law, the *higher the charge* on the ions (Ca^{2+} has a greater charge than K^+) and the *smaller their radii* (Ca^{2+} has a smaller radius than K^+) the *stronger the IMF* → the *higher the mp / fp (as well as, higher bp / cp).*

B. Hydrogen Bond [H-Bond]

A hydrogen bond occurs between the hydrogen atom in a polar bond such as H-F, O-H or N-H, and one of the following electronegative atoms F (EN = 4.0), O (EN = 3.5), or N (EN = 3.0) in another molecule. A hydrogen bond is a special, very strong case of a dipole-dipole interaction (discussed below). Dashed lines are used to represent intermolecular forces -- hydrogen bonding.

Examples of H-Bonding

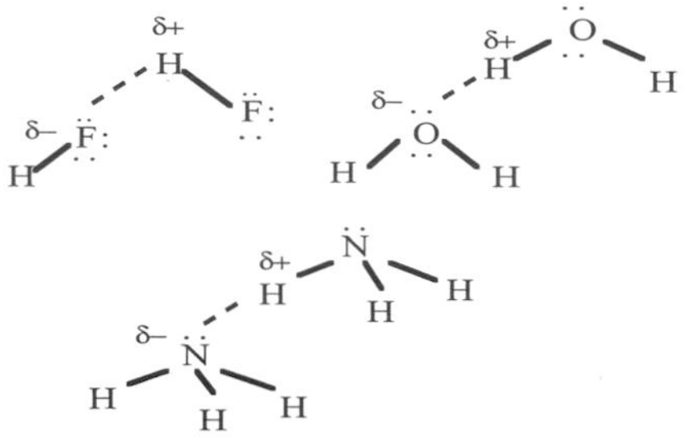

The following graph shows the anomaly in bp that occurs as a result of H-bonding.

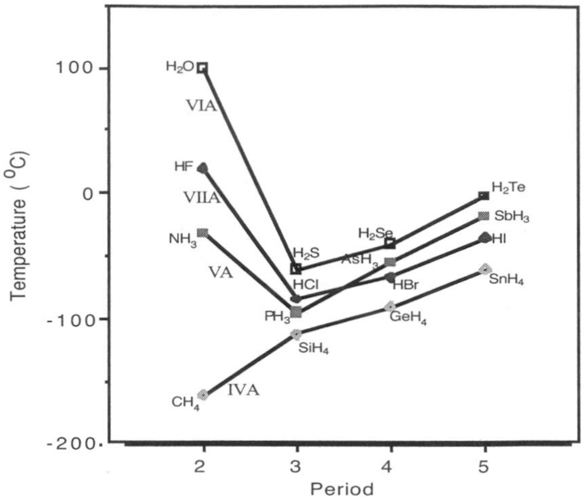

For covalent substances, their boiling point is expected to increase as we move down a group (due to increase in MM); however, three compounds (H_2O, HF, and NH_3) behave differently. The anomaly can be explained in terms of intermolecular hydrogen bonding.

C. Dipole-Dipole Interactions

Electrostatic in nature, molecules possessing dipoles exhibit dipole-dipole interactions. Molecules possessing large dipoles (large electronegativity differences among atoms in a covalent bond) have greater attraction for each other -- greater IMF. A hydrogen bond, discussed above can be considered as a super dipole-dipole interaction.

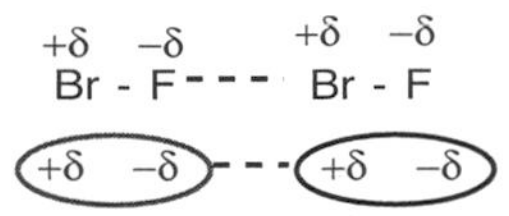

Dipole-dipole interactions are present in unsymmetrical compounds [i.e., binary compounds (e.g., BrF), compounds having one or more lone electron pair surrounding its central element (e.g., NBr_3, CH_3-O-CH_3) or compounds in which its surrounding elements are not the same (e.g. CH_2Cl_2)].

D. London Dispersion Forces (or van der Waals Forces)

London dispersion forces are typically weak attractive forces that are important only over extremely short distances. London dispersion forces exist for all types of molecules in condensed phases but are very weak for small molecules. For symmetrical compounds [i.e., compounds in which their central element has no lone pair of electrons and their surrounding atoms are the same (SO_3, BF_3, C_xH_y – hydrocarbons), diatomic elements (O_2, N_2, F_2, etc.) and most monatomic non-metals (He, Ar, etc.) they are the only kind of IMF.

London dispersion forces result from the attraction of the positively charged nucleus of one atom with the electron cloud of another nearby atom or molecule. The attraction induces a temporary dipole in the atom or molecule.

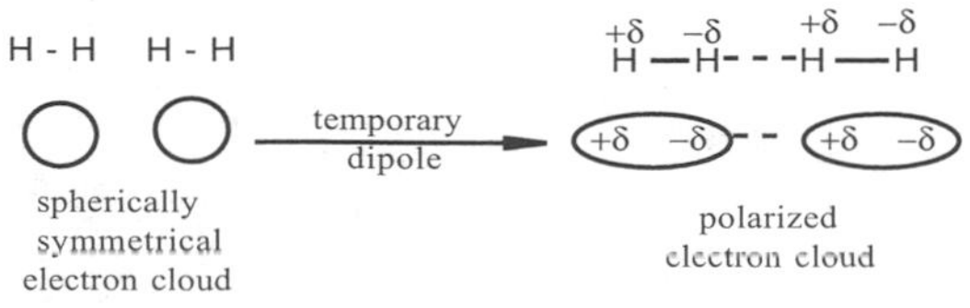

The larger the electron cloud (the larger the atom) the more easily distorted (polarized) a nuclei becomes; hence the larger the London dispersion force. *Basically, the larger the molar mass (MM) of a specie is, the greater its London dispersion force will be.*

E. Induced Dipoles [OPTIONAL]

The following are examples of temporary dipole induction [all are London dispersion forces, but some have specific "subnames" (i.e., ion-induced dipole and dipole-induced dipole)]:

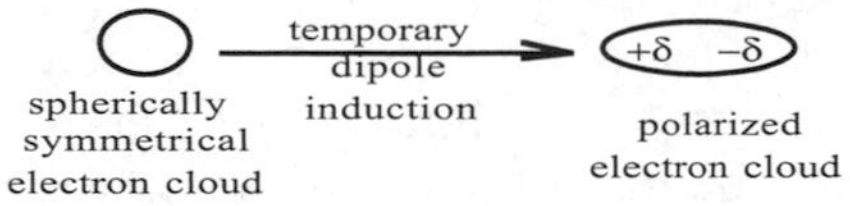

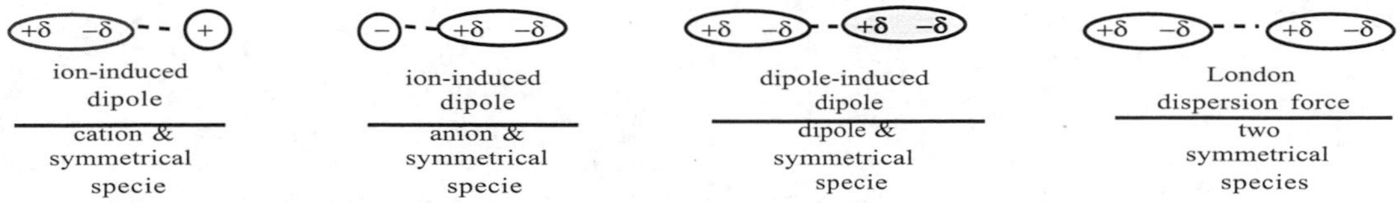

F. Relative Strength of Intermolecular Forces

ion-ion interactions > H-bonding > dipole-dipole > London Forces

With molecules possessing similar molar masses, the molecule possessing the stronger IMF will usually have the larger bp and fp. This is especially true when the IMF force is ion-ion or H-bonding.

With *covalent* molecules in which one of the atoms has been changed with another atom within the same group, the molecule having the larger molar mass will usually have the larger bp and fp *except when the IMF is hydrogen bonding*. Thus, NH_3 (IMF -- H-bonding) will have a higher bp and fp than PH_3 (IMF -- dipole-dipole) even though NH_3 has a smaller MM. However, AsH_3 will have a higher bp and fp than PH_3 because both have same IMF (dipole-dipole) and AsH_3 has a larger molar mass - the larger dispersion forces that result with the larger MM of AsH_3 overrides its decreasing permanent dipole-dipole intermolecular force.

Example Problems:

1. Give the strongest intermolecular force existing between the following: [OPTIONAL]

   a) NO_3^- and Br_2 - ion-induced dipole

   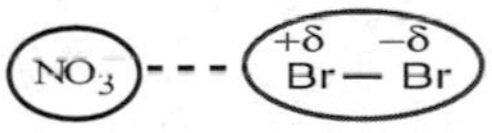

   b) NH_3 and $(CH_3)_2O$ - H-bonding $H_2N\text{-}H\text{----}O(CH_3)_2$

   c) HCl and HBr - dipole-dipole $\overset{\delta+\ \delta-}{\text{H-Cl}}\cdots\cdots\overset{\delta+\ \delta-}{\text{H-Br}}$

   d) HCl and He - dipole-induced dipole

   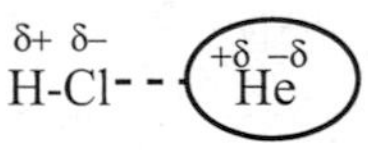

2. Which of the following is expected to have the highest boiling point?

   a) CH_3-O-H or CH_3-S-H

      CH_3-O-H -- Although normally we expect the boiling point to increase as we move down a group (due to an increase in MM) CH_3-O-H has intermolecular H-bonding which is a stronger IMF than the dipole-dipole IMF existing in CH_3-S-H.

   b) $CH_3(CH_2)_2CH_2OH$ (l) or HBr (g)

      $CH_3(CH_2)_2CH_2OH$ -- Although both have similar MM (74 & 80), $CH_3(CH_2)_2CH_2OH$ has H-bonding which is a stronger IMF than the dipole-dipole IMF existing in HBr.

   c) LiCl or Rn

      LiCl -- Although Rn has a much larger MM, LiCl has ion-ion interactions which is a much stronger force than the London dispersion forces existing in Rn.

d) CH_3F or CH_3Cl

CH_3Cl -- Both have dipole-dipole as their strongest IMF; when one atom has been replaced with another atom within the same family, the molecule having the larger MM is expected to have the greater bp.

III. The Liquid State

A. Vapor Pressure (P^o) & Boiling Point (bp)

Vapor pressure (P^o) is defined as the partial pressure of vapor molecules above the surface of the liquid under the dynamic equilibrium condition of condensation and evaporation. At the boiling point (condensation point), both the liquid and vapor (gas) phases are existing in equilibrium with each other.

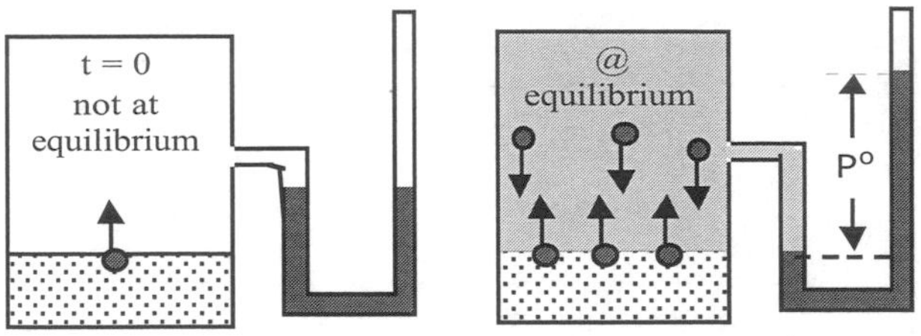

Vapor Pressure
The pressure exerted by the vapor above a liquid; it is measured at equilibrium in a closed system when rate of vaporization = rate of condensation

The lower the vapor pressure, the higher the bp, the stronger the IMF.

With liquids having similar molar masses, the substance having the stronger intermolecular force (IMF) will have the lower vapor pressure and higher boiling point. The vapor pressure of a liquid *always* increases as the temperature increases.

<u>Vapor Pressure vs. Temperature Diagram</u>

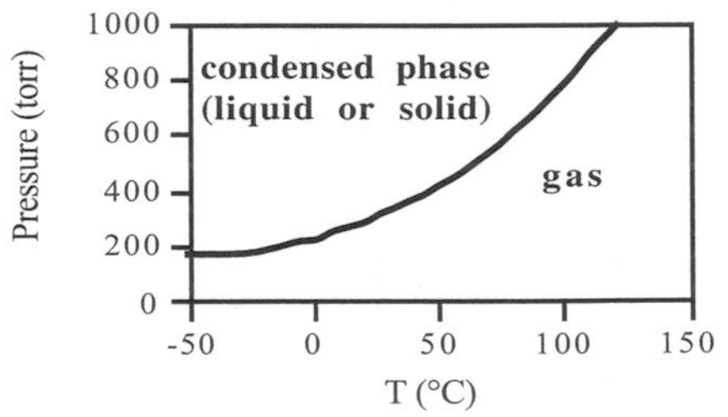

The diagram to the right illustrates the relationship between vapor pressure and temperature. Points along the "line" show the temperatures and pressures where the liquid (or solid) and gas are in equilibrium with each other. At temperatures and pressures to the right and below the "line", the substance exists as a gas; whereas, at temperatures to the left and pressures above of the "line", the substance exists in a condensed phase (liquid or solid).

Boiling Point (bp) is defined as the temperature at which the vapor pressure of the liquid is equal to the applied pressure.

The *Normal Boiling Point* is defined as the temperature at which the vapor pressure of the liquid is equal to one atmosphere (or 760 torr = 760 mm Hg) of pressure .

<u>Example Problems</u>: *(Refer to the vapor pressure v. for Example Problems: 1 - 4)*

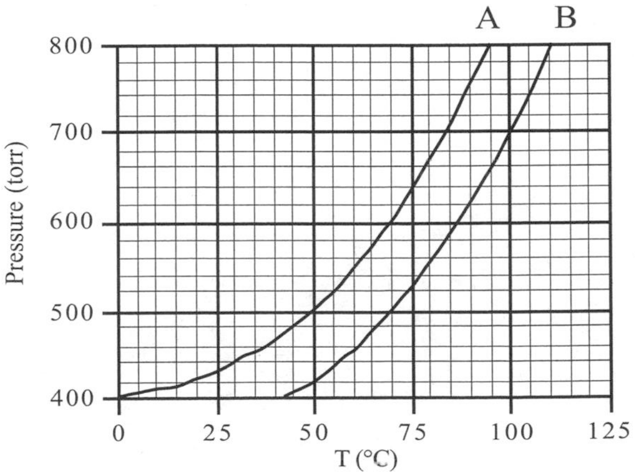

1. If A and B have a similar molar mass, which has the strongest IMF?

   B because at any given temperature, it has the lowest vapor pressure.

2. What is the normal bp of A?

   90°C [Normal bp is the temp at which the vapor pressure is equal to 1 atm (760 torr).]

3. What is the vapor pressure of B at 50°C?

   420 torr

4. What is the physical state of B at 75°C and 50(

   Gas, this temperature is to the right and the p

5. Which is expected to have the highest vapor pressure CH_3-CH_2-OH or CH_3-O-CH_3?

   CH_3OCH_3 - both have the same molar mass; however, CH_3OCH_3 has the weaker intermolecular force (dipole-dipole) vs. CH_3-CH_2-OH which can H-bond.

B. **Other Properties of Liquids**

1. Molecules that are liquids have less kinetic energy than those in the gas state; in the liquid state the attractive forces keep the molecules close, but not in a fixed position (as in the solid state).
2. For liquids as the temperature increases, the molecules move faster - expansion occurs for most liquids - the volume increases, and hence the density decreases (d = m/V). Galileo's thermometer ingeniously uses the expansion of liquids and floating spheroids to measure temperature. The density of each spheroid has been adjusted to exactly correspond to the density of the supporting liquid at certain designated temperatures.

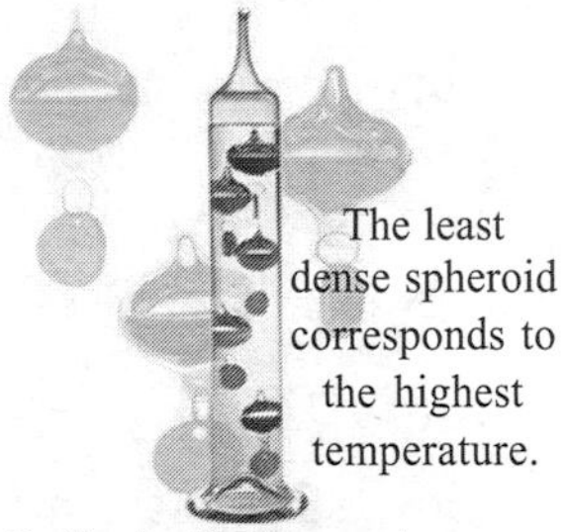

Galileo's Thermometer

3. The rate of diffusion for liquids is less than that for gases, for the mean free path is less. The mean free path is the average distance the molecule travels between collisions.

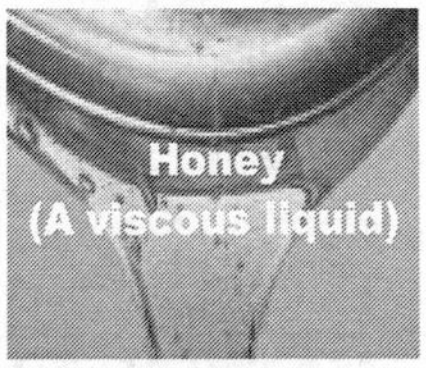

4. The viscosity of liquids depends on the strength of intermolecular attractive forces (viscous liquids have stronger IMF) and on the sizes & shapes of the particles. *Viscosity* is defined as the resistance to flow of a liquid. Honey has a high viscosity vs. water, which is free flowing and thus has a lower viscosity. As the temperature increases, viscosity decreases.
5. Those molecules on the surface of a liquid experience different attractive forces than those molecules not on the surface. Surface molecules are attracted more by the liquid beneath than to the vapor molecules above; whereas, the attractive forces for non-surface molecules is the same in all directions. *Surface tension* is the energy required to increase the surface area of a liquid by a unit amount. Molecules with strong IMF have high surface tensions. The more stable situation is one in which there is minimal surface area. Since a sphere has the least possible surface area, liquids tend to assume spherical shapes especially when they are in small droplets. As the droplet size gets larger, droplets tend to flatten out due to the effects of gravity.

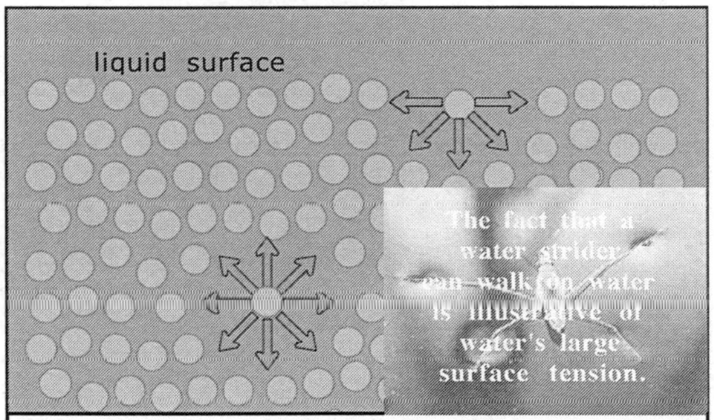

A molecule within the bulk of a liquid experiences attractions to neighboring molecules in all directions, but since these average out to zero, there is no net force on the molecule. For a molecule at the surface, the situation is quite different; it experiences forces only sideways and downward, and this is what creates the stretched-membrane effect which resists deformation when small weights are placed on it.

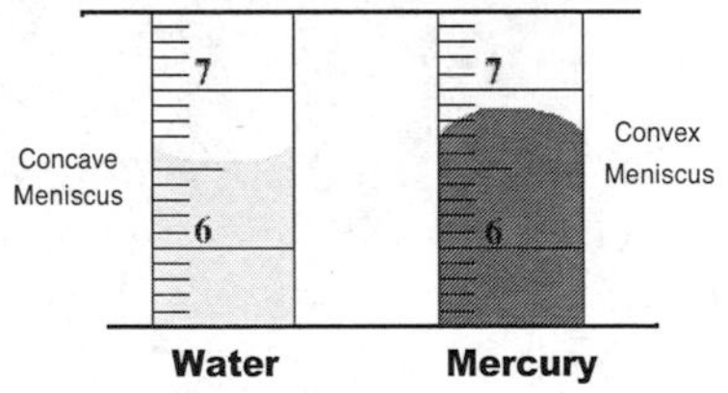

6. Water not only sticks to itself, but also to other surfaces. This allows water to move against gravity, which is very important to plants when transporting water from the soil to its leaves. This upward motion is known as *capillary action*. There are two types of forces (cohesive and adhesive) responsible for the type of meniscus displayed by water and mercury. *Cohesive forces* are intermolecular forces between liquid molecules; whereas, *adhesive forces* are intermolecular forces between the liquid and the container it is in. For mercury, its cohesive forces are greater than its adhesive forces and thus a convex meniscus results. Water experiences favorable adhesive forces with the glass (which is polar). Water creeps up the sides of the glass and forms a concave meniscus.

IV. The Solid State

A. Melting Point, Freezing Point, & Vapor Pressure

The melting point (mp) or freezing point (fp) is the temperature at which both solid and liquid phase exist in equilibrium. mp = fp.

In contrast to a substance's bp, its mp/fp is not affected by small (~ 20 torr) pressure changes.

Normal Melting Point - the melting point of the solid at a pressure of 1 atmosphere (760 torr).

Normal Freezing Point - the freezing point of the liquid at a pressure of 1 atmosphere (760 torr).

As cooling occurs, molecular motion slows down. Once the molecules slow down enough, the intermolecular attractive forces cause the molecules to go into fix lattice positions; causing solidification to take place.

Just as liquids, solids also have a vapor pressure, except they are much lower in value.

B. Crystalline & Amorphous Solids

Crystalline solids are those solids that are arranged in an orderly array (crystal lattices). Amorphous solids do not have a continuous orderly array (examples: tars & glass).

Crystal Type	Particles Occupying Lattice Sites	Attractive Forces	Examples	Properties
Ionic	Positive & Negative Ions	Electrostatic Attraction	NaCl, $CaCl_2$, $NaNO_3$	Hard; high mp; brittle; nonconductors as solids, but conductors when melted
Molecular	Atoms or Molecules	Hydrogen bond dipole-dipole London forces	H_2O (s) HCl (s) Ar (s), N_2 (s)	Soft; low mp; non-conductors in solid and liquid phase
Covalent (Network)	Atoms	Covalent bonds between atoms (one giant covalent molecule)	C, B and Si SiC (silicon carbide) SiO_2 (sand, quartz)	Very hard; **very high mp**; nonconductors [exception: $C_{(graphite)}$ is a conductor]
Metallic	Positive Ions "in a sea of electrons"	Attraction between positive ions and electron cloud that extends throughout crystal	Cu, Ag, Fe (all metals)	Range from very hard (e.g., W) to very soft (e.g., Au); mp range from high (e.g., W, mp >3000°C) to very low (e.g., Hg, mp = -39°C); conductors in both solid & liquid phase

V. Heat Transfer (ΔH_{fus}, ΔH_{sol}, ΔH_{vap}, & ΔH_{cond})

Chemical reactions and physical changes occur with either the simultaneous evolution of heat (*exothermic process*) or the absorption of heat (*endothermic process*). The amount of heat transferred in a process is usually expressed in *calories (cal)* or in the SI unit of *joules (J)*.

$$1 \text{ cal} = 4.184 \text{ J}$$

Specific heat is defined as the amount of heat necessary to raise the temperature of 1 g of substance by 1°C. Each substance has a specific heat, which is a physical intensive property, like density and melting point. From a knowledge of a subtance's specific heat, the heat (q) that is absorbed or released in a given process can be calculated by use of the following equation.

$$q = m \times s \times \Delta T$$

q (heat energy) $\rightarrow$ cal, kcal, J, or kJ

m (mass) $\rightarrow$ g

s (specific heat) $\rightarrow \dfrac{\text{cal}}{\text{g} \cdot {}^\circ\text{C}}$ (kcal, J, or kJ can be used in lieu of cal)

$\Delta T = T_2 - T_1$ (change in temp - make ΔT a positive #) $\rightarrow$ °C

An assumption is made that the specific heat of a substance is temperature independent while the substance is in the same phase.

Substances with large specific heats require more heat to raise their temperature. Water has one of the highest specific heats, 1.00 cal / g °C. The high specific heat of water (which constitutes ~60% of our body weight) makes our body's task of maintaining a constant body temperature of ~37°C much easier. Thus, our body has the ability to absorb or release considerable amounts of energy with little change in temperature.

substance	water	wood	gold	graphite
specific heat (cal / g °C)	1.00	0.421	0.0306	0.172

Heat of fusion (q_{fus}) - the heat that must be added to one gram of solid (at its melting point) to convert it to liquid with no change in temperature.

Molar heat of fusion (ΔH_{fus}) - the heat that must be added to one mole of solid (at its melting point) to convert it to liquid with no change in temperature.

Heat of solidification (q_{sol}) - the heat that is released when one gram of liquid (at its freezing point) is converted to solid with no change in temperature.

Molar heat of solidification (ΔH_{sol}) - the heat that is released when one mole of liquid (at its freezing point) is converted to solid with no change in temperature.

$$q_{fus} = -q_{sol} \quad \text{or} \quad \Delta H_{fus} = -\Delta H_{sol}$$

Heat of vaporization (q_{vap}) - the heat that must be added to one gram of liquid (at its boiling point) to convert it to vapor with no change in temperature.

Molar heat of vaporization (ΔH_{vap}) - the heat that must be added to one mole of liquid (at its boiling point) to convert it to vapor with no change in temperature.

Heat of condensation (q_{cond}) - the heat that is released when one gram of vapor (at its condensation point) is converted to liquid with no change in temperature.

Molar heat of condensation (ΔH_{cond}) - the heat that is released when one mole of vapor (at its condensation point) is converted to liquid with no change in temperature.

$$q_{vap} = -q_{cond} \quad \text{or} \quad \Delta H_{vap} = -\Delta H_{cond}$$

Table 1. Molar Heat of Fusion and Vaporization of Selected Substances

Substance	bp (°C)	ΔH_{vap} (kJ/mol)	fp (°C)	ΔH_{fus} (kJ/mol)
Ar	-186	6.3	-190	1.3
CH_4	-164	9.2	-183	0.84
CH_3CH_2-O-CH_2CH_3	34.6	26.0	-116.2	6.90
CH_3CH_2OH	78.3	39.3	-117.3	7.61
H_2O	100	40.7	0	6.01

As can be seen from Table 1, that as the intermolecular force increases, ΔH_{vap} increases. This is so because the stronger the intermolecular force is, the more difficult it is for a liquid to escape into the vapor phase.

Also, as can be seen from Table 1, $\Delta H_{vap} > \Delta H_{fus}$. This is so because molecules in the liquid phase are more attracted to each other (closer together) than gaseous molecules, hence it requires a greater amount of energy to convert a liquid into a gas. Less energy is required to convert a solid into a liquid because upon going from the solid to the liquid phase, the liquid molecules are not that separated from each other relative to the solid phase.

There is a quantitative relationship that exists between vapor pressure and temperature. This relationship can be obtained by using the *Clasius-Claperyon equation* [**ENRICHMENT - OPTIONAL**].

$$\ln\left(\frac{P_2}{P_1}\right) = \frac{\Delta H_{vap}}{R}\left(\frac{1}{T_1} - \frac{1}{T_2}\right)$$

[NOTE: The energy units for R (i.e., the units on top) must match those for ΔH_{vap} and T must be in K]

$$R = 0.0821\,\frac{\text{L·atm}}{\text{mol·K}} = 1.99 \times 10^{-3}\,\frac{\text{kcal}}{\text{mol·K}} = 1.99\,\frac{\text{cal}}{\text{mol·K}} = 8.31 \times 10^{-3}\,\frac{\text{kJ}}{\text{mol·K}} = 8.31\,\frac{\text{J}}{\text{mol·K}}$$

The heating curve below illustrates the changes in state of matter as a function of temperature and amount of heat added.

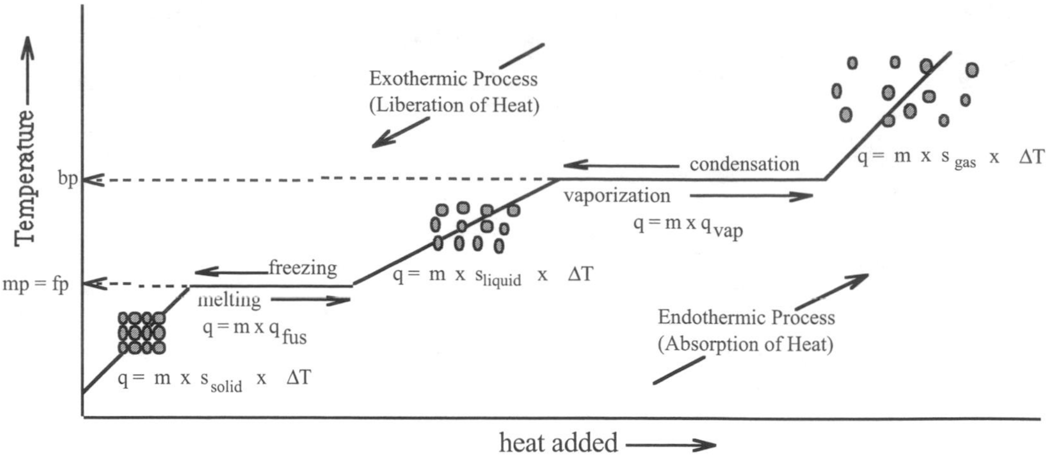

As heat energy is added to the solid at a constant rate, the temperature rises at a constant rate according to the specific heat of the solid, and its kinetic energy also rises. Eventually enough heat is added so that the solid begins to melt. At this point, the solid and liquid are in dynamic equilibrium, and further addition of heat (heat of fusion) does *not* change the temperature, but serves only to change the state of the substance from solid to liquid. This energy breaks some of the attractive forces between particles in the solid state and conversion to the liquid state is possible due to increase freedom of movement.

After all the solid has been changed to liquid, if heat is added at a constant rate, the temperature rises at a constant rate according to the specific heat of the liquid, and its kinetic energy also rises. Eventually, enough heat is added so that the liquid begins to vaporize. At this point, the liquid and vapor are in dynamic equilibrium, and further addition of heat (heat of vaporization) does *not* change the temperature, but serves only to change the state of the substance from liquid to gas. This energy breaks some of the attractive forces between particles in the liquid state and conversion to the gas state is possible due to increase freedom of movement.

Example Problems:

1. If the molar heat of fusion for water is 6.01 kJ/mol, then what is its molar heat of solidification?
   -6.01 kJ/mol (ΔH_{fus} of a solid is equal in magnitude but opposite in sign to ΔH_{sol} of a liquid)

2. Arrange the following in order of increasing ΔH_{vap}: SiO_2, CCl_4, NH_3
   CCl_4 (London) < NH_3 (H-bonding) < SiO_2 (covalent network - see section of crystalline solids)

3. What is the relationship that exists between ΔH_{vap}, bp, and vapor pressure?
   The larger the ΔH_{vap} is (the more energy that is required to convert a liquid into a gas), the greater the boiling point will be, and the lower the vapor pressure will be.

4. Insert the following -- NH_3, H_2, 0.028, 5.581 -- into the appropriate blanks below:

substance	ΔH_{vap} (kcal/mol)	ΔH_{fus} (kcal/mol)
1.	0.216	
2.		1.351

   Remember that $\Delta H_{vap} > \Delta H_{fus}$; therefore, ΔH_{fus} for substance 1 must be 0.028 kcal/mol and ΔH_{vap} for substance 2 must be 5.581 kcal/mol. The stronger the IMF is, the larger the ΔH_{vap}; therefore, substance 1 is H_2 and substance 2 is NH_3.

5. The molar heat of fusion, ΔH_{fus}, of naphthalene (MM = 128) at its melting point, 80°C, is 18,816 J/mol. How much heat (in J) must be absorbed by 3.00 g of naphthalene at 80°C to convert it into a liquid?

$$? J = 3.00 \text{ g naphthalene} \left(\frac{1 \text{ mol naphthalene}}{128 \text{ g naphthalene}}\right)\left(\frac{18816 \text{ J}}{1 \text{ mol naphthalene}}\right) = 441 \text{ J}$$

6. The molar heat of vaporization, ΔH_{vap}, of ethyl alcohol at its normal boiling point (78.3°C) is 39.3 kJ/mol. What is the vapor pressure (in torr) of ethyl alcohol at 60°C? **[OPTIONAL]**

$$\ln\left(\frac{P_2}{P_1}\right) = \frac{\Delta H_{vap}}{R}\left(\frac{1}{T_1} - \frac{1}{T_2}\right)$$

$$\ln\left(\frac{P_2}{760 \text{ torr}}\right) = \frac{39.3 \frac{kJ}{mol}}{8.31 \times 10^{-3} \frac{kJ}{mol \cdot K}}\left(\frac{1}{351 \text{ K}} - \frac{1}{333 \text{ K}}\right)$$

$$\ln P_2 - \ln(760) = 4.73 \times 10^3 (2.85 \times 10^{-3} - 3.00 \times 10^{-3})$$

$$\ln P_2 = -0.71 + 6.63 \quad \rightarrow \quad P_2 = e^{5.92} = 372 \text{ torr}$$

7. Calculate the amount of heat that must be absorbed by 50.0 g of ice at -12.0°C to convert it to water at 20.0°C. $s_{ice} = 2.09$ J/g·°C, $s_{water} = 4.18$ J/g·°C, $q_{fus} = 333$ J/g, $MM_{water} = 18.0$ g/mol.

ice, -12°C $\xrightarrow[\text{step 1}]{q = m \times s_{ice} \times \Delta T}$ ice, 0°C $\xrightarrow[\text{step 2}]{q = m \times q_{fus, ice}}$ water, 0°C $\xrightarrow[\text{step 3}]{q = m \times s_{water} \times \Delta T}$ water, 20°C

Step 1: $q = m \times s_{ice} \times \Delta T = (50.0 \text{ g}) \times (2.09 \text{ J/g °C}) \times [0.0 - (-12.0)]°C = 1.25 \times 10^3$ J

Step 2: $q = m \times q_{fus} = 50.0 \text{ g} \left(\frac{333 \text{ J}}{1 \text{ g}}\right) = 1.66 \times 10^4$ J

Step 3: $q = m \times s_{water} \times \Delta T = (50.0 \text{ g}) \times (4.18 \text{ J/g °C}) \times (20.0 - 0)°C = 4.18 \times 10^3$ J

$q_{tot} = q_{step 1} + q_{step 2} + q_{step 3}$ $= 2.21 \times 10^4$ J

8. a) Calculate the amount of heat (in J) that must be absorbed when 40.0 g of ice at -15.0°C is converted to steam at 135°C.
$s_{ice} = 2.09$ J/g·°C, $s_{water} = 4.18$ J/g·°C, $s_{steam} = 2.03$ J/g·°C, $q_{fus} = 333$ J/g, $q_{vap} = 2.26 \times 10^3$ J/g, $MM_{water} = 18.0$ g/mol.

ice, -15°C $\xrightarrow[\text{step 1}]{q = m \times s_{ice} \times \Delta T}$ ice, 0°C $\xrightarrow[\text{step 2}]{q = m \times q_{fus, ice}}$ water, 0°C $\xrightarrow[\text{step 3}]{q = m \times s_{water} \times \Delta T}$ water, 100°C

steam, 135°C $\xleftarrow[\text{step 5}]{q = m \times s_{steam} \times \Delta T}$ steam, 100°C $\xleftarrow[\text{step 4}]{q = m \times q_{vap, water}}$

Step 1: $q = m \times s_{ice} \times \Delta T = (40.0 \text{ g}) \times (2.09 \text{ J/g °C}) \times [0.0 - (-15.0)]°C = 1.25 \times 10^3$ J

Step 2: $q = m \times q_{fus} = 40.0 \text{ g} \left(\frac{333 \text{ J}}{1 \text{ g}}\right) = 1.33 \times 10^4$ J

Step 3: $q = m \times s_{water} \times \Delta T = (40.0 \text{ g}) \times (4.18 \text{ J/g °C}) \times (100 - 0)°C = 1.67 \times 10^4$ J

Step 4: $q = m \times q_{vap} = 40.0 \text{ g steam} \left(\frac{2.26 \times 10^3 \text{ J}}{1 \text{ g}}\right) = 9.04 \times 10^4$ J

Step 5: $q = m \times s_{steam} \times \Delta T = (40.0 \text{ g}) \times (2.03 \text{ J/g °C}) \times (135 - 100)°C = 2.84 \times 10^3$ J

$q_{tot} = q_{step 1} + q_{step 2} + q_{step 3} + q_{step 4} + q_{step 5}$ $= 1.24 \times 10^5$ J

b) How much heat must be transferred when 40.0 g of steam at 135°C is converted to ice at -15°C.

Since this is the reverse of the process occurring in question 8a, $q = -1.24 \times 10^5$ J; that is 1.24×10^5 J of energy must be removed from the steam @ 135°C to convert it to ice @ -15°C.

VI. Heat Transfer Involving Mixing Of Phases [OPTIONAL]

If a hot object is dropped into a cold object or vice-versa, then the heat given up by the hot object to the cold object can be expressed as follows: [Note: object → solid, liquid, or gas]

heat lost by hot object (q_{lost} or q_{hot}) = heat gained by cold object (q_{gained} or q_{cold})

Example Problems:

1. If 8.50 g of ice at -10.0°C is mixed with 50.0 g of water at 65.0°C, what will the final temperature be?

$s_{ice} = 2.09$ J/g · °C, $s_{water} = 4.18$ J/g · °C, $q_{fus} = 333$ J/g, $MM_{water} = 18.0$ g/mol

$$q_{hot,\ water} = q_{cold,\ ice}$$

$$m \times s_{water} \times \Delta T = m \times s_{ice} \times \Delta T + m \times q_{fus} + m \times s_{water} \times \Delta T$$

$$(50.0\text{ g})\ (4.18\text{ J/g °C})\ (65.0 - T_f) = (8.50\text{ g})\ (2.09\text{ J/g °C})\ (0 - (-10)\text{°C}) + (8.50\text{ g})\ (333\text{ J/g}) + (8.50\text{ g})\ (4.18\text{ J/g °C})\ (T_f - 0)$$

$$13585 - 209\ T_f = 178 + 2830 + 35.53\ T_f$$

$$10577 = 244.53\ T_f$$

$$T_f = 43.3\text{°C}$$

VII. Phase Diagrams

A phase diagram shows equilibrium temperature-pressure relationships for different phases of a substance. [NOTE: The dashed lines on Phase Diagram 1, have been included strictly as a guide to help do the example problems below.]

Curve AB (sublimation/deposition curve) represents the solid-gas equilibrium conditions. Points along the curve represent the temperature-pressure combinations for which the solid and gas are coexisting in equilibrium.

Curve BC (vapor pressure or vapor/liquid curve) represents the liquid-gas equilibrium conditions. Points along the curve represent the temperature-pressure combinations for which the liquid and gas are coexisting in equilibrium.

Line BD (melting/freezing curve) represents the solid-liquid equilibrium conditions. Points along this line represent the temperature-pressure combinations for which the solid and liquid are coexisting in equilibrium. Note that line BD in Phase Diagram 1 has a negative slope. Water is one of the very few substances in which this is the case. This kind of negative slope means that an increase in pressure, causes a drop in the melting point.

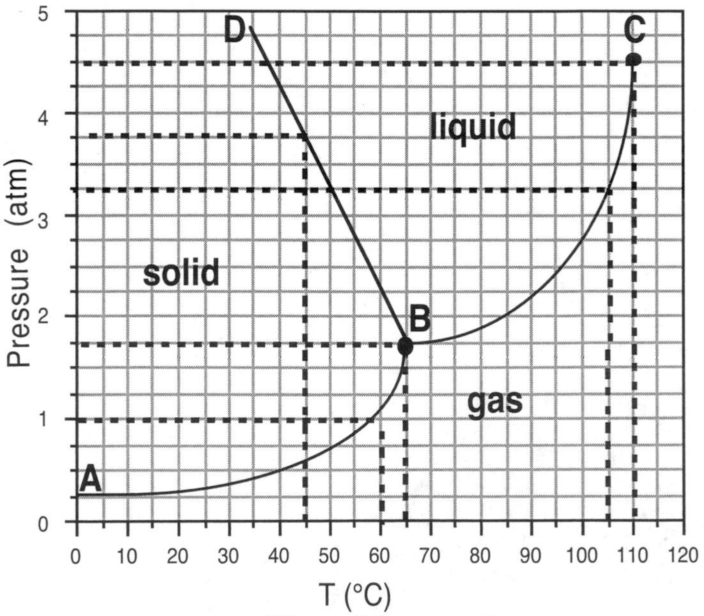

Phase Diagram 1

There is only one point (*triple point*), B, at which all three phases (solid, liquid, & gas) can coexist at equilibrium. At pressures below the triple point pressure, the liquid phase is not stable; rather the substance goes from the solid to gas (sublimes) or the reverse (a solid deposits from the gas).

The critical temperature and pressure occurs at point C (*critical point*). The *critical temperature* is the temperature above which a gas cannot be liquified. The *critical pressure* is the pressure required to liquefy a gas at its critical temperature. A substance at a temperature above its critical temperature and critical pressure is called a *supercritical fluid.*

Example Problems: *(Refer to Phase Diagram 1 in the previous page)*

1. What is the normal boiling point of the substance?

   This substance does not have a normal bp because at 1 atm the only phase change that occurs is that between solid→ gas (sublimation) or gas → solid (deposition). The normal sublimation/deposition point occurs at 60°C

2. What is the melting point of the substance at 3.75 atm of pressure?

   Line BD is the melting/freezing line, at 3.75 atm, the melting point would be 45°C.

3. At what temperature and pressure do all three phases exist at equilibrium?

   At point B the triple point, which occurs at T = 65°C & P = 1.75 atm.

4. At what temperature and pressure does the critical point occur?

   At T = 110°C & P = 4.5 atm.

5. What is the vapor pressure of the substance at 105°C?

   Curve BC is the vapor pressure curve; at 105°C the vapor pressure is equal to 3.25 atm.

6. How many phases and/or phase mixtures can exist at a temperature of 105°C?

   3 (gas, gas-liquid, and liquid).
   [To answer this question, start at a pressure of 0 atm and a temperature of 105°C, while proceeding upwards (constant T of 105°C and increasing pressures) count the number of different phases and phase mixtures that occur until you reach the top of the graph.]

7. How many phases and/or phase mixtures can exist at a pressure of 3.25 atm?

   5 (solid, solid-liquid, liquid, liquid-gas, and gas).
   [To answer this question, start at the lowest temperature given in the graph (0°C in this case) and a pressure of 3.25 atm, while proceeding to the right (constant P of 3.25 atm and increasing temperatures) count the number of different phases and phase mixtures that occur until you reach the end of the graph.]

8. What phase or phase mixture is existing at T = 40°C and P = 1.75 atm?

   solid

9. At what pressures is the liquid phase nonexistent?

   At any pressure below the triple point (1.75 atm).

10. At a temperature of 110°C, what pressure is required to liquefy the gas?

    4.5 atm (the critical pressure, 4.5 atm, is the pressure required to liquefy a gas at its critical temperature, 110°C).

11. At what temperatures and pressures will the substance exist as a supercritical fluid?

    T > 110°C (critical temperature) and P > 4.5 atm (critical pressure).

12. What happens to the melting point of the substance as its pressure is decreased?

    it increases (a negative slope for the melting/freezing line [BD] indicates that a decrease in pressure causes an increase in the melting point).

EXERCISES

Gases, Liquids, & Solids

1. Fill in the following blanks:
   a) The application of heat converts a ________ into a liquid. (solid or gas)
   b) A(n) _________ in pressure converts a gas into a liquid. (increase or decrease)
   c) _________ converts a liquid into a solid. (Heating or Cooling)
   d) The phase transition from the gaseous state to the liquid state is called _______.
   e) The phase transition from the liquid state to the solid state is called _________.
   f) The phase transition from the solid state to the liquid state is called _________.

2. Which of the following phase transitions requires the input of energy (i.e., is endothermic)?
   a) solid → liquid b) solid → gas c) liquid → gas d) gas → solid

3. Given the followng melting point and boiling point information, what physical state would each of the following substances be in under each of the following conditions:
   A. CF_4 (mp = -184°C, bp = -128°C) B. CCl_4 (mp = -23°C, bp = 77°C)
   C. $Fe(CO)_5$ (mp = -21°C, bp =105°C) D. Ga (mp = 30°C, bp = 2403°C)

   a) At 25°C (P = 760 torr) -- typical laboratory conditions
   b) At 100°C (P = 760 torr)
   c) At -50°C (P = 760 torr)

Intermolecular Forces

4. List the strongest intermolecular force that exists between the molecules, atoms, or ions in each of the following.
   a) NaCl b) HBr c) HF d) F_2 e) CH_3OH f) $SiCl_4$
   g) $CHCl_3$ h) $FeCl_3$ i) CH_3NH_2 j) PBr_3 k) CH_4 l) He
   m) Br_2 n) $AsCl_3$ o) NH_4OH

5. The following substances are known to possess dipole-dipole interactions as the strongest IMF. Substance A is a solid, B is a liquid, and C is a gas. Arrange the substances in order of increasing dipole-dipole interaction.

6. ICl and Br_2 have almost the same molar mass yet ICl has a melting point equal to 27°C and Br_2 has a melting point equal to -7.2°C. Explain.

7. In each pair, which would you expect to have the higher boiling point?
   a) He or Ar b) PH_3 or NH_3 c) HBr or HI d) RbCl or FeS e) CHF_3 or $CHCl_3$
   f) KCl or NaF g) CH_3OH or CH_3F || h) SiC or H_2O i) Si or Cl_2 [*Read IVB before answering h and i*]

8. The following boiling points belong to one of the following compounds: 117°C, 78°C, 34.5°C, -23°C.

CH_3-O-CH_3	CH_3CH_2OH	CH_3CH_2-O-CH_2CH_3	$CH_3CH_2CH_2CH_2OH$
A	B	C	D

   a) Which bp goes with what compound?
   b) If each of the following substances were placed in separate sealed translucent bottles at room temperature, could you identify one of the substances right away? Explain. (Hint: Think of what physical state each of the substances is in from the bp information given.)

9. What is the strongest intermolecular force existing between the following pairs? **[OPTIONAL]**
   a) He & Ar b) Ar & HCl c) Ar & Na^+ d) Ar & H_2O
   e) H_2O & HCl f) H_2O & Ar g) H_2O & CCl_4 h) H_2O & NH_3
   i) CCl_4 & $SiCl_4$ j) CCl_4 & He k) CCl_4 & NH_3 l) CCl_4 & HBr

The Liquid & Solid State

10. Given the following vapor pressure curve, answer the following questions.
    a) What is the normal bp of X?
    b) What is the normal bp of Y?
    c) What is the vapor pressure of X at 25°C?
    d) Predict which would have the stronger intermolecular force. Explain.
    e) Which is more volatile (i.e., which has the higher vapor pressure)?
    f) What is the bp of X at an external pressure of 500 torr?
    g) At a pressure of 700 torr and 70°C, what is the physical state of X?

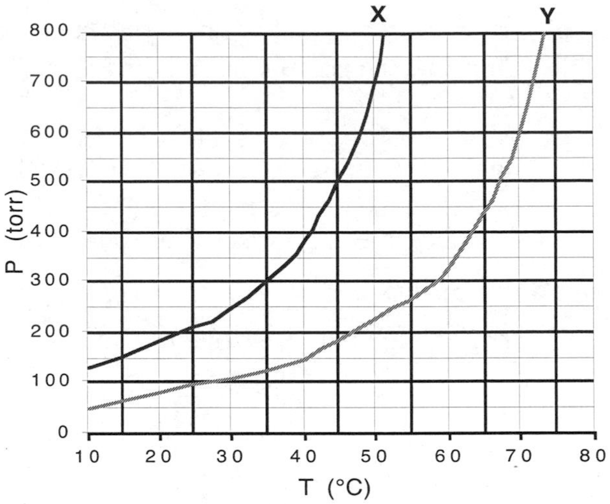

11. In each pair, which would you expect to have the higher vapor pressure?
    a) He or Ar b) PH_3 or NH_3 c) HBr or HI d) CCl_4 or $SiCl_4$

12. Given the following vapor pressure & temperature information, under typical laboratory conditions (T = 25°C and P = 760 torr), predict whether each of the following substances would be in the gas phase or in one of the condensed phases (i.e., liquid phase or solid phase)?
    a) Substance A, P° @ 25°C = 700 torr b) Substance B, P° @ 25°C = 800 torr
    c) Substance C, P° @ 100°C = 100 torr d) Substance D, P° @ 24°C = 1000 torr
    e) Substance E, P° @ 30°C = 760 torr f) Substance F, P°@ 20°C = 760 torr

Heat Transfer

13. Arrange the following substances in order of increasing ΔH_{vap}: $SiCl_4$, Ne, $CHCl_3$, CH_3OH
14. The molar heat of fusion (ΔH_{fus}) for C_6H_6 (MM = 78.1) is 10.9 kJ/mol at its freezing point of 5.5°C. How much heat (in J) must be removed in order to convert 100. g of $C_6H_{6\,(l)}$ at 5.5°C into $C_6H_{6\,(s)}$?
15. The molar heat of fusion (ΔH_{fus}) for C_6H_6 (MM = 78.1) is 10.9 kJ/mol at its freezing point of 5.5°C. How much heat (in J) must be added to 100. g of solid C_6H_6 at 5.5°C in order to melt it?
16. The heat of vaporization (ΔH_{vap}) of water is 40.3 kJ/mol at its normal boiling point of 100°C. What is the vapor pressure (in torr) of water at 60°C? **[OPTIONAL]**
17. Calculate the heat of vaporization (ΔH_{vap}) of a substance (in kJ/mol) given that at 90°C and 50°C its vapor pressure is 700 torr and 200 torr, respectively? **[OPTIONAL]**
18. The heat of vaporization (ΔH_{vap}) of ethanol is 39.3 kJ/mol at its normal boiling point of 78°C. At what temperature (in °C) will its vapor pressure be 372 torr? **[OPTIONAL]**
19. Given the following information for the substance, ethanol (CH_3CH_2OH, MM = 46.1)
    $s_{ethanol,\,lq} = 2.44$ J/g · °C, $q_{vap} = 838$ J/g, $q_{fus} = 109$ J/g, fp = -114°C, bp = 78°C
    Calculate the amount of heat (in J) that is released when 50.0 g of liquid ethanol at -14°C is converted into solid ethanol at -114°C.
20. Given the following information,
    $s_{steam} = 2.03$ J/g · °C, $s_{water} = 4.18$ J/g · °C, $s_{ice} = 2.09$ J/g · °C
    $q_{vap,\,water} = 2260$ J/g, $q_{fus,\,water} = 333$ J/g, fp = 0°C, bp = 100°C
    a) Calculate the amount of heat (in J) that is released when 50.0 g of steam at 110°C is converted to liquid water at 100°C.
    b) Calculate the amount of heat (in J) that is released when 10.0 g of steam at 110°C is converted to ice at 0.0°C.

c) Calculate the amount of heat (in J) required to convert 1.00 mol of ice at -10°C to water at 25°C.
d) Calculate the amount of heat (in J) required to convert 1.00 mole of water at 25°C to steam at 110°C.
e) Calculate the amount of heat (in J) required to convert 18.0 g of ice at -20°C to steam at 105°C.
f) Calculate the amount of heat (in J) that is released when 1 mol of steam at 100°C is converted to water at 100°C.
g) What mass of ice (in g) at 0.00°C needs to be added to 150. g of water at 25.0°C in order for the final temperature to be 17.0°C? **[OPTIONAL]**
h) Calculate the mass of water (in g) at 25.0°C needed to obtain a final temperature of 41.0°C when 5.00 g of steam at 100.0°C are added to it. **[OPTIONAL]**

Phase Diagrams

21. Given the following phase diagram of an unknown substance, answer the following questions.

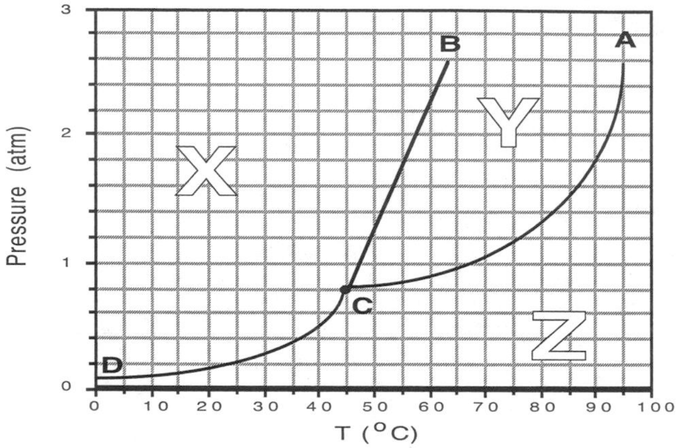

a) What phase is indicated by X, Y, and Z, respectively?
b) What is the normal sublimation point of the substance?
c) What is the normal freezing point of the substance?
d) What is the normal melting point of the substance?
e) What is the normal boiling point of the substance?
f) What is the normal condensation point of the substance?
g) At a pressure of 0.20 atm, what is the sublimation point of the substance?
h) At what temperatures & pressures are the solid & liquid phase in equilibrium with each other?
i) What is curve CA called?
j) How many phases and/or phase mixtures can exist at 45°C?
k) At what temperature and pressure does the triple point occur?
l) What is the critical temperature?
m) What is the critical pressure?
n) Where is the critical point?
o) If the initial temperature of the substance was 50°C and its pressure was held constant at 0.5 atm, what needs to occur for a solid to be deposited?
p) What happens to the melting point of the substance as the pressure increases?
q) At 100°C and pressures below 2 atm, how many phases and/or phase mixtures can exist?
r) At 2 atm, how many phases and/or phases mixtures can exist?
s) What phase(s) and/or phase mixture(s) exist below the triple point?
t) True or False. The substance may be converted from a gas into a liquid if its pressure is increased from 1 atm to 2 atm at 100°C.
u) True or False. At temperatures above the critical temperature, the substance can't be liquified.
v) True or False. At temperatures above 95°C, the substance will always be a supercritical fluid.

MULTIPLE CHOICE PRACTICE EXAM FOR MODULE 1

1. Which of the following statements is usually true?
   a. The density of a substance in its solid phase is greater than that in its gas phase.
   b. Liquids are less compressible than solids.
   c. Solids have vibrational and translational motion.
   d. Liquids have an indefinite shape and volume.
   e. The volume that is occupied by the same mass of a substance in its solid state is greater than that in its liquid state.
   f. Of the three common states of matter, a substance's solid state has the weakest attractive forces.
   g. Of the three common states of matter, a substance's gaseous state has the shortest intermolecular distance between formula units (i.e., molecules, atoms, or ions).

   1) only a 2) only a and c 3) only e
   4) only c and d 5) none of the statements is true.

2. The phase transition in which a gas goes to the solid state is called ____.
   1) sublimation 2) freezing 3) melting 4) condensation 5) deposition

3. Which of the following will convert a gas into liquid?
   1) cooling 2) heating 3) decrease in pressure
   4) increasing the volume of the container (while maintaining a constant temperature)
   5) two of the above

4. Which of the following is the strongest force (interaction)?
   1) hydrogen bond 2) covalent bond 3) London dispersion force
   4) dipole-dipole 5) dipole-induced dipole

5. What is the strongest intermolecular force existing in CH_4?
   1) hydrogen bond 2) ion-induced dipole 3) London dispersion force
   4) dipole-dipole 5) dipole-induced dipole

6. Which of the following exhibit hydrogen bonding?
   a. HI b. CH_3NH_2 c. AsH_3
   1) only b 2) only b & c 3) only a & c 4) a, b, & c
   5) none of the above

7. What is the strongest intermolecular force existing between HCl and $(CH_3)_2O$? **[OPTIONAL]**
   1) hydrogen bond 2) ion-induced dipole 3) London dispersion force
   4) dipole-dipole 5) dipole-induced dipole

8. Which of the following has the largest London dispersion force?
   1) F_2 2) Cl_2 3) Br_2 4) I_2
   5) All have equally "sized" London dispersion forces

9. Which of the following is expected to have the highest boiling point?
   1) Cl_2 2) Ar 3) $CH_3(CH_2)_2CH_3$ 4) $CH_3(CH_2)_2CH_2OH$ 5) H_2S

10. Which of the following is expected to have the highest melting point? [Hint: Covalent (network) solids have very high melting points.]
    1) H_2O 2) Rn 3) H_2Se 4) HCl 5) SiC

11. Which of the following is expected to have the lowest vapor pressure?
    1) H_2O 2) Rn 3) H_2Se 4) HCl 5) H_2

For Questions 12 - 14 consider the vapor pressure curve to your right.

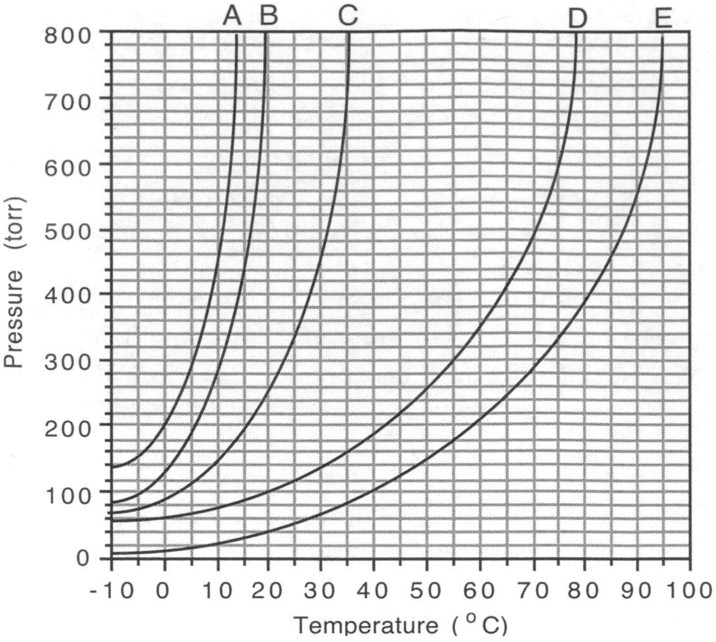

12. The boiling point of D at 220 torr is:
    1) 73°C 2) 45°C 3) 15°C
    4) 20°C 5) 63°C

13. A, B, C, D, & E have similar molar masses. Which has the strongest intermolecular force?
    1) A 2) B 3) D 4) E
    5) All have equal strength intermolecular forces.

14. Under typical laboratory conditions, which of the following exists as a gas?
    1) only A 2) only B
    3) only A & B 4) only E
    5) There is not enough information given.

15. Which of the following statements is (are) true about liquids?
    1) Molecules in the liquid state have an equal kinetic energy relative to those in the gaseous state.
    2) For most liquids expansion occurs with a decrease in temperature.
    3) The viscosity of liquids increases with an increase in temperature.
    4) Two or more of the above.
    5) None of the above.

16. Which of the statements below is (are) true concerning the vaporization (at the boiling point) of a liquid?
    1) The temperature is increasing. 2) Energy is being released.
    3) The vapor and liquid phase are existing in equilibrium with each other.
    4) Two or more of the above. 5) None of the above.

17. Which of the following is expected to have the largest ΔH_{vap} (heat of vaporization)?
    1) CH_3NH_2 2) Rn 3) H_2Se 4) HCl 5) H_2

18. Which of the following is (are) true?
    1) fp = -mp 2) $\Delta H_{fus} = -\Delta H_{sol}$ 3) ΔH_{fus} is always greater than ΔH_{vap}
    4) Two or more of the above. 5) None of the above.

19. The molar heat of fusion for C_6H_6 (MM = 78.1) is 10.9 kJ/mol at its freezing point of 5.5°C. How much heat (in J) is released by 25.0 g of C_6H_6 at 5.5°C when it is converted into a solid?
    1) 3.49×10^3 2) 2.72×10^5 3) 2.13×10^4 4) 29.4 5) 3.49×10^{-3}

Consider the following information when answering questions 20 - 21

$s_{steam} = 2.03\ \frac{J}{g \cdot °C}$, $s_{water} = 4.18\ \frac{J}{g \cdot °C}$, $s_{ice} = 2.09\ \frac{J}{g \cdot °C}$, $q_{vap} = 2260\ \frac{J}{g}$, $q_{fus} = 333\ \frac{J}{g}$

20. Calculate the amount of heat (in J) that needs to be removed in order to convert 25.0 g of water at 25.0°C into ice at -50.0°C.
    1) 8.32×10^3 2) 6.12×10^4 3) 2.01×10^4 4) 1.35×10^4 5) 5.22×10^3

21. Calculate the amount of heat (in J) that is required when 10.0 g of water at 35.0°C is converted to steam at 125.°C.
    1) 3.22×10^3 2) 3.76×10^4 3) 2.82×10^4 4) 5.12×10^4 5) 2.58×10^4

Consider the phase diagram given on page 1-14 to answer questions 22 - 25

22. If the unknown substance is at a pressure of 0.2 atm and a temperature of 50°C, which of the following statements would be correct?
    1) At a constant pressure if the temperature is lowered to 30°C a solid will deposit.
    2) At a constant temperature if the pressure is increased to 760 torr the substance will solidify.
    3) If the temperature is decreased to 45°C and the pressure is increased to 0.8 atm, all three phases will be in equilibrium with each other.
    4) Two or more of the above statements are correct.
    5) None of the above statements are correct.

23. How many phases and/or phase mixtures can occur at 1 atm?
    1) 1 2) 2 3) 3 4) 4 5) 5

24. What is the boiling point of the substance at a pressure of 1.4 atm?
    1) 83°C 2) 52°C 3) 45°C 4) 0°C 5) This substance does not boil at this pressure.

25. Which of the following statements is correct?
    a. Line CA is the vapor pressure curve which indicate the temperatures and pressures where the liquid and vapor are in equilibrium.
    b. Point C is called the critical point and indicates the temperature and pressure where the solid, liquid, and vapor phases are in equilibrium.
    c. At temperatures above 95°C, the substance only exists as a liquid.
    d. At pressures below 0.8 atm, the substance will never exist as a liquid.
    e. The melting point of the substance increases with an increase in pressure.

    1) only a, c, d, e 2) only a, d, e 3) only b and c 4) only b, c, d 5) only a and e

26. Which of the following statements is true?
    1) At temperatures greater than the critical temperature, a substance can not be liquified.
    2) At temperatures and pressures greater than the triple point, a substance will not sublime.
    3) A substance that readily sublimes has a triple point greater than the barometric pressure.
    4) All of the above statements are correct.
    5) None of the above statements are correct.

27. Which of the following statements is/are correct?
    1) Liquids with strong intermolecular forces are more apt to have a high resistance to flow (i.e., they tend to have a high viscosity) than liquids with weak intermolecular forces.
    2) Water forms a concave meniscus with glass because it experiences unfavorable adhesive forces.
    3) Mercury forms a convex meniscus with glass because its cohesive forces are smaller than its adhesive forces.
    4) Two or more of the above statements are correct.
    5) None of the above statements are correct.

28. On a relative basis, the stronger the intermolecular forces in a substance are,
    1) the smaller its heat of vaporization will be.
    2) the higher its molar heat of fusion will be.
    3) the higher its vapor pressure.
    4) the more closely it will follow the ideal gas laws.
    5) Two of the above statements are correct.

29. Which of the following is most likely applicable to $NaCl_{(s)}$?
    1) It is hard, brittle, and a poor conductor.
    2) The attractive forces that are present are electrostatic in nature.
    3) The particles occupying its lattice sites are Na^+ and Cl^-.
    4) Two of the above statements are correct.
    5) All of the above statements are correct.

30. Which of the following is most likely applicable to $SiO_{2(s)}$ (quartz)?
   1) The strongest attractive forces that are present are due to covalent bonding.
   2) It has a very low melting point.
   3) It is a poor conductor.
   4) Two of the above statements are correct.
   5) All of the above statements are correct.

31. Which of the following is most likely applicable to $N_{2(s)}$?
   1) High melting point.
   2) Good conductor.
   3) Its strongest intermolecular force is dipole-dipole.
   4) Two of the above statements are correct.
   5) None of the above statements are correct.

32. Which of the following is most likely a molecular solid?
   1) $Fe_{(s)}$ 2) $N_{2\,(s)}$ 3) $NaCl_{(s)}$ 4) $C_{(s,\ diamond)}$ 5) $SiC_{(s)}$

33. Arrange the following (H_2O, NaCl, $C_{(diamond)}$, Ar, HCl) in order of increasing melting point.
   1) $H_2O < NaCl < C_{(diamond)} < Ar < HCl$ 2) $Ar < HCl < H_2O < NaCl < C_{(diamond)}$
   3) $C_{(diamond)} < Ar < H_2O < NaCl < HCl$ 4) $Ar < H_2O < HCl < NaCl < C_{(diamond)}$
   5) $Ar < NaCl < C_{(diamond)} < Ar < H_2O$

34. Given the following table, which of the following statements is true?

Substance	mp (°C)	bp (°C)	Electrical Conductivity (s)	Electrical Conductivity (l)
OsF_6	32	46	none	none
B	2076	3927	none	none
I_2	114	184	none	none

   1) OsF_6 is an ionic solid.
   2) The ΔH_{vap} for I_2 is greater than that of for B.
   3) OsF_6 has stronger intermolecular forces than B.
   4) B is a covalent (network) solid.
   5) Two of the above choices is correct.

35. Given the following information about a compound, which of the following statements is true?

   Normal mp = 50°C Normal bp = 70°C ΔH_{vap} = 10 kJ/mol

   a. The compound is a liquid at 760 mm Hg and 80°C.
   b. The compound releases 10 kJ/mol of heat when it condenses.
   c. At 68°C the compound has a vapor pressure greater than 770 torr.
   d. The compound has a molar heat of fusion greater than 10 kJ/mol.
   e. The compound is a gas at 1 atm and 80°C.
   f. The compound is most likely a covalent (network) solid.
   g. The compound will most likely not conduct electricity in either its solid or liquid state.
   h. The compound is a liquid under normal laboratory conditions.

   1) only b and c 2) only a, e, and g 3) only b, e. and g
   4) only e, g, and h 5) only c, f, and g

36. The heat of vaporization of a substance is 39.3 kJ/mol. If the vapor pressure of the substance is 234 torr at 50°C, then what is the vapor pressure (in torr) of the substance at 60°C? **[OPTIONAL]**

1) 151 2) 1.10 3) 760 4) 363 5) 244

37. The heat of vaporization of water is 40.8 kJ/mol at its normal boiling point of 100°C. At what temperature (in °C) will its vapor pressure be 0.032 atm? **[OPTIONAL]**

1) 296 2) 33 3) -62 4) -0.0034 5) 23

MODULE 1 - ANSWERS

1. a) solid b) increase c) cooling d) condensation e) freezing, solidification, or crystallization f) melting or fusion
2. a, b, c
3. a) A. gas B. liquid C. liquid D. solid
   b) A. gas B. gas C. liquid D. liquid
   c) A. gas B. solid C. solid D. solid
4. a) ion-ion b) dipole-dipole c) hydrogen bond d) London forces e) hydrogen bond
   f) London forces g) dipole-dipole h) ion- ion i) hydrogen bond j) dipole-dipole
   k) London forces l) London forces m) London forces n) dipole-dipole o) ion-ion
5. C < B < A
6. ICl has stronger IMF than Br_2 (dipole-dipole vs London forces); the stronger the IMF the higher the mp and bp.
7. a) Ar b) NH_3 c) HI d) FeS e) $CHCl_3$ f) NaF
   g) CH_3OH h) SiC (very strong covalent network) i) Si (very strong covalent network)
8. a) A → -23°C, B → 78°C, C → 34.5°C, D → 117°C
   b) Yes, since room temperature is ~ 25°C, any compound with a bp less than room temperature is a gas. Compound A is therefore a gas and a bottle containing it would appear as though it was empty.
9. a) London forces b) dipole-induced dipole c) ion-induced dipole d) dipole-induced dipole
   e) dipole-dipole f) dipole-induced dipole g) dipole-induced dipole h) hydrogen bond
   i) London forces j) London forces k) dipole-induced dipole l) dipole-induced dipole
10. a) 51°C b) 73°C c) 210 torr
    d) Y (assuming similar MM, the substance with the lowest vapor pressure has stronger IMF)
    e) X f) 45°C
    g) gas (at 700 torr at any temperature greater than 51°C, its bp, compound X will be a gas)
11. a) He b) PH_3 c) HBr d) CCl_4
12. a) condensed phase b) gas c) condensed phase d) gas e) condensed phase f) gas
13. Ne < $SiCl_4$ < $CHCl_3$ < CH_3OH
14. 1.40×10^4 J
15. 1.40×10^4 J
16. 159 torr
17. 30.5 kJ/mol
18. 60°C
19. 1.76×10^4 J
20. a) 1.14×10^5 J b) 3.03×10^4 J c) 8.25×10^3 J d) 4.67×10^4 J e) 5.51×10^4 J f) 4.07×10^4 J
    g) 12.4 g h) 187 g
21. a) X → solid; Y → liquid; Z → gas
    b) this substance doesn't have a normal sublimation point
    c) 47°C
    d) 47°C
    e) 68°C
    f) 68°C
    g) 25°C
    h) at T & P along line CB (melting/freezing curve)
    i) vapor pressure curve (boiling-condensation curve or liquid-gas curve)
    j) 3 (gas, gas-liquid-solid, solid)
    k) T = 45°C, P = 0.8 atm
    l) 95°C
    m) 2.6 atm
    n) at point A (P = 2.6 atm, T = 95°C)
    o) T must be decreased to below 40°C
    p) increases
    q) 1 (gas)
    r) 5 (solid, solid-liquid, liquid, liquid-gas, gas)
    s) solid, solid-gas, gas
    t) False
    u) True
    v) False (If P > 2.5 atm (critical pressure), then statement will be true)

ANSWERS TO MULTIPLE CHOICE PRACTICE EXAM

1	2	3	4	5	6	7	8	9	10	11	12	13	14	15	16	17	18	19	20	21	22	23	24	25
1	5	1	2	3	1	4	4	4	5	1	2	4	3	5	3	1	2	1	4	5	3	5	1	2

26	27	28	29	30	31	32	33	34	35	36	37
4	1	2	5	4	5	2	2	4	3	4	5

MODULE 2. *Solutions*

I. Types of Solutions / Homogeneous Mixture

When we think of a solution (homogeneous mixture -- a mixture that is uniform throughout), we normally think of a liquid. Liquid solutions are the most common, but there are also gas and solid solutions.

Solute	Solvent	Appearance	Example
Gas	Liquid	Liquid	Pepsi
Liquid	Liquid	Liquid	90 proof rum
Solid	Liquid	Liquid	Seawater
Gas	Gas	Gas	Air
Solid	Solid	Solid	18-karat gold

Saturated Solution - when the solvent contains all the solute it can hold at a given temperature.

Unsaturated Solution - any solution that contains a lesser amount (than maximum) of solute.

Supersaturated Solution - an unstable solution holding more solute than its normal maximum amount at a given temperature. Since this is an unstable solution, at some period in time, some solute will eventually come out of the solution; thus giving undissolved solute and a saturated solution.

For example, the solubility of NaCl at 40°C is 40 g per 100 mL of water.

Saturated Solution - 40 g NaCl dissolved in 100 mL of water

Unsaturated Solution - Any amount of NaCl less than 40 g dissolved in 100 mL of water

Supersaturated Solution - more than 40 g of NaCl **dissolving** in 100 mL of water

II. Dissolution Process

Two conditions favor *dissolution* (formation of a homogenous mixture--solution): a) a decrease in the energy of the system, which corresponds to an exothermic process and b) an increase in entropy (i.e., disorder or randomness) of the system - which is usually the case.

The relative strength of the following interactions affect the dissolution of a solute in a solvent:

a) solute-solute interactions b) solvent-solvent interactions c) solvent-solute interactions

Dissolution will be favored when the first two of the above factors are relatively small and the third is relatively large. This is the case for many ionic compounds in water. Generally, those ionic compounds that don't dissolve in water contain highly charged ions [e.g., $Ca_3(PO_4)_2$)] in which the energy (i.e., lattice energy) holding the oppositely charged ions together is relatively large (i.e., factor a is very large in comparison to factor c).

The process in which solvent molecules surround and interact with solute molecules/ions is called *solvation*. When the solvent is water, the more specific term is called *hydration*. The larger the ion is the more H_2O molecules it can accomodate (i.e., the more hydrated it is). Most ions in an aqueous solution are surrounded by four to nine H_2O molecules.

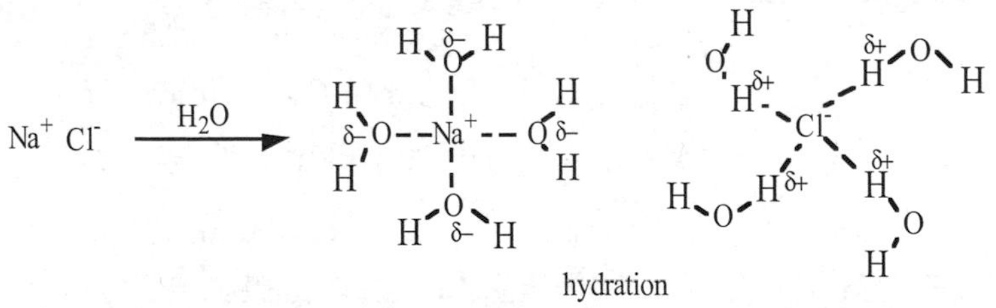

hydration

When predicting if two substances will be soluble in each other, the following rule of thumb is used: ***Like Dissolves Like*** -- polar solutes tend to dissolve in polar solvents and non-polar solutes tend to dissolve in non-polar solvents. *If two substances have similar intermolecular forces, chances are that the solute will have a high solubility in the solvent.*

When both the solute and solvent are liquids, and they form a homogenous mixture (i.e., the solute dissolves in the solvent), they are said to be *miscible* in each other. If the liquid solute and liquid solvent form a heterogenous mixture, they are said to be *immiscible* in each other.

Gases are soluble in each other. Few gases appreciably dissolve in water [e.g., HF, NH_3, HCl, HBr and HI]. These gases which are covalent in their pure form ionize either partially (e.g., HF and NH_3) or completely (e.g., HCl, HBr and HI) when they are placed in water.

Example Problems:

1. Under typical lab conditions (25°C and 760 torr), predict whether the solubility of the solute is expected to be high or low in the given solvent.

   a) $CaCl_2$ in CCl_4

      $CaCl_2$, which contains a very strong intermolecular force - ion-ion interactions, is expected to have a low solubilty in the non-polar solvent CCl_4, which has very weak London forces. The solute-solute interaction and solvent-solvent interactions will be large relative to the solvent-solute interaction.

   b) $BaCl_2$ in H_2O

      Generally speaking, ionic compounds are expected to be water soluble (according to the solubility rules, we've seen exceptions); since $BaCl_2$ is ionic (and both the cation and anion don't have a high charge), its solubility should be high in H_2O.

   c) CH_3OH in H_2O

      Organic compounds that have H-bonding as an IMF are expected to be soluble in water provided that they have 5 C or less. The more carbons present in an organic compound, the more non-polar nature that it has and the less water soluble it becomes. Since CH_3OH is capable of H-bonding and has 5 C or less it is expected to have a high solubility in H_2O.

   e) C_4H_{10} in CCl_4

      Both are non-polar; therefore, the solubility of C_4H_{10} should be very high in CCl_4. [NOTE: Hydrocarbons, C_xH_y, are non-polar.]

   f) O_2 in H_2O

      O_2 (a gas - you should remember which elements are gases under typical lab conditions) does not appreciably dissolve in water because it is non-polar.

2. Arrange the following compounds in order of decreasing solubility in water: CH_3OH, Br_2, H_2S.

   CH_3OH (polar, H-bonding) > H_2S (polar, dipole-dipole) > Br_2 (non-polar, London forces)

III. Effect of Temperature and Pressure on Solubility

LeChatelier's Principle states that when a stress is applied to a system at equilibrium, the system responds in a way that best relieves the stress. If the dissolution process for liquids or solids releases heat (exothermic), then according to LeChatelier's Principle the solubility of the solute will decrease with an increase in temperature. If the dissolution process for liquids or solids absorbs heat (endothermic) -- this is usually the case, then according to LeChatelier's Principle the solubility of the solute will increase with an increase in temperature.

$$A_{(s\ or\ l)} + \text{solvent} \rightleftharpoons \text{solution} + \text{heat} \qquad \text{(Exothermic Dissolution Process)}$$

$$A_{(s\ or\ l)} + \text{solvent} + \text{heat} \rightleftharpoons \text{solution} \qquad \text{(Endothermic Dissolution Process)}$$

For gas solutes in liquid solvents, their solubility in a solvent decreases with increasing temperature.

Changing the pressure has no appreciable effect on the solubility of either solid or liquid solutes in liquid solvents. However, the solubilities of a gas solute in all solvents will increase with an increase in the partial pressure of the gas according to Henry's Law:

$$P_{gas} = k \cdot C_{gas}$$

where,
- $P_{gas} \rightarrow$ partial pressure of gas above the soln
- $k \rightarrow$ Henry's Law constant for the gas in a solvent at a given T
- $C_{gas} \rightarrow$ concentration or solubility of the dissolved gas

To find the concentration/solubility of a gas in a particular solvent and partial pressure given its concentration/solubility and partial pressure at another condition, the following equation can be used:

$$\frac{P_{gas\text{-}cond\ 1}}{P_{gas\text{-}cond\ 2}} = \frac{k_{cond\ 1}}{k_{cond\ 2}} \cdot \frac{C_{gas\text{-}cond\ 1}}{C_{gas\text{-}cond\ 2}} \qquad \text{where, } k_{cond\ 1} = k_{cond\ 2}$$

thus

$$\frac{P_{gas\text{-}cond\ 1}}{P_{gas\text{-}cond\ 2}} = \frac{C_{gas\text{-}cond\ 1}}{C_{gas\text{-}cond\ 2}}$$

Example Problems:

1. How would you increase the solubility of a sample of oxygen dissolved in water under normal laboratory conditions?

   Decrease the solution's temperature or increase the partial pressure of oxygen.

2. The solubility of nitrogen gas at 25°C and a partial pressure of 0.687 atm is 4.7 x 10^{-4} mol/L. What is the value of Henry's Law constant in torr•L/mol?

$$P_{gas} = k \cdot C_{gas} \quad \rightarrow \quad 0.687\ \text{atm} = k \cdot 4.7 \times 10^{-4}\ \frac{\text{mol}}{\text{L}}$$

$$k = \frac{0.687\ \text{atm}}{4.7 \times 10^{-4}\ \frac{\text{mol}}{\text{L}}} = 1.5 \times 10^{3}\ \frac{\text{atm}\cdot\text{L}}{\text{mol}}$$

$$?\ \frac{\text{torr}\cdot\text{L}}{\text{mol}} = 1.5 \times 10^{3}\ \frac{\text{atm}\cdot\text{L}}{\text{mol}}\left(\frac{760\ \text{torr}}{1\ \text{atm}}\right) = 1.1 \times 10^{6}\ \frac{\text{torr}\cdot\text{L}}{\text{mol}}$$

3. At a partial pressure of acetylene of 1.2 atm, 1.04 mol of it dissolves in 1.00 L of acetone. If the partial pressure of acetylene in acetone is increased to 15 atm, then what is its solubility (in mol/L)?

$$\frac{P_{gas\text{-}cond\ 1}}{P_{gas\text{-}cond\ 2}} = \frac{C_{gas\text{-}cond\ 1}}{C_{gas\text{-}cond\ 2}} \quad \rightarrow \quad \frac{1.2\ \text{atm}}{15\ \text{atm}} = \frac{1.04\ \frac{\text{mol}}{\text{L}}}{C_{acetylene@15\ atm}}$$

$$C_{acetylene@15\ atm} = \frac{1.04 \times 15}{1.2} = 13\ \text{mol/L}$$

4. Nitrogen is added to the solution in problem 3, so that its partial pressure is 2 atm, while that of acetylene remains 15 atm. Given this information, what is the solubility of acetylene in acetone?

   The solubility of acetylene is not dependent upon the partial pressure of any other gas and thus its solubility/concentration remains the same → 13 mol/L

IV. Concentration Units

Quantitative study of a solution requires that we know the amount of solute that is present in a given amount of solution, i.e., its concentration. In your first semester chemistry course you were exposed to weight (mass) percent and molarity. Now we will expose you to other concentration units (m - molality and X - mole fraction) and how to interconvert between them.

A. Percent by Mass or Weight Percent (wt %)

$$\text{wt}\ \% = \frac{\text{g solute}}{\text{g soln}} \times 100$$

where → g soln = g solute(s) + g solvent

B. Molarity (M)

$$M = \frac{\text{mol solute}}{\text{L soln}} = \frac{\left(\frac{g_{solute}}{MM_{solute}}\right)}{L_{soln}}$$

(1 L soln = 1000 mL soln)

C. Molality (m)

$$m = \frac{\text{moles of solute}}{\text{kg of solvent}} = \frac{\left(\frac{g_{solute}}{MM_{solute}}\right)}{kg_{solvent}}$$

(1 kg solvent = 1000 g solvent)

Example Problems:

1. What is the molality of a solution that contains 128 g of CH_3OH (MM = 32.0) in 202 g of water?

$$? \text{ m}\left(\frac{\text{mol } CH_3OH}{\text{kg } H_2O}\right) = \frac{128 \text{ g } CH_3OH\left(\frac{1 \text{ mol } CH_3OH}{32.0 \text{ g } CH_3OH}\right)}{202 \text{ g } H_2O\left(\frac{1 \text{ kg } H_2O}{10^3 \text{ g } H_2O}\right)} = 19.8 \text{ m}$$

2. How many grams of water must be used to dissolve 50.0 mL of CH_3OH (MM = 32.0, density = 0.791 g/ mL) in order to obtain a 3.05 m solution of CH_3OH?

$$? \text{ g } H_2O = 50.0 \text{ mL } CH_3OH\left(\frac{0.791 \text{ g } CH_3OH}{1 \text{ mL } CH_3OH}\right)\left(\frac{1 \text{ mol } CH_3OH}{32.0 \text{ g } CH_3OH}\right)\left(\frac{1 \text{ kg } H_2O}{3.05 \text{ mol } CH_3OH}\right)\left(\frac{1000 \text{ g } H_2O}{1 \text{ kg } H_2O}\right) = 405. \text{ g}$$

D. **Mole Fraction (X)**

Mole fraction is a unitless concentration unit expressed as the number of moles of the component in question divided by the total number of moles of all the components present. For a two component system containing A and B, X_A & X_B are expressed as:

$$X_A = \frac{\text{moles of A}}{\text{moles A + moles B}} \quad \text{and} \quad X_B = \frac{\text{moles of B}}{\text{moles A + moles B}}$$

$$X_A + X_B = 1$$

Example Problem:

1. What are the mole fractions of CH_3OH and H_2O in a solution containing 128 g CH_3OH and 202 mL of water (d = 1.00 g/mL)?

$$? \text{ mol } CH_3OH = 128 \text{ g } CH_3OH\left(\frac{1 \text{ mol } CH_3OH}{32.0 \text{ g } CH_3OH}\right) = 4.00 \text{ mol } CH_3OH$$

$$? \text{ mol } H_2O = 202 \text{ mL } H_2O\left(\frac{1.00 \text{ g } H_2O}{1 \text{ mL } H_2O}\right)\left(\frac{1 \text{ mol } H_2O}{18.0 \text{ g } H_2O}\right) = 11.2 \text{ mol } H_2O$$

$$X_{CH_3OH} = \frac{\text{mol } CH_3OH}{\text{mol } CH_3OH + \text{mol } H_2O} = \frac{4.00}{4.00 + 11.2} = 0.263$$

$$X_{H_2O} = \frac{\text{mol } H_2O}{\text{mol } CH_3OH + \text{mol } H_2O} = \frac{11.2}{4.00 + 11.2} = 0.737$$

$$\text{or } X_{H_2O} = 1 - X_{CH_3OH} = 1 - 0.263 = 0.737$$

V. **Interconversion Among Concentration Units**

To interconvert among certain concentration units, the density (or specific gravity) of the solution must be known.

Example Problems:

1. Commercial sulfuric acid is 96.4% H_2SO_4 (MM = 98.1) by weight, and its specific gravity is 1.84. Calculate the molarity of commercial sulfuric acid.

$$\text{specific gravity is numerically equal to density} \rightarrow \frac{1.84 \text{ g soln}}{1 \text{ mL soln}}$$

$$96.4\%\ H_2SO_4 = \frac{96.4\ g\ H_2SO_4}{100\ g\ soln} \quad \rightarrow \quad ?\ M = \frac{mol\ H_2SO_4}{L\ soln}$$

$$M = \frac{mol\ H_2SO_4}{L\ soln} = \frac{96.4\ g\ H_2SO_4\left(\frac{1\ mol\ H_2SO_4}{98.1\ g\ H_2SO_4}\right)}{100\ g\ soln\left(\frac{1\ mL\ soln}{1.84\ g\ soln}\right)\left(\frac{10^{-3}\ L\ soln}{1\ mL\ soln}\right)} = 18.1\ M$$

OR

$$M = \frac{mol\ H_2SO_4}{L\ soln} = \frac{96.4\ g\ H_2SO_4}{100\ g\ soln}\left(\frac{1\ mol\ H_2SO_4}{98.1\ g\ H_2SO_4}\right)\left(\frac{1.84\ g\ soln}{1\ mL\ soln}\right)\left(\frac{1\ mL}{10^{-3}\ L}\right) = 18.1\ M$$

2. What is the weight percent of a solution that is 14.7 M H_3PO_4 (MM = 98.0) and has a specific gravity of 1.70?

specific gravity is numerically equal to density $\rightarrow \frac{1.70\ g\ soln}{1\ mL\ soln}$

$$14.7\ M\ H_3PO_4 = \frac{14.7\ mol\ H_3PO_4}{1\ L\ soln} = \frac{14.7\ mol\ H_3PO_4}{1000\ mL\ soln} \rightarrow ?\ wt\ \% = \frac{g\ H_3PO_4}{g\ soln}\ x\ 100\%$$

$$?\ \frac{g\ H_3PO_4}{g\ soln} = \frac{14.7\ mol\ H_3PO_4\left(\frac{98.0\ g\ H_3PO_4}{1\ mol\ H_3PO_4}\right)}{1000\ mL\ soln\left(\frac{1.70\ g\ soln}{1\ mL\ soln}\right)} = 0.847$$

$$wt\ \% = \frac{g\ H_3PO_4}{g\ soln}\ x\ 100\% = 0.847\ x\ 100 = 84.7\%$$

3. What is the molality of an 84.7% H_3PO_4 by mass (MM = 98.0) whose density is 1.70 g/mL?

$$84.7\%\ H_3PO_4 = \frac{84.7\ g\ H_3PO_4}{100\ g\ soln} \quad \rightarrow \quad ?\ m = \frac{mol\ H_3PO_4}{kg\ of\ H_2O}$$

g soln = g H_3PO_4 + g H_2O $\rightarrow$ 100 g soln = 84.7 g H_3PO_4 + ? g H_2O $\rightarrow$

g H_2O = 100 - 84.7 = 15.3 g

$$m = \frac{mol\ H_3PO_4}{kg\ of\ H_2O} = \frac{84.7\ g\ H_3PO_4\left(\frac{1\ mol\ H_3PO_4}{98.0\ g\ H_3PO_4}\right)}{15.3\ g\ H_2O\left(\frac{1\ kg\ H_2O}{10^3\ g\ H_2O}\right)} = 56.5\ m$$

4. What is the molarity of a 56.8 m H_3PO_4 (MM = 98.0) whose density is 1.70 g/mL?

$$56.8\ m\ H_3PO_4 = \frac{56.8\ mol\ H_3PO_4}{1000\ g\ H_2O} \quad \rightarrow \quad ?\ M\ H_3PO_4 = \frac{mol\ H_3PO_4}{L\ soln}$$

? g soln = g H_3PO_4 + g H_2O

$$?\ g\ soln = \left(56.8\ mol\ H_3PO_4\left(\frac{98.0\ g\ H_3PO_4}{1\ mol\ H_3PO_4}\right)\right) + 1000\ g\ H_2O$$

$$? \text{ g soln} = 5566 \text{ g } H_3PO_4 + 1000 \text{ g } H_2O = 6566 \text{ g soln}$$

$$? \text{ L soln} = 6566 \text{ g soln}\left(\frac{1 \text{ mL soln}}{1.70 \text{ g soln}}\right)\left(\frac{10^{-3} \text{ L soln}}{1 \text{ mL}}\right) = 3.86 \text{ L soln}$$

$$? \text{ M } H_3PO_4 = \frac{\text{mol } H_3PO_4}{\text{L soln}} = \frac{56.8 \text{ mol } H_3PO_4}{3.86 \text{ L soln}} = 14.7 \text{ M}$$

5. What is the mole fraction of H_3PO_4 (MM = 98.0) in a 14.7 M H_3PO_4 solution whose density is 1.70 g/mL?

$$14.7 \text{ M} = \frac{14.7 \text{ mol } H_3PO_4}{1000 \text{ mL soln}} \quad \rightarrow \quad X_{H_3PO_4} = \frac{\text{moles of } H_3PO_4}{\text{moles } H_3PO_4 + \text{moles } H_2O}$$

$$? \text{ g soln} = 1000 \text{ mL soln}\left(\frac{1.70 \text{ g soln}}{1 \text{ mL soln}}\right) = 1.70 \times 10^3 \text{ g soln}$$

$$\text{soln wt.} = \text{g } H_3PO_4 + \text{g } H_2O$$

$$1.70 \times 10^3 \text{ g soln} = \left(14.7 \text{ mol } H_3PO_4\left(\frac{98.0 \text{ g } H_3PO_4}{1 \text{ mol } H_3PO_4}\right)\right) + ? \text{ g } H_2O$$

$$\text{g } H_2O = 1.70 \times 10^3 - (14.7 \times 98) = 259. \text{ g}$$

$$? \text{ mol } H_2O = 259. \text{ g } H_2O\left(\frac{1 \text{ mol } H_2O}{18.0 \text{ g } H_2O}\right) = 14.4 \text{ mol}$$

$$X_{H_3PO_4} = \frac{\text{moles of } H_3PO_4}{\text{moles } H_3PO_4 + \text{moles } H_2O} = \frac{14.7}{14.7 + 14.4} = 0.505$$

VI. Colligative Properties of Nonelectrolyte Solutions

Unless otherwise noted, the solvent in solution will be water. Nonelectrolytes ionize very close to 0% in water. [Strong electrolytes ionize 100% in water. Weak electrolytes ionize only slightly in water.]

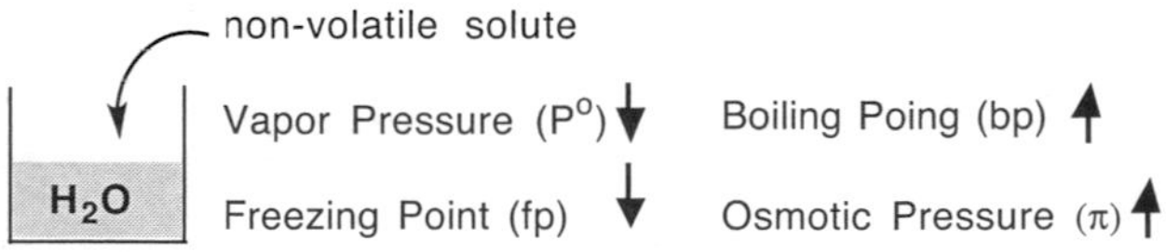

Colligative Properties are physical properties of solutions that depend upon the *number* of solute particles present in solution rather than the kind of solute particles. The four colligative properties of a solution containing nonvolatile solutes affect the solution by: a) *lowering its vapor pressure*, b) *raising its boiling point*, c) *lowering its freezing (melting) point*, and d) *generating an osmotic pressure*.

A. Raoult's Law and Vapor Pressure Lowering

In a solution composed of two substances, one will be the solute and the other the solvent. The total vapor pressure of a solution is equal to the sum of the partial pressures of its pure components (P_{solute} and $P_{solvent}$).

$$P_{solution} = P_{solute} + P_{solvent}$$

Raoult's Law states that at a given temperature and pressure, the partial pressure of a substance (i.e., solute or solvent) in an *ideal solution* can be defined as:

$$P_A = X_A P^o_A$$ where,

$P_A \rightarrow$ partial pressure of substance A in solution

$X_A \rightarrow$ mole fraction of substance A in solution

$P^o_A \rightarrow$ vapor pressure of pure substance A

Example Problem:

1. The vapor pressures of acetone (C_3H_6O, MM = 58.1) and that of water at 25.0°C are 345 torr and 23.8 torr, respectively. If 15.0 g of acetone are dissolved in 10.0 g of water at 25.0°C, then what is the vapor pressure of the solution?

$$P_{solution} = P_{acetone} + P_{water}$$

$$P_{solution} = X_{acetone}P^{o}_{acetone} + X_{water}P^{o}_{water}$$

$$P_{solution} = \frac{\frac{15.0\text{ g}}{58.1\text{ g/mol}}}{\left(\frac{15.0\text{ g}}{58.1\text{ g/mol}}\right)+\left(\frac{10.0\text{ g}}{18.0\text{ g/mol}}\right)}(345\text{ torr}) + \frac{\frac{10.0\text{ g}}{18.0\text{ g/mol}}}{\left(\frac{15.0\text{ g}}{58.1\text{ g/mol}}\right)+\left(\frac{10.0\text{ g}}{18.0\text{ g/mol}}\right)}(23.8\text{ torr})$$

$$P_{solution} = (0.318)(345\text{ torr}) + (0.682)(23.8\text{ torr}) = 109.4\text{ torr} + 16.3\text{ torr} = 125.7\text{ torr}$$

Solutions containing nonvolatile liquids or solids as solutes (i.e., solutes with low vapor pressures) always lower the vapor pressure of the solution.

$$P_{solution} = \underset{\text{negligible}}{P_{solute}} + P_{solvent} \qquad \text{thus,} \quad P_{solution} \approx P_{solvent}$$

What this means is that the total vapor pressure of the solution is basically only dependent on the partial pressure of the solution's volatile solvent.

The *lowering* of the vapor pressure of the solution (or of the "relatively volatile" solvent present in the solution) that results when *nonvolatile-nonionizing* solutes are added, $\Delta P_{solvent}$, is defined as:

$$\Delta P_{solvent} = \underset{\text{(pure)}}{P^{o}_{solvent}} - \underset{\text{(in soln)}}{P_{solvent}} = P^{o}_{solvent} - X_{solvent}P^{o}_{solvent} = P^{o}_{solvent}X_{solute}$$

↑ This represents how much the vapor pressure of the solvent was lowered as a result of having added a nonvolatile-nonelectrolyte

factor out $P^{o}_{solvent}$ ↓ $P^{o}_{solvent}(1 - X_{solvent})$ → $X_{solute} = 1 - X_{solvent}$

Example Problems: [NOTE: Unless otherwise informed, assume that the solute is a nonvolatile-nonelectrolyte]

1. The vapor pressure of benzene at 20°C is 74.6 torr. If 60.0 g of sucrose (MM = 342) is dissolved in 120 g of benzene (MM = 78.0) at 20°C, then:
   a) Calculate the vapor pressure (in torr) of the solution.

$$?\text{ mol sucrose} = 60.0\text{ g sucrose}\left(\frac{1\text{ mol sucrose}}{342\text{ g sucrose}}\right) = 0.175\text{ mol sucrose}$$

$$?\text{ mol benzene} = 120\text{ g benzene}\left(\frac{1\text{ mol benzene}}{78.0\text{ g benzene}}\right) = 1.54\text{ mol benzene}$$

$$X_{benzene} = \frac{\text{mol benzene}}{\text{mol sucrose} + \text{mol benzene}} = \frac{1.54\text{ mol}}{0.175\text{ mol} + 1.54\text{ mol}} = 0.895$$

$$P_{soln} = \underset{\sim 0}{P_{sucrose}} + P_{benzene} = X_{benzene}P^{o}_{benzene} = 0.895 \times 74.6\text{ torr} = 66.8\text{ torr}$$

   b) Calculate the vapor pressure lowering of the solution (i.e., calculate by how much the vapor pressure of the solvent in the solution was lowered as a result of having added a nonvolatile-nonelectrolyte solute).

$$\Delta P_{benzene} = \underset{\text{(pure)}}{P^{o}_{benzene}} - \underbrace{X_{benzene}P^{o}_{benzene}}_{P_{benzene}\text{ (in soln)}} = 74.6\text{ torr} - (0.895 \times 74.6\text{ torr}) = 7.8\text{ torr}$$

OR

$$\Delta P_{benzene} = P^{o}_{benzene}X_{sucrose} = 74.6\text{ torr}(1 - 0.895) = 7.83\text{ torr}$$

2. Determine the vapor pressure lowering associated with a 1.25 m sucrose solution at 25°C. P^o_{water} @ 25°C = 23.8 torr.

$$1.25 \text{ m sucrose} = \frac{1.25 \text{ mol sucrose}}{1 \text{ kg } H_2O} \rightarrow \text{mole of sucrose} = 1.25$$

$$? \text{ mol } H_2O = 1 \text{ kg } H_2O \left(\frac{10^3 \text{ g } H_2O}{1 \text{ kg } H_2O}\right)\left(\frac{1 \text{ mol } H_2O}{18.0 \text{ g } H_2O}\right) = 55.6 \text{ mol}$$

$$X_{H_2O} = \frac{\text{mol } H_2O}{\text{mol sucrose + mol } H_2O} = \frac{55.6 \text{ mol}}{1.25 \text{ mol} + 55.6 \text{ mol}} = 0.979$$

$$\Delta P_{H_2O} = \underset{\text{(pure)}}{P^o_{H_2O}} - \underbrace{X_{H_2O} P^o_{H_2O}}_{\substack{P_{H_2O} \\ \text{(in soln)}}} = 23.8 \text{ torr} - (0.979 \text{ x } 23.8 \text{ torr}) = 0.5 \text{ torr}$$

OR

$$\Delta P_{H_2O} = P^o_{H_2O} X_{sucrose} = 23.8 \text{ torr } (1 - 0.979) = 0.50 \text{ torr}$$

B. **Boiling Point Elevation**

Above, we saw that the vapor pressure of a solution (or solvent) decreased by the introduction of a nonvolatile solute. Such a solution must be heated to a higher temperature than the pure solvent to cause its vapor pressure to be equal to the atmospheric pressure (see figure to the right). In accord with Raoult's Law, the elevation of the boiling point of the solution (or solvent) caused by the dissolution of a nonvolatile nonelectrolyte is given as:

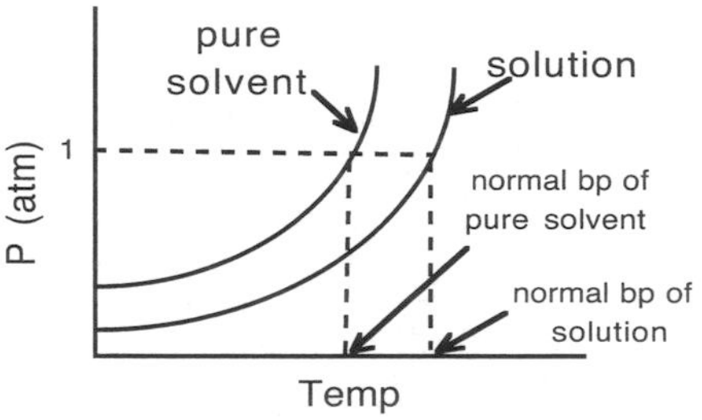

$$\Delta T_b = K_b m$$

where $\Delta T_b = bp_{(soln)} - bp_{(solvent)}$ [boiling point elevation]

K_b = molal boiling point constant (different for every solvent)

m = molality of solute

Table 1. Some Common Properties of Solvents

Solvent	bp (°C)	K_b (°C/m)	fp (°C)	K_f (°C/m)
Carbon Tetrachloride (CCl_4)	76.5	5.03	-23.0	32
Benzene (C_6H_6)	80.1	2.53	5.50	5.12
Cyclohexane (C_6H_{12})	80.7	2.79	6.50	20.0
Ethanol (CH_3CH_2OH)	78.4	2.98	-115	1.99
Water (H_2O)	100	0.512	0.00	1.86
Acetic Acid (CH_3COOH)	118	3.07	16.6	3.90

Boiling Point elevation experiments can be used to determine the molar mass of solutes.

$$\Delta T_b = K_b m = K_b \left(\frac{\text{mol solute}}{\text{kg solvent}}\right) = K_b \left(\frac{\frac{\text{g solute}}{\text{MM solute}}}{\text{kg solvent}}\right) \rightarrow \Delta T_b = K_b \left(\frac{\frac{\text{g solute}}{\text{MM solute}}}{\text{kg solvent}}\right)$$

Therefore,

$$MM_{solute} = \frac{K_b \text{ x g solute}}{\Delta T_b \text{ x kg solvent}}$$

Example Problems: [Refer to ***Table 1*** to obtain the K_b and normal bp for the solvent, which is water unless otherwise informed. Assume that the solute is a nonvolatile-nonelectrolyte.]

1. What is the normal boiling point of a 1.25 m sucrose solution?

$$\Delta T_b = K_b m = \left(0.512 \frac{°C}{m}\right)(1.25\ m) = 0.640\ °C$$

$$\Delta T_b = bp_{(soln)} - bp_{(solvent)} \rightarrow 0.640 = bp_{(soln)} - 100.0 \rightarrow bp_{(soln)} = 100.0 + 0.640 = 100.640°C$$

2. By how many °C would the bp of a solution containing 100.3 g of nonvolatile nonelectrolyte solute, $C_6H_{12}O_6$ (MM = 180), in 1.00 kg of water be raised over that of pure water?

$$m\left(\frac{mol\ C_6H_{12}O_6}{kg\ H_2O}\right) = \frac{100.3\ g\ C_6H_{12}O_6 \left(\frac{1\ mol\ C_6H_{12}O_6}{180\ g\ C_6H_{12}O_6}\right)}{1\ kg\ H_2O} = 0.557\ m$$

$$\Delta T_b = K_b m = \left(0.512 \frac{°C}{m}\right) \times (0.557\ m) = 0.285°C$$

3. Which has the largest normal boiling point? a) 5 m $C_3H_6O_3$ or b) 2 m $C_6H_{12}O_6$

   Since $\Delta T_b \propto m$, the solution with the largest molality will have the largest bp; therefore, the 5 m $C_3H_6O_3$ solution will have the largest bp.

4. Which of the solvents listed in Table 1 would give the largest boiling point elevation for a 1 m solution?

   Since $\Delta T_b \propto K_b$, the solvent that would give the largest bp elevation would be CCl_4.

C. **Freezing Point Lowering**

The freezing point of a solution will always be less than the freezing point of the pure solvent. The use of antifreeze (ethylene glycol) in car radiators is an excellent example of the utility of this concept. Antifreeze lowers the freezing point of the solution (good trait for freezing weather); antifreeze also raises the boiling point of the solution (good trait for hot weather). The freezing point depression of solutions of nonelectrolytes have been found to be equal to:

$$\Delta T_f = K_f m$$

where $\Delta T_f = fp_{(solvent)} - fp_{(soln)}$ [freezing point lowering]
K_f = molal freezing point constant (different for every solvent)
m = molality of solute

Freezing point elevation experiments can be used to determine the molar mass of solutes. In a derivation similar to that done for boiling point elevation, the molar mass of a solute can be obtained using the following equation:

$$MM_{solute} = \frac{K_f \times g\ solute}{\Delta T_f \times kg\ solvent}$$

Example Problems: [Refer to ***Table 1*** to obtain the K_f and normal fp for the solvent, which is water unless otherwise informed. Assume that the solute is a nonvolatile-nonelectrolyte.]

1. A solution of 0.85 g of the organic compound mestiol in 100.0 g of benzene is observed to have a fp of 5.16°C. What is the molality of the mestiol solution?

$$\Delta T_f = fp_{(solvent)} - fp_{(soln)} \rightarrow \Delta T_f = 5.50 - 5.16 = 0.34°C$$

$$\Delta T_f = K_f m \rightarrow 0.34°C = \left(5.12 \frac{°C}{m}\right) \times m \rightarrow m = \frac{0.34}{5.12} = 0.066\ m$$

2. When 15.0 g of ethyl alcohol (C_2H_5OH, MM = 46.0) is dissolved in 780 g of formic acid (HCO_2H), the fp of the solution is 7.20°C. If the freezing point of pure formic acid is 8.40°C, then calculate K_f for formic acid?

$$m\left(\frac{\text{mol } C_2H_5OH}{\text{kg } HCO_2H}\right) = \frac{15.0 \text{ g } C_2H_5OH\left(\frac{1 \text{ mol } C_2H_5OH}{46.0 \text{ g } C_2H_5OH}\right)}{0.780 \text{ kg } HCO_2H} = 0.418 \text{ m}$$

$$\Delta T_f = fp_{(solvent)} - fp_{(soln)} \rightarrow \Delta T_f = 8.40 - 7.20 = 1.20°C$$

$$\Delta T_f = K_f m \rightarrow 1.20°C = K_f \times 0.418 \text{ m}$$

$$K_f = \frac{1.20}{0.418} = 2.87°C/m$$

3. If 8.26 g of naphthalene (MM = 128) were dissolved in 95.2 g of benzene, then calculate the freezing point of the solution ?

$$m\left(\frac{\text{mol naphthalene}}{\text{kg benzene}}\right) = \frac{8.26 \text{ g naphthalene}\left(\frac{1 \text{ mol naphthalene}}{128 \text{ g naphthalene}}\right)}{95.2 \text{ g benzene}\left(\frac{1 \text{ kg}}{10^3 \text{ g}}\right)} = 0.678 \text{ m}$$

$$\Delta T_f = K_f m = \left(5.12 \frac{°C}{m}\right) \times 0.678 \text{ m} = 3.47°C$$

$$\Delta T_f = fp_{(solvent)} - fp_{(soln)} \rightarrow 3.47°C = 5.50°C - fp_{(soln)}$$

$$fp_{(soln)} = 5.50 - 3.47 = 2.03°C$$

4. A solution containing 5.00 g of a nonvolatile nonelectrolyte solute, X, in 120 grams of acetic acid is observed to have a freezing point of 14.0°C. What is the molar mass of X?

$$\Delta T_f = fp_{(solvent)} - fp_{(soln)} \rightarrow \Delta T_f = 16.6 - 14.0 = 2.6°C$$

$$MM_X = \frac{K_f \times \text{g solute}}{\Delta T_f \times \text{kg solvent}} = \frac{3.90°C/m \times 5.00 \text{ g}}{2.6°C \times 0.120 \text{ kg}} = 62. \text{ g/mol}$$

D. Generation of an Osmotic Pressure

The phenomenon of osmotic pressure (π) is illustrated below.

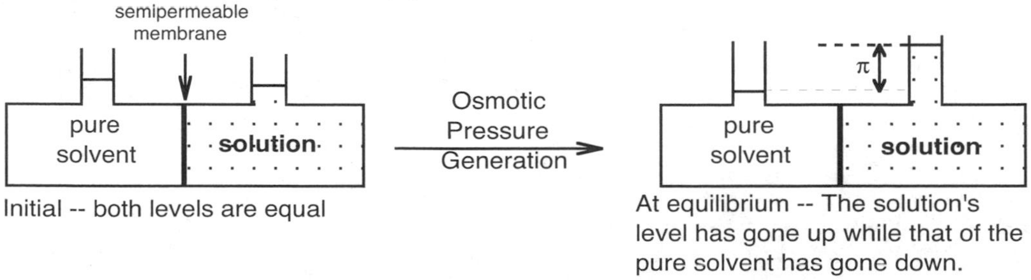

In the above diagram, the two compartments are separated by a *semipermeable membrane*, which allows small solvent molecules (e.g., H_2O) to pass through but blocks the passage of larger solute molecules. At the start both levels are equal. After some time, the level in the right tube begins to rise; this continues until equilibrium is reached. The net movement of solvent molecules through a semipermeable membrane is from a pure solvent or from a dilute solution to a more concentrated solution is called *osmosis*. The *osmotic pressure (π)* of a solution is the pressure required to stop osmosis (i.e., passage of solvent molecules from pure solvent or a dilute solution to a more concentrated solution). For very dilute solutions, the osmotic pressure can be found by use of either one of the following equations:

$$\pi V = nRT \qquad \text{or} \qquad \pi V = \left(\frac{g}{MM}\right)RT \qquad \text{or} \qquad \pi = MRT \leftarrow \pi = \left(\frac{n}{V}\right)RT$$

where π = osmotic pressure (atm or torr), n = moles of solute, T = temperature (K)
V = volume of solution (L), MM = molar mass of solute (g/mol)
M = molarity of solution $\left(\frac{\text{mol solute}}{\text{L soln}}\right)$
R = gas constant $\left(0.0821 \frac{\text{L} \cdot \text{atm}}{\text{mol} \cdot \text{K}} \text{ or } 62.4 \frac{\text{L} \cdot \text{torr}}{\text{mol} \cdot \text{K}}\right)$

If two solutions have equal osmotic pressures (i.e., equal *effective* concentrations or osmolarities - see below for definition of osmolarity) they are said to be *isotonic*. Assume that solutions made up of solutes that are neither acids, bases, or salts (i.e., not ionic) and whose concentration (i.e., wt%, m, or M) is the same have the same effective concentration. If two solutions have unequal osmotic pressures the more concentrated solution is said to be *hypertonic*, while the more dilute solution is said to be *hypotonic*.

Example Problems:

1. The average osmotic pressure of seawater is about 30.0 atm at 25°C. Calculate the molar concentration of an aqueous solution of urea that is isotonic with seawater.

   Isotonic solutions have equal effective concentrations and thus equal osmotic pressures.

   $$\pi = MRT \quad \rightarrow \quad 30.0 \text{ atm} = M \; (0.0821 \text{ L} \cdot \text{atm/mol} \cdot \text{K}) \; (25 + 273 \text{ K})$$

   $$M = \frac{30.0}{0.0821 \bullet 298} = 1.23 \text{ M}$$

2. A solution of a 0.100 gram sample of an unknown dissolved in enough benzene to make 0.0300 L of solution exhibits an osmotic pressure of 5.50 torr at 27°C. What is the molar mass (in g/mol) of the unknown?

   $$\pi V = \left(\frac{g}{MM}\right)RT \rightarrow 5.50 \text{ torr x } 0.0300 \text{ L} = \frac{0.100 \text{ g}}{MM} \bullet 62.4 \frac{\text{L} \cdot \text{torr}}{\text{mol} \cdot \text{K}} \bullet (27 + 273 \text{ K})$$

   $$MM = \frac{0.100 \text{ x } 62.4 \text{ x } 300}{5.50 \text{ x } 0.0300} = 1.13 \text{ x } 10^4 \text{ g/mol}$$

3. In each of the cases given below, state in which compartment, if any, will the solution level be higher once equilibrium is reached. The solvent in each of the solutions is water.

	A	B
a)	1% sucrose	10% sucrose
b)	90 g $C_3H_6O_3$/L soln	180 g $C_6H_{12}O_6$/L soln

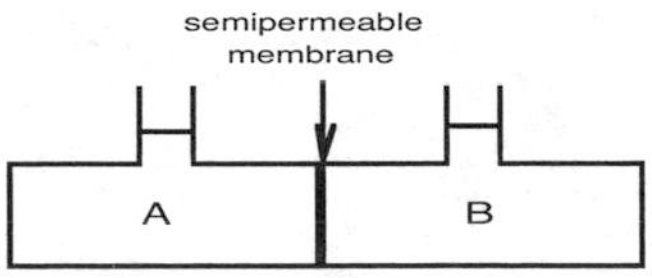

   The net movement of solvent molecules through a semipermeable membrane is from a pure solvent or from a dilute solution to a more concentrated solution.

   In a, the solution in compartment B is more concentrated than the solution in compartment A -- the level in compartment B will be higher.

   In b, the solution in compartment A (1 M soln) has the same effective concentration as the solution in compartment B (1 M soln) -- the levels will thus remain equal.

   $$M \text{ (compartment A)} = \frac{\frac{90 \text{ g}}{90 \text{ g/mol}}}{1\text{L}} = 1 \text{ M} \qquad M \text{ (compartment B)} = \frac{\frac{180 \text{ g}}{180 \text{ g/mol}}}{1\text{L}} = 1 \text{ M}$$

VII. Colligative Properties of Aqueous Electrolyte Solutions

As previously stated, colligative properties depend upon the *number* of solute particles. For nonionizing nonelectrolytes, 1 mol of solute gives rise to 1 mole of particles. For ionizing electrolytes, 1 mol of solute gives rise to *more* than 1 mole of particles. Consider the following examples:

Nonionizing Nonelectrolytes (General Formula: $C_xH_yO_z$)

$C_6H_{12}O_{6\,(s)} \xrightarrow{H_2O} C_6H_{12}O_{6\,(aq)}$ (1 mol $C_6H_{12}O_6 \rightarrow$ 1 mol of particles)

$C_3H_6O_{3\,(s)} \xrightarrow{H_2O} C_3H_6O_{3\,(aq)}$ (1 mol $C_3H_6O_3 \rightarrow$ 1 mol of particles)

Ionizing Strong Electrolytes (Strong acids & bases and soluble salts)

$KCl_{(s)} \xrightarrow{H_2O} K^+_{(aq)} + Cl^-_{(aq)}$ (1 mol KCl $\rightarrow$ 2 moles of particles)

$K_3PO_{4\,(s)} \xrightarrow{H_2O} 3\,K^+_{(aq)} + PO_4^{3-}{}_{(aq)}$ (1 mol $K_3PO_4 \rightarrow$ 4 moles of particles)

$V_2(SO_4)_{3\,(s)} \xrightarrow{H_2O} 2\,V^{3+}_{(aq)} + 3\,SO_4^{2-}{}_{(aq)}$ (1 mol $V_2(SO_4)_3 \rightarrow$ 5 moles of particles)

For strong electrolytes that ionize "completely", the effective concentration* of solute in solution is given by either its osmolarity or osmolality. For nonelectrolytes, its osmolarity equals its molarity and its osmolality equals its molality. For strong electrolytes, the osmolality and osmolarity are defined as follows:

Osmolality (Osm) - i (number of particles) x m (molality of the solution)

Osmolarity (OsM) - i (number of particles) x M (molarity of the solution)

For ionizing solutes, the boiling point elevation, the freezing point lowering, and the generation of osmotic pressure, are redefined as follows. (Actually the same equations can be used for nonionizing nonelectrolytes -- Osm = m and OsM = M).

boiling point elevation: $\Delta T_b = K_b \times Osm$

freezing point lowering: $\Delta T_f = K_f \times Osm$

osmotic pressure generation: $\pi = OsM \times R \times T$

----

* An assumption is made that the effective concentration of strong electrolytes is equal to its osmolarity or osmolality -- in actuality its effective concentration is less (especially the more concentrated the solution) due to ion association. The van't Hoff factor, i, is a multiplier that converts the stated concentration to the effective concentration. Thus we can also say:

$m_{effective} = i \times m$ where, $i <$ # of particles

$M_{effective} = i \times M$ where, $i <$ # of particles

Consult your textbook for a more detailed explanation of the van't Hoff factor if warranted.

Example Problems:

1. What is the boiling point elevation of a 1.00 m solution of KBr?

   $\Delta T_b = K_b \times Osm$ where, $Osm = i \times m$

   $0.512\ °C/m \times (2 \times 1.00\ m) = 1.02°C$

2. Which of the following solutions -- 2.00 m $C_3H_6O_3$ or 1.00 m K_2SO_4 -- will have a) the lowest freezing point, b) the highest boiling point, and c) the greatest osmotic pressure (assume the concentration is given in M (mole/L) soln instead of m (mol/kg solvent)?

   a) Since $\Delta T_f \propto$ Osm, the solution with the largest osmolality will have the lowest fp. Since the osmolality of K_2SO_4 (3 x 1.00 m) is greater than that for $C_3H_6O_3$ (1 x 2.00m), K_2SO_4 will have the lowest freezing point.

   b) Since $\Delta T_b \propto$ Osm, the solution with the largest osmolality will have the highest bp; therefore, K_2SO_4 will have the highest boiling point.

   c) Since $\pi \propto$ OsM, the solution with the largest osmolarity will have the greatest osmotic pressure; therefore, K_2SO_4 will have the largest osmotic pressure.

3. Compartment A (left compartment) is separated from compartment B (right compartment) by a semipermeable membrane. If a 1 M NaCl solution is in compartment A and a 1 M Na_2SO_4 solution is in compartment B, which compartment at equilibrium will the solution level be highest?

   In compartment B, because a 1 M NaCl solution (2 OsM) is more dilute than a 1 M Na_2SO_4 solution (3 OsM). Solvent flows from the more dilute to the more concentrated solution.

EXERCISES

Solutions, Dissolution Process, & The Effect of Temperature & Pressure on Solubility

1. The solubility of the amino acid dl-alanine in water at 25°C, is 16.7 g per 100 mL of water. Given this information, answer the following questions. (Assume that the temperature was 25°C.)
   a) A solution made by dissolving 16.7 g of dl-alanine in 100 mL of water would result in what kind of solution?
   b) A solution made by dissolving 16.6 g of dl-alanine in 100 mL of water would result in what kind of solution?
   c) A solution made by adding 19.0 g of dl-alanine in 100 mL of water should result in what kind of solution?
   d) When 16.9 g of dl-alanine were added to 100 mL of water, everything dissolved. What kind of solution was formed?

2. For each of the following predict whether the solubility of solute is high or low in the given solvent.

a) NaCl in H_2O	b) CH_3NH_2 in H_2O	c) HBr in H_2O	d) I_2 in H_2O
e) CCl_4 in H_2O	f) Ar in H_2O	g) HF in H_2O	h) NH_4Cl in H_2O
i) I_2 in CCl_4	j) Ar in CCl_4	k) NaCl in CCl_4	l) C_6H_6 in CCl_4
m) BF_3 in CCl_4	n) $MgCl_2$ in CCl_4	o) C_6H_6 in H_2O	p) $MgCl_2$ in H_2O
q) O_2 in N_2	r) Ar in $H_2O_{(g)}$		

3. Under typical lab conditions (25°C and 760 torr), given the following information, predict what happens to the solubility of the solute as a result of the following changes.
   [NOTE: Under typical lab conditions, generally, all salts are solids and the following common substances are gases (e.g., elements: H_2, O_2, N_2, F_2, Cl_2, noble gases; compounds: CO_2, CO, CH_4].

   A. When KI dissolves in water the beaker gets cold.
   B. Na_2SO_4 dissolves in water via an exothermic process.

   a) What happens to the solubility of KI in H_2O as the temperature is increased?
   b) What happens to the solubility of Na_2SO_4 in H_2O as the temperature is increased?
   c) What happens to the solubility of KI in H_2O as the pressure is increased?
   d) What happens to the solubility of Na_2SO_4 in H_2O as the pressure is decreased?
   e) What happens to the solubility of CO_2 in H_2O as the temperature is increased?
   f) What happens to the solubility of CO_2 in H_2O as the pressure is increased?

Concentration Units

4. What is the molality of a solution prepared by dissolving 2.00 mol of $C_6H_{12}O_6$ (MM = 180) in 100. mL of water (MM = 18.0, d = 1.00 g/mL)?
5. What is the molality of a solution prepared by dissolving 20.0 g of $C_6H_{12}O_6$ (MM = 180) in 100. g of water?
6. If 10.0 mL of Br_2 (d = 3.10 g/mL, MM = 160) are mixed with 100. mL of CCl_4 (d = 1.59 g/mL, MM = 154), then what is the molality of the resulting solution?
7. In order to prepare a 2.00 m solution of $C_6H_{12}O_6$ (MM = 180), how many grams of water are needed to dissolve 10.0 g of $C_6H_{12}O_6$?
8. A 2.00 m solution of CH_3OH (MM = 32.0) can be prepared by dissolving how many grams of CH_3OH in 1.00 kg of H_2O?
9. A 2.00 m solution of CH_3OH (MM = 32.0, d = 0.791 g/mL) can be prepared by dissolving how many mL of CH_3OH in 1.00 kg of H_2O?
10. If 0.100 mol of $C_6H_{12}O_6$ is dissolved in 200. mL of water, what is the mole fraction of each component in the solution?

11. If 5.50 g of $C_6H_{12}O_6$ (MM = 180) are dissolved in 20.0 mL of water, what is the mole fraction of each component in the solution?

12. If 10.0 mL of Br_2 (d = 3.10 g/mL, MM = 160) are mixed with 100. mL of CCl_4 (d = 1.59 g/mL, MM = 154), then what is the mole fraction of each component in the solution?

13. If 5.00 g of NaCl (MM = 58.5) and 5.00 g of NaBr (MM = 103) are dissolved with 100.0 g of water, then what is the mole fraction of each component in the solution?

Interconversion Among Concentration Units

14. What is the mole fraction of H_2O & CH_3OH in a solution whose molality is 2.00 m?
15. Calculate the molarity of a 15.0% NH_4OH (MM = 35.0) solution by weight if the density of the solution is 1.14 g/mL.
16. What is the weight percent of a 1.20 M NaOH (MM = 40.0) that has a density of 1.06 g/mL?
17. Given the following information,

    Concentrated HNO_3 (MM = 63.0) is 17.0 M and has a specific gravity of 1.42

    Calculate:
    a) its weight percent
    b) its molality
    c) the mole fraction of HNO_3 in solution
18. Given the following information,

    Concentrated HCl (MM = 36.5) is 37.0% HCl by weight and its density is 1.19 g/mL

    Calculate:
    a) its molarity
    b) its molality
    c) the mole fraction of H_2O in solution
19. Given the following information,

    Concentrated H_3PO_4 (MM = 98.0) is 56.8 m and its density is 1.70 g/mL

    Calculate:
    a) its molarity
    b) its weight percent
    c) the mole fraction of H_2O in solution

Colligative Properties of Nonelectrolyte Solutions

Lowering of Vapor Pressure & Raoult's Law

Solutions Containing Volatile Solutes

20. The vapor pressure of pure liquid A is 550 torr and the vapor pressure of pure liquid B is 320 torr at room temperature. If the vapor pressure of a solution containing A and B is 465 torr, what is the mole fraction of A in the solution?

21. A solution was prepared by dissolving 1.67 mole of liquid C with 3.15 mole of liquid D. At 55.0°C, if the vapor pressure of the solution was 355 torr and the vapor pressure of pure liquid C was 515 torr, then calculate the vapor pressure (in torr) of pure liquid D at this temperature?

Solutions Containing Non-Volatile Solutes

22. What is the vapor pressure (in torr) of a solution made by dissolving the following amounts of solute in 55.6 mol of water at 25°C? The vapor pressure of water at 25°C is 23.8 torr.
    a) 1 mol $C_6H_{12}O_6$ (MM =180)
    b) 1 mol $C_3H_6O_3$ (MM = 90.1)
    c) 2 mol $C_6H_{12}O_6$ (MM =180)
    d) 180. g $C_6H_{12}O_6$ (MM =180)
    e) 90.0 g $C_6H_{12}O_6$ (MM =180)
    f) 90.0 g $C_3H_6O_3$ (MM = 90.1)

23. Arrange the following in order of increasing vapor pressure:

1 m $C_3H_6O_3$,	1 m $C_6H_{12}O_6$,	2 m $C_6H_{12}O_6$,	180. g $C_6H_{12}O_6$ in 10.0 mol H_2O,	H_2O
A	B	C	D	E

24. The vapor pressure of water at 27°C is 26.7 torr. Determine the vapor pressure (in torr) of a solution (at 27°C) prepared by dissolving 18.0 g $C_6H_{12}O_6$ (MM =180) in 100. g of H_2O (MM = 18.0).

25. The vapor pressure of water at 27°C is 26.7 torr. Determine the vapor pressure lowering (in torr) associated with a solution (at 27°C) prepared by dissolving 18.0 g $C_6H_{12}O_6$ (MM =180) in 100. g of H_2O (MM = 18.0).

26. The vapor pressure of carbon tetrachloride at 23°C is 100 mm Hg. What is the vapor pressure (in torr) of a solution (at 23°C) prepared by dissolving 10.0 g of $C_{10}H_{22}$ (MM = 142) in 100. mL of CCl_4 (MM = 154, d = 1.59 g/mL)?

27. The vapor pressure of carbon tetrachloride at 23°C is 100 mm Hg. What is the vapor pressure lowering (in torr) associated with a solution (at 23°C) prepared by dissolving 10.0 g of $C_{10}H_{22}$ (MM = 142) in 100. mL of CCl_4 (MM = 154, d = 1.59 g/mL)?

28. What is the mole fraction of water in a solution whose temperature is 25°C and whose vapor pressure is 23.3 torr? The vapor pressure of water at 25°C is 23.8 torr.

Boiling Point Elevation

29. What is the boiling point elevation (in °C) of the following solutions made by dissolving each of the following amounts of solute in 1.00 kg of H_2O? (K_b, H_2O = 0.512 °C/m)
    a) 1 mol $C_6H_{12}O_6$ (MM =180)
    b) 1 mol $C_3H_6O_3$ (MM = 90.1)
    c) 2 mol $C_6H_{12}O_6$ (MM =180)
    d) 180. g $C_6H_{12}O_6$ (MM =180)
    e) 90.0 g $C_6H_{12}O_6$ (MM =180)
    f) 90.0 g $C_3H_6O_3$ (MM = 90.1)

30. What is the normal boiling point of each of the solutions in question 29?

31. Arrange the following in order of increasing boiling point:

1 m $C_3H_6O_3$,	1 m $C_6H_{12}O_6$,	2 m $C_6H_{12}O_6$,	180. g $C_6H_{12}O_6$ in 10.0 mol H_2O,	H_2O
A	B	C	D	E

32. By how many degrees Celsius would the bp of a solution prepared by dissolving 10.0 g of $C_{10}H_{22}$ (MM = 142) in 100. mL of CCl_4 (MM = 154, d = 1.59 g/mL, bp = 76.5°C, K_b = 5.03°C/m) be raised over that of pure CCl_4?

33. A solution of 1.00 g of an unknown organic compound in 100.0 g of CCl_4 (MM = 154, bp = 76.5°C, K_b = 5.03°C/m) is observed to have a bp of 77.2°C. Given this information, what must have been the molality of the solution?

34. A solution containing 10.0 g of a nonvolatile nonelectrolyte, Z, in 100.0 mL of CCl_4 (MM = 154, d = 1.59 g/mL, bp = 76.5°C, K_b = 5.03°C/m) is observed to have a bp of 77.2°C. What is the molar mass of Z?

35. A solution prepared by dissolving 142. g of $C_{10}H_{22}$ (MM = 142) in 1.00 kg of C_8H_{18} (MM = 114, bp = 125.6°C) is found to have a bp of 129.6°C. Given this information, what is the boiling point constant for C_8H_{18}?

36. How many grams of urea (MM = 60.1) must be added to 25.0 g of H_2O (MM = 18.0, K_b = 0.512 °C/m, bp = 100°C) to give a boiling-point elevation of 0.200°C?

Freezing Point Lowering

37. What is the freezing point depression (in °C) of the following solutions made by dissolving each of the following amounts of solute in 1.00 kg of H_2O? (K_f, H_2O = 1.86 °C/m)
    a) 1 mol $C_6H_{12}O_6$ (MM =180)
    b) 1 mol $C_3H_6O_3$ (MM = 90.1)
    c) 2 mol $C_6H_{12}O_6$ (MM =180)
    d) 180. g $C_6H_{12}O_6$ (MM =180)
    e) 90.0 g $C_6H_{12}O_6$ (MM =180)
    f) 90.0 g $C_3H_6O_3$ (MM = 90.1)

38. What is the normal freezing point of the each of the solutions in question *37*?

39. Arrange the following in order of increasing freezing point:

1 m $C_3H_6O_3$,	1 m $C_6H_{12}O_6$,	2 m $C_6H_{12}O_6$,	180. g $C_6H_{12}O_6$ in 10.0 mol H_2O,	H_2O
A	B	C	D	E

40. By how many degrees Centigrade would the freezing point of a solution prepared by dissolving 10.0 g of $C_{10}H_{22}$ (MM = 142) in 100. mL of C_6H_6 (MM = 78.1, d = 0.879 g/mL, fp = 5.5°C, K_f = 5.12°C/m) be lowered?

41. A solution of 1.00 g of an unknown organic compound in 100. g of C_6H_6 (MM = 78.1 fp = 5.5°C, K_f = 5.12°C/m) is observed to have a fp of 5.2°C. Given this information, what must have been the molality of the solution?

42. A solution containing 20.0 g of a nonvolatile nonelectrolyte, Z, in 100. mL of C_6H_6 (MM = 78.1, d = 0.879 g/mL, fp = 5.5°C, K_f = 5.12°C/m) is observed to have a fp of 2.5°C. What is the molar mass (in g/mol) of Z?

43. A solution prepared by dissolving 142. g of $C_{10}H_{22}$ (MM = 142) in 1.00 kg of C_6H_{12} (MM = 114, fp = 6.55°C) is found to have a fp of -13.45 °C. Given this information, what is the freezing point constant (in °C/m) for C_6H_{12}?

44. How many grams of urea (MM = 60.1) must be added to 25.0 g of water (MM = 18.0, K_f = 1.86 °C/m, fp = 0.00°C) to give a freezing-point depression of 0.200°C?

Osmotic Pressure Generation

45. What is the molarity of a solution whose osmotic pressure at 27.0°C is 5.0 atm?

46. At what temperature (in K) will a solution whose molarity is 0.0560 have an osmotic pressure of 957 torr?

47. The osmotic pressure at 20.0°C of a solution prepared by dissolving 0.270 g of unknown in enough water to make 50.0 mL of solution is 20.5 torr. Given this information, what is the molar mass (in g/mol) of the unknown?

48. In each of the cases given below, state in which compartment, if any, will the solution level be higher once equilibrium is reached. The solvent in each of the solutions is water and the solute does not ionize in water.

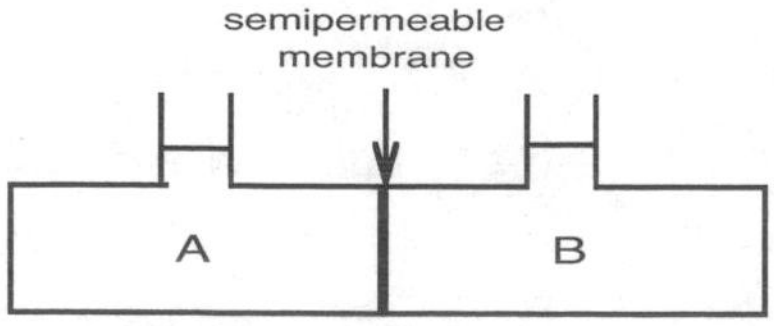

	A	B
a)	180 g $C_3H_6O_3$/L soln	180 g $C_6H_{12}O_6$/L soln
b)	1 M glucose	1 M sucrose
c)	2.0 M sucrose	1.5 M glucose

Colligative Properties of Aqueous Electrolyte Solutions

49. When each of the following are placed in water, will they be nonelectrolytes or strong electrolytes?

a) CH_3OH b) $C_5H_{10}O_5$ c) Li_3AsO_4 d) K_3PO_4 e) HI

f) $Fe(NO_3)_3$ g) CH_3CH_2OH h) Na_2HPO_3 i) $Ca(C_2H_3O_2)_2$ j) $KMnO_4$

50. Assuming that the effective concentration is equal to the osmolality of the solution, calculate the normal boiling point of a 1 m solution of each of the following compounds. (for H_2O: bp = 100.0°C and K_b = 0.512 °C/m)

a) CH_3OH b) $Fe(NO_3)_3$ c) Na_2HPO_3 d) K_3PO_4 e) $KMnO_4$

51. Assuming that the effective concentration is equal to the osmolality of the solution, calculate the normal freezing point of a 1 m solution for each of the compounds given in question *50.* (for H_2O: fp = 0.0°C and K_f = 1.86 °C/m)

52. Assuming that the effective concentration is equal to the osmolarity of the solution, calculate the osmotic pressure (in torr) that is generated by a 1 M solution at 25°C for each of the compounds given in question *50.*

53. Which of the following solutions is expected to have:

A. 3 m CH_3OH B. 1 m $Fe(NO_3)_3$ C. 2 m Na_2HPO_3 D. 3 m $Ca(C_2H_3O_2)_2$

a) the highest freezing point?
b) the lowest boiling point?
c) the lowest osmotic pressure (consider that the concentration of the solution is in molarity instead of molality)?

54. Consider the diagram given in question *48.* In each of the cases given below, state in which compartment, if any, will the solution level be expected to be higher once equilibrium is reached.

	A	B
a)	1 M CH_3OH	1 M Na_2HPO_3
b)	1 M $RbC_2H_3O_2$	2 M CH_3OH
c)	3 M $Ca(C_2H_3O_2)_2$	6 M $C_5H_{10}O_5$
d)	100 g K_3PO_4 (MM = 164) / L solution	100 g CH_3OH (MM = 32) / L solution

----

ENRICHMENT

55. See the footnote on page 2-12 before doing b and c.

a) Assuming that CsCl completely dissociates in water, what is the freezing point of a 0.121 m solution of CsCl? ($K_{f,\ water}$ = 1.86 °C/m)
b) Given that a 0.121 m solution of CsCl freezes at -0.403°C, calculate its van't Hoff factor (i).
c) Given that a 0.121 m solution of CsCl freezes at -0.403°C, calculate its apparent % dissociation.

MULTIPLE CHOICE PRACTICE EXAM FOR MODULE 2

1. Which of the following solute/solvent pairs are expected to have a high solubility in each other?
   a. SiH_4 in CCl_4 b. CH_3OH in H_2O c. BCl_3 in CCl_4
   1) only b 2) only c 3) only b & c 4) only a & c 5) a, b, & c

2. Which of the following are expected to be water soluble (or miscible)?
   1) SiH_4 2) CH_3NH_2 3) $Ba_3(PO_4)_2$ 4) $KMnO_4$
   5) Only two of the above.

3. When the solute KBr is placed in water:
   1) an increase in entropy is likely to occur and since each ion has a low charge, KBr is expected to be soluble in water .
   2) each potassium ion will be surrounded by water molecules in which the hydrogen atom of water will be interacting with the potassium ion.
   3) Each bromide ion will be surrounded by water molecules in which the oxygen atom of water will be interacting with the bromide ion.
   4) Two or more of the above statements are true.
   5) None of the above statements are true.

4. Which of the following statements is true in regards to how temperature and pressure is expected to affect the solubility of a solute in a solvent?
   1) Oxygen is more soluble in water at 25°C than it is at 50°C.
   2) Sodium chloride is appreciably more soluble in water at a pressure of 760 torr than it is at a pressure of 730 torr.
   3) As a scuba diver descends deeper into the ocean less gas will dissolve in the diver's bloodstream.
   4) When $CaCl_2$ is placed in a beaker containing water, the beaker noticeably gets hotter. An increase in temperature will more likely cause the solubility of $CaCl_2$ in water to increase.
   5) Two of the above statements are true.

Consider the following information when answering Questions 5 - 6. When 28.0 g of Br_2 (MM = 160) is dissolved in 150. g of CCl_4 (MM = 154), then

5. What is the molality of the solution?
   1) 0.0348 2) 0.432 3) 1.17 4) 1.41 5) 34.8

6. What is the mole fraction of Br_2?
   1) 1.17×10^{-3} 2) 0.152 3) 0.157 4) 0.181 5) 0.848

7. In order to prepare a 0.175 m solution of Br_2 (MM = 160) in CCl_4 (MM = 154), how many grams of CCl_4 are needed to dissolve 0.250 mol of Br_2?
   1) 1.43×10^3 2) 9.28 3) 700 4) 43.8 5) 8.93

8. What is the molality of a 20.0% by weight $(NH_4)_2SO_4$ (MM = 132) solution (d = 1.117 g/mL)?
   1) 1.69 2) 0.150 3) 1.51 4) 2.10 5) 1.89

9. What is the molarity of a 20.0% by weight $(NH_4)_2SO_4$ (MM = 132) solution (d = 1.117 g/mL)?
   1) 1.69 2) 0.150 3) 1.51 4) 2.10 5) 1.89

10. Calculate the molarity of a 7.98 m H_2SO_4 (MM = 98.1) solution (d = 1.34 g/mL).
    1) 14.2 2) 4.44 3) 6.0 4) 5.96 5) 0.168

11. As the concentration of a non-volatile solute in a solution is increased, ________.
    1) the vapor pressure of the solution increases.
    2) the freezing point of the solution increases.
    3) the osmotic pressure that is generated increases.
    4) Two of the above choices.
    5) None of the above choices.

12. If 28.2 g of $C_{20}H_{42}$ (MM = 282) are dissolved in 500. g of C_6H_6 (MM = 78.0, $P^{o}_{25.0°C}$ = 93.4 torr), then what is the vapor pressure (in torr) of the solution at 25.0°C? (Assume that the solute is a nonvolatile-nonelectrolyte.)
1) 0.00 2) 92.0 3) 93.4 4) 94.8 5) 760

13. If 6.0 g of urea (MM = 60.1) are dissolved in 32.0 g of CH_3OH (MM = 32.0, $P^{o}_{20°C}$ = 89 torr), then what is vapor pressure depression (in torr) of the solution at 20°C? (Assume that the solute is a nonvolatile-nonelectrolyte.)
1) 6.0 2) 14 3) 8.1 4) 75 5) 81

14. Which of the following has the highest boiling point? (The solvent is water.)
1) 0.5 m $ZnCl_2$ 2) 1 m $C_3H_6O_3$ 3) 0.5 m $NaNO_3$ 4) 0.2 m Na_3PO_4 5) pure H_2O

15. If 1.00 mol of substance A (MM = 200) is dissolved in 500. g of CCl_4 (MM = 157, K_b = 5.03 °C/m, bp = 76.5°C), then what is the boiling point (in °C) of the solution? (Assume that the solute is a nonvolatile-nonelectrolyte.)
1) 71.5 2) 81.5 3) 66.4 4) 86.6 5) 76.6

16. The boiling point for a solution prepared by dissolving 9.81 g of compound D into 90.0 g of water (MM = 18, K_b = 0.512 °C/m, bp = 100°C) was found to be 100.37°C. Given this information, what is the molar mass (in g/mol) of compound D? (Assume that the solute is a nonvolatile-nonelectrolyte.)
1) 175 2) 34 3) 150 4) 240 5) 79

17. Which of the following has the lowest freezing point? (The solvent is water.)
1) 0.5 m $ZnCl_2$ 2) 1 m $C_3H_6O_3$ 3) 0.5 m $NaNO_3$ 4) 0.2 m Na_3PO_4 5) pure H_2O

18. What is the molality of an aqueous solution whose freezing point is -0.093°C? (Assume that the solute is a nonvolatile-nonelectrolyte.) For water, K_f = 1.86 °C/m & fp = 0.00°C
1) 0.093 2) 0.17 3) 1.86 4) 20 5) 0.050

19. Calculate K_f (in °C/m) for the solvent bromoform (MM = 253, fp = 8.3°C, d = 2.89 g/mL) given the following information: When 28.2 g of $C_{20}H_{42}$ (MM = 282) are dissolved in 173. mL of bromoform, the freezing point of the solution is 5.4°C. (Assume that the solute is a nonvolatile-nonelectrolyte.)
1) 17.8 2) 0.069 3) 5.0 4) 14.5 5) 2.9

20. Which of the following generates the highest osmotic pressure? (The solvent is water.)
1) 0.5 M $ZnCl_2$ 2) 1 M $C_3H_6O_3$ 3) 0.5 M $NaNO_3$ 4) 0.2 M Na_3PO_4 5) pure H_2O

21. What is the molarity of a solution that generates an osmotic pressure of 2000. mm Hg at 20.0°C? (Assume that the solute is a nonvolatile-nonelectrolyte.)
1) 0.109 2) 1.60 3) 83.1 4) 0.624 5) 9.17

22. If 0.20 g of an unknown compound, dissolved in enough water so as to produce 100. mL of solution (MM = 18.0, d = 1.00 g/mL) at 25.°C, generates an osmotic pressure of 9.8 torr, then calculate the molar mass of this unknown compound. (Assume that the solute is a nonvolatile-nonelectrolyte.)
1) 3.5×10^3 2) 3.8×10^3 3) 4.0×10^4 4) 4.5×10^4 5) 40.

23. Which of the following is (are) true?
1) During osmosis there is a net flow of water through a semipermeable membrane from a 0.5 M $C_6H_{12}O_6$ solution in one compartment to another compartment containing pure water.
2) The mole fraction of a solute can never be greater than one.
3) The freezing point of an aqueous solution must always be less than 0.00°C.
4) Two of the above statements.
5) All of the above statements.

MODULE 2 - ANSWERS

1. a) saturated b) unsaturated c) saturated d) supersaturated
2. a) high b) high c) high d) low e) low f) low
   g) high h) high i) high j) high k) low l) high
   m) high n) low o) low p) high q) high
   r) high (gases are soluble in each other)
3. a) increase b) decrease c) no effect d) no effect e) decrease f) increase
4. 20.0 m
5. 1.11 m
6. 1.22 m
7. 27.8 g
8. 64.0 g
9. 80.9 mL
10. $X_{C_6H_{12}O_6} = 8.92 \times 10^{-3}$ $X_{H_2O} = 0.991$
11. $X_{C_6H_{12}O_6} = 2.68 \times 10^{-2}$ $X_{H_2O} = 0.973$
12. $X_{Br_2} = 0.159$ $X_{CCl_4} = 0.841$
13. $X_{NaCl} = 1.50 \times 10^{-2}$ $X_{NaBr} = 8.52 \times 10^{-3}$ $X_{H_2O} = 0.976$
14. $X_{CH_3OH} = 3.47 \times 10^{-2}$ $X_{H_2O} = 0.965$
15. 4.89 M
16. 4.53%
17. a) 75.4% b) 48.7 m c) 0.467
18. a) 12.1 M b) 16.1 m c) 0.775
19. a) 14.7 M b) 84.8% c) 0.495
20. 0.630
21. 270 torr
22. a) 23.4 torr b) 23.4 torr c) 23.0 torr d) 23.4 torr e) 23.6 torr f) 23.4 torr
23. D < C < A = B < E
24. 26.2 torr
25. 0.5 torr
26. 93.6 torr
27. 6.39 torr
28. 0.979
29. a) 0.512°C b) 0.512°C c) 1.024°C d) 0.512°C e) 0.256°C f) 0.511°C
30. a) 100.512°C b) 100.512°C c) 101.024°C d) 100.512°C e) 100.256°C f) 100.511°C
31. E < A = B < C < D
32. 2.23°C
33. 0.139 m
34. 452 g/mol
35. 4.00 °C/m
36. 0.587 g
37. a) 1.86°C b) 1.86°C c) 3.72°C d) 1.86°C e) 0.930°C f) 1.86°C
38. a) -1.86°C b) -1.86°C c) -3.72°C d) -1.86°C e) -0.930°C f) -1.86°C
39. D < C < A = B < E
40. 4.10°C
41. 0.0586 m
42. 388 g/mol
43. 20.0 °C/m
44. 0.162 g
45. 0.203 M
46. 274 K
47. 4816 g/mol
48. a) A b) equal c) A
49. a) non b) non c) strong d) strong e) strong f) strong
   g) non h) strong i) strong j) strong
50. a) 100.512°C b) 102.048°C c) 101.536°C d) 102.048°C e) 101.024°C
51. a) -1.86°C b) -7.44°C c) -5.58°C d) -7.44°C e) -3.72°C
52. a) 1.86×10^4 torr b) 7.44×10^4 torr c) 5.58×10^4 torr d) 7.44×10^4 torr e) 3.72×10^4 torr
53. a) A b) A c) A
54. a) B b) equal c) A d) B
55. a) -0.450°C b) 1.79 c) 90%

ANSWERS TO MULTIPLE CHOICE PRACTICE EXAM

1	2	3	4	5	6	7	8	9	10	11	12	13	14	15	16	17	18	19	20	21	22	23
5	5	1	1	3	2	1	5	1	3	3	2	3	1	4	3	1	5	4	1	1	2	4

MODULE 3. Chemical Thermodynamics

I. Definitions

Thermochemistry - the study of heat changes in chemical and physical processes. Thermochemistry is part of a much more general subject called thermodynamics.

Thermodynamics - the study of the interconversion of heat and other kinds of energy. Thermodynamics can be used to: study the strength of interactions, predict the spontaneity of reactions or electrochemical processes, study the extent to which a reaction goes to completion.

Thermodynamics is also applied to many engineering, physical, and biochemical systems (e.g., the cytochrome system in the body).

Energy - the capacity to do work or transfer heat. [Common units -- Joule (J) or calorie (cal)]

Potential Energy (PE) - the energy an object possesses because of its position or composition. This is the kind of energy found in chemicals such as natural gas and gasoline.

Kinetic Energy (KE) - the energy of motion ($E_{kinetic} = \frac{1}{2} mv^2$)

Law of Conservation of Energy / First Law of Thermodynamics - although energy can assume many forms that are interconvertible, energy can neither be created or destroyed; thus, the total energy of the universe is constant.

Endothermic Process - a chemical reaction or physical change that occurs with the absorption of heat (i.e., a decrease in temperature is observed). A process that requires (absorbs) heat, by convention, is assigned a "+" sign.

Exothermic Process - a chemical reaction or physical change that occurs with the simultaneous evolution of heat (i.e., an increase in temperature is observed). A process that releases (evolves) heat, by convention, is assigned a "-" sign.

System - For chemists, systems include substances and the container in which those substances are in during a chemical or physical process. For example, in a neutralization experiment, the system may be a beaker containing the acid to which the base is added.

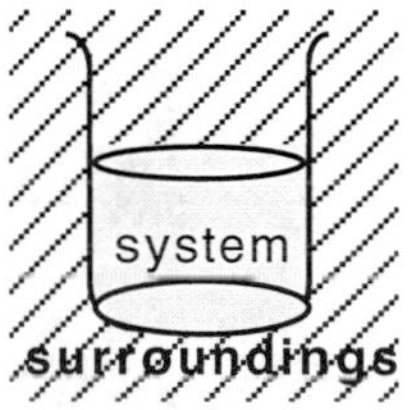

Open System - a system which can exchange mass and energy (heat) with its surroundings.

Closed System - a system which allows the transfer of energy (heat) but not mass.

Isolated System - a system that does not allow the transfer of either mass or energy (heat).

Surroundings - anything outside the system.

Universe - the system and its surroundings.

Isothermal Process - a chemical reaction or physical change that occurs at a constant temperature.

Isobaric Process - a chemical reaction or physical change that occurs at a constant pressure.

Isochoric (or Isovolumetric) Process - a chemical reaction or physical change that occurs at a constant volume.

Adiabatic (or Isocaloric) Process - a chemical reaction or physical change that occurs in such a manner such that no heat is gained or lost by the system.

Thermodynamic State - A set of conditions (temperature, pressure, composition, and physical state) that describe each part of the system.

II. Calorimetry

Calorimetry is defined as the measurement of heat changes. Chemical reactions and physical changes usually occur with either the simultaneous evolution of heat (*exothermic process*) or the absorption of heat (*endothermic process*). The amount of heat transferred in a process is usually expressed in *calories (cal)* or in the SI unit of *joules (J)*.

$$1 \text{ cal} = 4.184 \text{ J}$$

A. Specific Heat and Heat Capacity

Specific heat, given the symbol s, is defined as the amount of heat necessary to raise the temperature of 1 g of a substance by 1°C. Each substance has a specific heat, which is a physical intensive property, like density and melting point. The specific heat for a substance, while in the same physical state, varies with temperature. However, these variations are so small that we will assume that while a substance is in a particular physical state that its specific heat is temperature independent. From a knowledge of the specific heat, the heat (q) that is absorbed or released in a given process can be calculated by use of the following equation.

$$q = m \times s \times \Delta T$$

q (heat energy) → cal or J

m (mass) → g

s (specific heat) → $\frac{cal}{g \cdot {}^\circ C}$ or $\frac{J}{g \cdot {}^\circ C}$

$\Delta T = T_{final} - T_{initial}$ (change in temp - make ΔT a positive #) → °C

Substances with large specific heats require more heat to raise their temperature. The high specific heat of water (which constitutes ~60% of our body weight) makes our body's important task of maintaining a constant body temperature of ~37°C much easier. Thus, our body has the ability to absorb and release considerable amounts of energy with little change in temperature.

Heat capacity is defined as the amount of heat required to raise the temperature of a given quantity of a substance by 1°C. The relationship between heat capacity, given the symbol C, and specific heat is:

$$C = m \times s \qquad \left(\text{Units for } C = \frac{cal}{{}^\circ C} \text{ or } \frac{J}{{}^\circ C}\right)$$

Thus, the amount of heat released or absorbed in a given process can also be defined as:

$$q = C \times \Delta T$$

According to the Law of Conservation of Energy, if a hot object is dropped into a cold object or vice-versa, then the heat given up by the hot object to the cold object can be expressed as follows: [Note: object → solid, liquid, or gas]

heat lost by hot object (q_{lost}) = heat gained by cold object (q_{gained})

The specific heat of certain objects can be obtained by dropping a known amount of the hot object at a known temperature into a known amount of "cold" water at a known temperature. The heat that is transferred by the hot object (e.g., a metal) to the cold object (i.e., water in this case) can be expressed as follows: [Note: object → solid or liquid]

heat given up by hot object = heat taken in by cold object

$$q_{hot} = q_{cold}$$

$$(m \times s \times \Delta T)_{hot} = (m \times s \times \Delta T)_{cold}$$

<u>Schematic of how the specific heat of an object can be obtained</u>

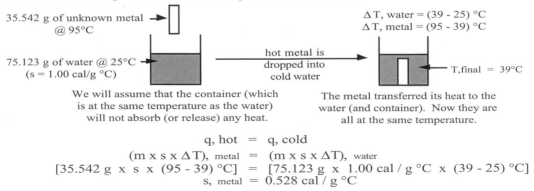

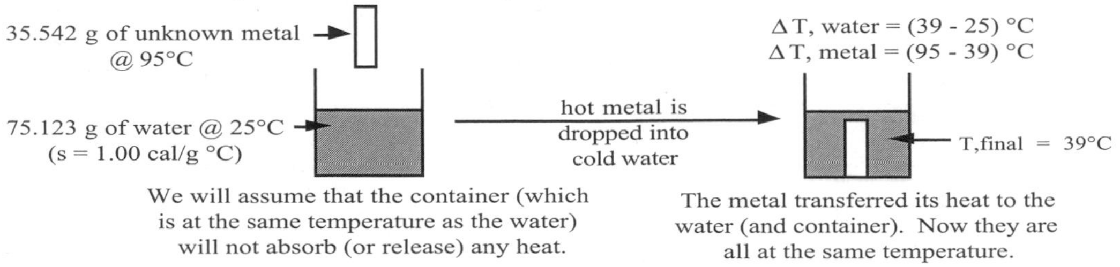

$$q, hot = q, cold$$

$$(m \times s \times \Delta T)_{metal} = (m \times s \times \Delta T)_{water}$$

$$[35.542\ g \times s \times (95 - 39)\ {}^\circ C] = [75.123\ g \times 1.00\ cal / g\ {}^\circ C \times (39 - 25)\ {}^\circ C]$$

$$s_{metal} = 0.528\ cal / g\ {}^\circ C$$

For now, we are going to ignore the sign conventions ("+" sign for an endothermic process and "-" sign for an exothermic process) and we are going to assume that we will be working with isolated systems [systems that do not allow the transfer of either mass or energy (heat)].

Example Problems:

1. How many joules are required to heat 352. g of water (s = 1.00 cal/g · °C) from 32°C to 95°C?

$$q = m \times s \times \Delta T$$

$$q = (352.\ g)\left(1.00 \frac{cal}{g \cdot {}^\circ C}\right)(95°C - 32°C) = 2.2 \times 10^4\ cal$$

$$?\ J = 2.2 \times 10^4\ cal \left(\frac{4.184\ J}{1\ cal}\right) = 9.2 \times 10^4\ J$$

2. If we add 450 cal of heat to 37 g of ethyl alcohol (s = 0.59 cal/ g · °C) at 20°C, what would its final temperature be?

$$q = m \times s \times \Delta T \rightarrow 450\ cal = 37\ g \times 0.59 \frac{cal}{g \cdot {}^\circ C} \times \Delta T$$

$$\Delta T = \frac{450\ cal}{\left(0.59 \frac{cal}{g \cdot {}^\circ C}\right) \times 37\ g} = 21°C$$

Since heat was added, the final temperature must be greater than the initial temperature.

$$\Delta T = T_{final} - T_{initial} \rightarrow 21°C = T_{final} - 20°C \rightarrow T_{final} = 21°C + 20°C = 41°C$$

3. What is the heat capacity (in J/°C) of a 1.00-kg block of aluminum (s_{Al} = 0.89 J/g ·°C)?

$$C = m \times s = \left(1.00\ kg\left(\frac{10^3\ g}{1\ kg}\right)\right) \times 0.89 \frac{J}{g \cdot {}^\circ C} = 8.9 \times 10^2 \frac{J}{{}^\circ C}$$

B. Constant-Pressure Calorimetry

A device used for determining the heat transfer for a variety of physical and chemical processes (except for the notable exception of combustion reactions) under constant atmospheric pressures is a *constant-pressure calorimeter*. To express the heat that is released or absorbed under constant pressure conditions the symbols, ΔH (pronounced as "delta" H and referred to as enthalpy) or q_p (p → constant pressure) are used. Enthalpy, ΔH, will be more fully discussed later on in this module.

The constant-pressure calorimeter most often used in general chemistry labs to illustrate the principles of calorimetry is the "coffee-cup" calorimeter. This calorimeter is constructed from two nested Styrofoam cups, as shown in the figure to your right. Because the calorimeter is not sealed, the process whose heat transfer is to be measured, occurs essentially under constant atmospheric pressures (i.e. isobaric process). Reactions are chosen so that no gaseous reactants or products are involved.

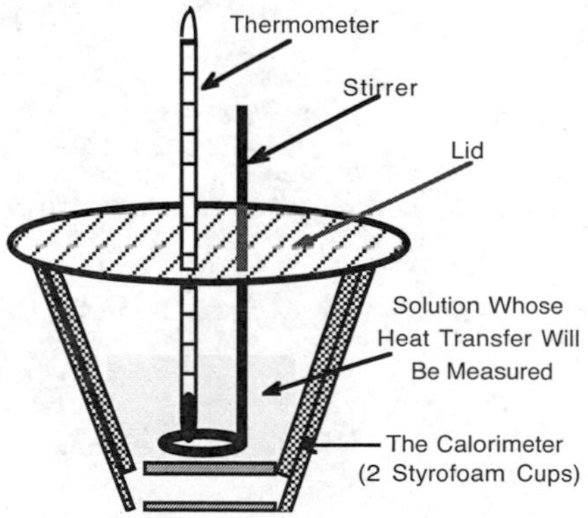

Since the same calorimeter is used throughout an experiment it thus becomes easier to use its heat capacity, C (where m x s is constant). The heat capacity of a coffee-cup calorimeter is often obtained by pouring a known amount of hot water into a known amount of cold water. Since the heat given up (i.e., lost) by the hot object (hot water) must be equal to the heat absorbed (i.e., gained) by the cold object (cold water & the calorimeter) we have the following relationships:

$$q_{lost} = q_{gained}$$

$$q_{hot\ water} = q_{cold\ water} + q_{cal}$$

$$(m\ x\ s\ x\ \Delta T)_{hot\ water} = (m\ x\ s\ x\ \Delta T)_{cold\ water} + (C\ x\ \Delta T)_{cal}$$

After rearranging the above equation, C_{cal} can be obtained as such:

$$C_{cal} = \frac{(m\ x\ s\ x\ \Delta T)_{hot\ water} - (m\ x\ s\ x\ \Delta T)_{cold\ water}}{\Delta T_{cal}}$$

Example Problems:

1. A 94.4 g piece of iron at 152.6°C was dropped into 140. mL of octane at 24.7°C contained in a coffee-cup calorimeter. The final temperature reached was 45.2°C. Given this information, what is the specific heat of octane in J/g · °C? *Assume that the calorimeter absorbs a negligible amount of heat.* $s_{Fe} = 0.44$ J/g · °C; $d_{octane} = 0.703$ g/mL

$$q_{lost} = q_{gained}$$

$$q_{Fe} = q_{octane} + q_{cal}{\nearrow}^{0}$$

$$(m\ x\ s\ x\ \Delta T)_{Fe} = (m\ x\ s\ x\ \Delta T)_{octane}$$

$$(94.4\ g)\left(0.44\ \frac{J}{g\cdot°C}\right)(152.6°C - 45.2°C) = \left(140\ mL\ x\ 0.703\ \frac{g}{mL}\right)(s_{octane})(45.2°C - 24.7°C)$$

$$4461\ J = 2018\ g\cdot°C\ x\ s_{octane}$$

$$s_{octane} = \frac{4461}{2018} = 2.2\ \frac{J}{g\cdot°C}$$

2. When 49.787 g of water at 64.5°C is poured into 50.045 g of water at 24.2°C contained in a coffee-cup calorimeter, the temperature rises to 43.5°C. Given this information, what is the heat capacity (in cal/°C) of the calorimeter? ($s_{water} = 1.00$ cal/g · °C)

$$q_{lost} = q_{gained}$$

$$q_{hot\ water} = q_{cold\ water} + q_{cal}$$

$$(m\ x\ s\ x\ \Delta T)_{hot\ water} = (m\ x\ s\ x\ \Delta T)_{cold\ water} + (C\ x\ \Delta T)_{cal}$$

$$(49.787\ g)\left(1.00\ \frac{cal}{g\cdot°C}\right)(64.5 - 43.5)\ °C = (50.045\ g)\left(1.00\ \frac{cal}{g\cdot°C}\right)(43.5 - 24.2)\ °C + (C_{cal})(43.5 - 24.2)°C$$

$$1046\ cal = 966\ cal + C_{cal}\ x\ 19.3\ °C$$

$$C_{cal} = \frac{1046 - 966}{19.3} = 4.2\ \frac{cal}{°C}$$

3. When a metal cylinder whose mass is 27.291 g and whose temperature is 94.2°C is dropped into 40.572 g of water at 24.1°C contained in the same coffee-cup calorimeter as in example problem 2 (above), the temperature of the water rises to 29.4°C. Given this information, what is the specific heat (in cal/g · °C) of the metal cylinder?

$$q_{lost} = q_{gained}$$

$$q_{metal} = q_{cold\ water} + q_{cal}$$

$$(m\ x\ s\ x\ \Delta T)_{metal} = (m\ x\ s\ x\ \Delta T)_{cold\ water} + (C\ x\ \Delta T)_{cal}$$

$$(27.291\ g)(s_{metal})(94.2 - 29.4)°C = (40.572\ g)\left(1.00\ \frac{cal}{g\cdot°C}\right)(29.4 - 24.1)\ °C + \left(4.2\ \frac{cal}{°C}\right)(29.4 - 24.1)\ °C$$

$$1768\ g\cdot°C\ x\ s_{metal} = 215\ cal + 22\ cal$$

$$s_{metal} = \frac{215 + 22}{1768} = 0.13\ \frac{cal}{g\cdot°C}$$

4. When 50.0 mL of 2.11 M HCl (T = 24.0°C) were mixed with 50.0 mL of 2.11 M NaOH (T = 24.0°C) in a coffee-cup calorimeter having a heat capacity of 4.2 cal/°C, the temperature rose to 38.2°C. Assume that: the density and the specific heat of the resulting solution are the same as that for water (d = 1.00 g/mL & s = 1.00 cal/g·°C) and that volumes are additive. Given all this information, then:

   a) How much heat (in cal) was released by this neutralization reaction?

   The amount of heat released by the neutralization reaction (q_{neut}) is equal to the heat absorbed by the resulting solution (q_{soln}) and the calorimeter. The mass of the solution can be obtained as follows:

$$? \, g_{soln} = (50.0 + 50.0) \text{ mL} \left(\frac{1.00 \text{ g}}{\text{mL}}\right) = 100. \text{ g}$$

$$q_{lost} = q_{gained}$$

$$q_{neut} = q_{soln} + q_{cal}$$

$$q_{neut} = (m \times s \times \Delta T)_{soln} + (C \times \Delta T)_{cal}$$

$$q_{neut} = (100 \text{ g})\left(1.00 \frac{\text{cal}}{\text{g·°C}}\right)(38.2 - 24.0)\ °\text{C} + \left(4.2 \frac{\text{cal}}{°\text{C}}\right)(38.2 - 24.0)\ °\text{C}$$

$$q_{neut} = 1420 \text{ cal} + 60 \text{ cal} = 1.48 \times 10^3 \text{ cal}$$

   b) Calculate the heat transfer per mol of HCl (i.e., # cal released/mol HCl)?

   Remember: M (mol/L) x V (L) = mol

$$? \frac{\text{cal}}{\text{mol HCl}} = \frac{1.48 \times 10^3 \text{ cal}}{2.11 \text{ M} \times 50.0 \times 10^{-3} \text{ L}} = 1.40 \times 10^4 \frac{\text{cal}}{\text{mol}}$$

   To make it emphatic that heat was released (i.e., T increased), a negative sign should be used; thus, the heat transfer (ΔH) for this process is equal to -1.40×10^4 cal/mol

C. **Constant-Volume Calorimetry**

Heats of combustion (the amount of heat that is released when a particular compound is burned in presence of oxygen) are measured by placing a known mass of compound under study in a steel container, called a *constant-volume bomb calorimeter*, which is filled with oxygen to a pressure of about 30 atm. To express the heat that is released or absorbed under constant volume (or isochoric) conditions the symbols, ΔE or ΔU (change in internal energy) or q_v (v → constant volume) are used. Internal energy will be more fully discussed later on in this module.

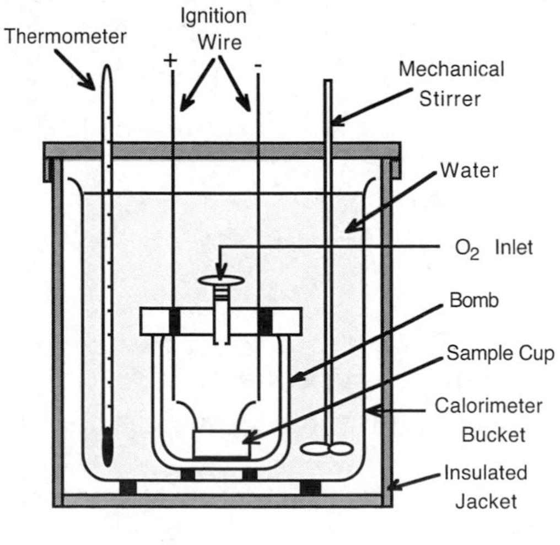

The closed bomb is immersed in a known amount of water, as shown in the figure to your right. The sample is electrically ignited and the heat produced by the combustion can be calculated accurately by recording the rise in the temperature of the water. The heat capacity of a bomb calorimeter is usually obtained by combusting a sample that gives off a known amount of heat. The temperature of both the sample and the calorimeter is the same as that of the water surrounding the calorimeter. Since the heat [q_{comb}] given up by the combusted sample ["the hot object"] is equal to the heat absorbed by the water and the calorimeter ["the cold object(s)"] then we basically have the same relationship as that of the constant-pressure calorimeter.

$$q_{lost} = q_{gained}$$

$$q_{comb} = q_{water} + q_{cal}$$

$$q_{comb} = (m \text{ x } s \text{ x } \Delta T)_{water} + (C \text{ x } \Delta T)_{cal}$$

Thus C_{cal} can be obtained by rearranging the above equation:

$$C_{cal} = \frac{q_{comb} - (m \text{ x } s \text{ x } \Delta T)_{water}}{\Delta T}$$

Example Problem:

1. 2.000 grams of an unknown sample at 20.5°C was burned in a bomb calorimeter. As a result the temperature of the 1000. g of water surrounding the bomb rose to 25.5°C. If the heat capacity of the bomb was equal to 4.50 cal/°C and s_{water} = 1.00 cal/g · °C, then:

   a) Was the reaction endothermic or exothermic?

      Exothermic because the temperature rose from 20.5°C to 25.5°C.

   b) How much heat (in cal) was released by the combustion of the 2.000 g of sample?

      The amount of heat released by the combustion reaction (q_{comb}) is equal to the heat gained by the bomb calorimeter and its contents ($q_{water} + q_{cal}$).

$$q_{lost} = q_{gained}$$

$$q_{comb} = q_{water} + q_{cal}$$

$$q_{comb} = (m \text{ x } s \text{ x } \Delta T)_{water} + (C \text{ x } \Delta T)_{cal}$$

$$q_{comb} = \left(1000.\ \text{g x } 1.00 \frac{\text{cal}}{\text{g} \cdot {}^\circ\text{C}} \text{ x } (25.5 - 20.5)^\circ\text{C}\right) + \left(4.50 \frac{\text{cal}}{{}^\circ\text{C}} \text{ x } (25.5 - 20.5)^\circ\text{C}\right)$$

$$q_{comb} = 5000 \text{ cal} + 23 \text{ cal} = 5.0 \text{ x } 10^3 \text{ cal}$$

III. State Functions

A *state function* is a variable that describes the state (i.e., temperature, pressure, composition, and physical state) of the system; it is a function that is independent of the pathway by which a process occurs. Several state functions that we have already encountered, are P, V, and T. We shall soon see that the energy that a system possesses is also a state function.

Many scales that we use in thermodynamics are defined arbitrarily. Arbitrary scales are useful when we are interested in changes in the quantity being described. Thus, the most important use of state functions is to describe changes (i.e., differences in initial and final conditions), for example:

$$\Delta X = X_{final} - X_{initial}$$

- ΔX: Change in X
- X_{final}: Value of X at the end of the process or reaction
- $X_{initial}$: Value of X at the start of the process or reaction

IV. Thermochemical Equations

Earlier in this module we mentioned that the heat transfer at constant pressure was given the symbol ΔH (change in enthalpy -- a state function) or q_p. Constant-pressure calorimetry is one of the ways in which the value of ΔH for a particular process can be obtained. Heat transfers for all physical and chemical processes can not always be obtained using constant-pressure calorimetry. Later on in this module you will explore other methods of obtaining ΔH's indirectly.

A chemical equation showing the value of ΔH is called a *thermochemical equation*. For example,

$$H_2O_{(l)} \rightarrow H_2O_{(s)} \qquad \Delta H = -6.01 \text{ kJ}$$

The above thermochemical equation states that when 1 mol of water is converted to 1 mol of ice (at constant pressure) the change in enthalpy is -6.01 kJ (the negative sign indicates that this is an exothermic process).

When dealing with thermochemical equations, the following concepts are important:

1. The coefficients in a balanced thermochemical equation strictly refer to the number of moles of reactants and products involved. It is acceptable to use fractions in thermochemical equations.

2. The physical state of all species is important and must be specified.

3. The value of ΔH does not change appreciably with temperature.

4. The sign on ΔH indicates whether the heat transfer (at constant pressure) was endothermic ($+\Delta H$) or exothermic ($-\Delta H$).

5. ΔH is an extensive property (i.e., a property that is dependent on the amount of material present). Thus a change in the stoichiometric coefficients of a thermochemical equation is reflected by a change in the value of ΔH. For example,

$$H_2O_{(l)} \rightarrow H_2O_{(s)} \qquad \Delta H = -6.01 \text{ kJ}$$

$$\tfrac{1}{2} H_2O_{(l)} \rightarrow \tfrac{1}{2} H_2O_{(s)} \qquad \Delta H = \tfrac{1}{2}(-6.01) \text{ kJ} = -3.01 \text{ kJ}$$

6. When a chemical equation is reversed (i.e., products become reactants and reactants become products), the magnitude of ΔH remains the same; however, the sign changes. For example,

$$H_2O_{(l)} \rightarrow H_2O_{(s)} \qquad \Delta H = -6.01 \text{ kJ}$$

$$H_2O_{(s)} \rightarrow H_2O_{(l)} \qquad \Delta H = 6.01 \text{ kJ}$$

V. Stoichiometry of Reaction Heats

The method that was used in the module on reaction stoichiometry can be extended to problems involving the quantity of heat released or absorbed during a reaction. Consider the following thermochemical equation:

$$CH_{4\,(g)} + 2\,O_{2\,(g)} \rightarrow CO_{2\,(g)} + 2\,H_2O_{(l)} \qquad \Delta H = -213 \text{ kcal}$$

The following conversion factors apply to the above thermochemical equation:

$$1 \text{ mol } CH_4 = 2 \text{ mol } O_2 = 1 \text{ mol } CO_2 = 2 \text{ mol } H_2O = -213 \text{ kcal}$$

Example Problem:

1. What is the heat transfer (in kJ) involved when 200. g of ammonia (MM = 17.0) are produced according to the following thermochemical equation?

$$N_{2\,(g)} + 3\,H_{2\,(g)} \rightarrow 2\,NH_{3\,(g)} \qquad \Delta H = -91.8 \text{ kJ}$$

Conversion factors: $2 \text{ mol } NH_3 = -91.8 \text{ kJ} \qquad 1 \text{ mol } NH_3 = 17.0 \text{ g}$

$$? \text{ kJ} = 200. \text{ g } NH_3 \left(\frac{1 \text{ mol } NH_3}{17.0 \text{ g } NH_3}\right)\left(\frac{-91.8 \text{ kJ}}{2 \text{ mol } NH_3}\right) = -540 \text{ kJ}$$

Thus 540 kJ of heat are evolved when 200. g of ammonia are produced.

VI. The First Law of Thermodynamics and Internal Energy, ΔE or ΔU

Because the Law of Conservation of Energy is the most elementary of thermodynamic concepts it is also known as the *First Law of Thermodynamics.*

The internal energy, given the symbol E (or U) of a substance represents all of the energy (kinetic and potential) contained within that substance. Because of the difficulties in measuring the kinetic energy (molecular motion and electron movement) and potential energy (subatomic and molecular attractive and repulsive forces) of a system accurately chemists concentrate in the changes in internal energy. The differences between the internal energy of physical or chemical processes is given by:

$$\Delta E = E_{final} - E_{initial} \qquad \text{(physical process)}$$

$$\Delta E_{rxn} = E_{products} - E_{reactants} \qquad \text{(chemical process)}$$

It should be noted that ΔE is an extensive property. Thus, the more you have of a substance, the greater the amount of internal energy that it possesses.

Energy is exchanged between the system and surroundings as heat (q) and as work (w). Therefore, a more useful form of the First Law of Thermodynamics is:

$$\Delta E = q + w$$

The following sign conventions are employed for q and w:

	Sign	Process
heat (q)	+	heat absorbed by the system from the surroundings (endothermic process)
	-	heat released by the system to the surroundings (exothermic process)
work (w)	+	work done on the system by the surroundings
	-	work done by the system on the surroundings

Actually, these sign conventions make a lot of sense. Consider your bank account (the system): withdrawals = less money → "-" money; deposits = more money → "+" money. Loss of heat = "-" heat; System does work ="-" work; System loses internal energy = "-" ΔE; etc.

It should be noted that *neither* q or w are state functions.

We saw previously how from calorimetry experiments q (heat) can be obtained. The only type of work involved in most physical and chemical processes is pressure-volume work. We see from dimensional analysis, that the product of pressure and volume is work:

$$w = \underset{\text{force}}{F} \times \underset{\text{distance}}{d} = \underset{\frac{F}{d^2}}{P} \times \underset{d^3}{V} \qquad \frac{F}{d^2} \times d^3 = F \times d$$

A physical process in which pressure-volume work is done is in the expansion or compression of a gas against a constant external pressure. The work done on the system by its surroundings is given as:

$$w = -P\,\Delta V \quad \text{(at constant T \& P)} \qquad \Delta V = V_{final} - V_{initial}$$

+ ΔV → expansion
ΔV › compression
Units: P (atm) and V (L)

In order to convert PΔV work which commonly has the units of L·atm into the more common units of Joules and/or calories, the following conversion factors are useful:

$$1 \text{ cal} = 4.184 \text{ J} = 4.129 \times 10^{-2} \text{ L·atm}$$

Given the above definition for w, ΔE can also be written as:

$$\Delta E = q + (-P\Delta V) = q - P\Delta V \qquad \text{(at constant T \& P)}$$

In ***constant volume reactions*** ($\Delta V = 0$) there is no $P\Delta V$ work done; thus, ΔE becomes the heat transfer at constant volume (q_V):

$$\Delta E = q_V \qquad \text{(at constant V)}$$

Remembering that a bomb calorimeter measures heat transfer under constant volume conditions; ΔE's can be obtained thusly.

Solids and liquids do not expand or contract significantly with pressure changes; their production and consumption involves a negligible amount of work ($\Delta V \approx 0$). Thus the only chemical processes in which a considerable amount of work can be done by or on the system is in the production or consumption of gases. The following definition for work derived from the ideal gas equation ($PV = nRT$) can also be written:

$$w = -P\,\Delta V = -(\Delta n)RT \qquad \text{(at constant T \& P)}$$

Δn = total moles of gaseous products - total moles of gaseous reactants

Thus,

$$\Delta E = q + w = q - P\Delta V = q - (\Delta n)RT \qquad \text{(at constant T \& P)}$$

$$R = 0.0821\,\frac{\text{L·atm}}{\text{mol·K}} = 1.99 \times 10^{-3}\,\frac{\text{kcal}}{\text{mol·K}} = 1.99\,\frac{\text{cal}}{\text{mol·K}} = 8.31 \times 10^{-3}\,\frac{\text{kJ}}{\text{mol·K}} = 8.31\,\frac{\text{J}}{\text{mol·K}}$$

Example Problems:

1. When a gas was compressed, 250 J of work energy were required. During this process 150 J of heat were released. Given this information calculate the change in internal energy.

   Sign Conventions: q → heat released → - sign
   w → compression (work done on system) → + sign

   $$\Delta E = q + w = -150\text{ J} + (+250\text{ J}) = +100\text{ J}$$

   Thus, 100 J of energy were gained by the system.

2. If 5.00 L of a gas contained in a cylinder fitted with a weightless movable piston is allowed to expand to 7.00 L under each of the following conditions, then:

   a) Calculate the work (in J) associated with the change under vacuum.

   NOTE: Vacuum → 0 pressure

   $$w = -P\Delta V = 0\text{ atm}(7.0\text{ L} - 5.0\text{ L}) = 0\text{ L·atm} \rightarrow 0\text{ Joules}$$

   Thus, there is no work associated when a gas is expanded under vacuum.

   b) Calculate the work (in J) associated with the change at 780 torr.

   NOTE: Conversion Factors → 1 cal = 4.184 J = 4.129×10^{-2} L·atm

   $$w = -P\Delta V = -\left(780\text{ torr} \times \left(\frac{1\text{ atm}}{760\text{ torr}}\right)\right) \times (7.00\text{ L} - 5.00\text{ L}) = -2.05\text{ L·atm}$$

   $$?\text{ J} = -2.05\text{ L·atm}\left(\frac{4.184\text{ J}}{4.129 \times 10^{-2}\text{ L·atm}}\right) = -208\text{ J}$$

3. For each of the following chemical or physical processes carried out at constant pressure indicate whether: a) work was done on the system, b) work was done by the system, or c) no work was done.

   NOTE: $w = -P\Delta V = -(\Delta n)RT \rightarrow w \propto -\Delta n_{(gases)}$

   Sign Conventions: - (work done by system) & + (work done on system)

   a) $2\ NH_4NO_{3\,(s)} \rightarrow 2\ N_{2\,(g)} + 4\ H_2O_{(g)} + O_{2\,(g)}$

   mol gas products = 2 mol $N_{2\,(g)}$ + 4 mol $H_2O_{(g)}$ + 1 mol $O_{2\,(g)}$ = 7 mol gas

   mol gas reactants = 0 mol gas (there are no gaseous reactants)

   Δn – mol gas products - mol gas reactants = 7 - 0 = 7

   Since Δn is a positive number, w is a negative number → thus work was done by the system.

   b) $H_{2\,(g)} + F_{2\,(g)} \rightarrow 2\ HF_{(g)}$

   $\Delta n = 2 - (1 + 1) = 0$

   Since $\Delta n = 0$, $w = 0$ → thus no work was done.

   c) $H_2O_{(g)} \rightarrow H_2O_{(l)}$

   $\Delta n = 0 - 1 = -1$

   Since Δn is a negative number, w is a positive number → thus work was done on the system.

4. If the combustion of 5.00 g of C_2H_5OH (MM = 46.1) conducted in a bomb calorimeter liberated 148. kJ of heat, then what is ΔE in kcal/mol C_2H_5OH?

   NOTE: bomb calorimeter → constant volume conditions

   At constant volume: $\Delta E = q_v$

   Conversion Factors: 1 cal = 4.184 J → 1 kcal = 4.184 kJ

$$? \frac{\text{kcal}}{\text{mol } C_2H_5OH} = \frac{148.\text{ kJ}}{5\text{ g } C_2H_5OH}\left(\frac{46.1\text{ g } C_2H_5OH}{1\text{ mol } C_2H_5OH}\right)\left(\frac{1\text{ kcal}}{4.184\text{ kJ}}\right) = 326\ \frac{\text{kcal}}{\text{mol } C_2H_5OH}$$

Since heat was liberated, q_v must be a negative number → $\Delta E = -326$ kcal/mol C_2H_5OH

5. If the combustion of 1 mol of C_2H_5OH was carried out under constant atmospheric pressures in a cylinder fitted with a weightless movable piston at 25°C, then:

   a) how much pressure-volume work (in J) was done?

   Combustion Reaction: $C_2H_5OH_{(l)} + 3\ O_{2\,(g)} \rightarrow 2\ CO_{2\,(g)} + 3\ H_2O_{(l)}$

   $w = -P\Delta V = -(\Delta n)RT$

   $\Delta n = 2\text{ mol } CO_{2\,(g)} - 3\text{ mol } O_{2\,(g)} = -1\text{ mol gas}$

$$w = -(\Delta n)RT = -(-1\text{ mol})\left(8.31\frac{\text{J}}{\text{mol·K}}\right)(25+273)\ \text{K} = 2.48 \times 10^3\ \text{J}$$

   b) was work done by the system or by the surroundings?

   Since w is a positive number, then work was done by the surroundings on the system (i.e., the system gained work energy; work was done on the system).

c) would the piston move up, down, or remain stationary?

The piston would move down. This motion is caused by the net consumption of gas. Recall that for gases, $V \propto n$ [$PV = nRT$]; thus, less moles of gas → less volume.

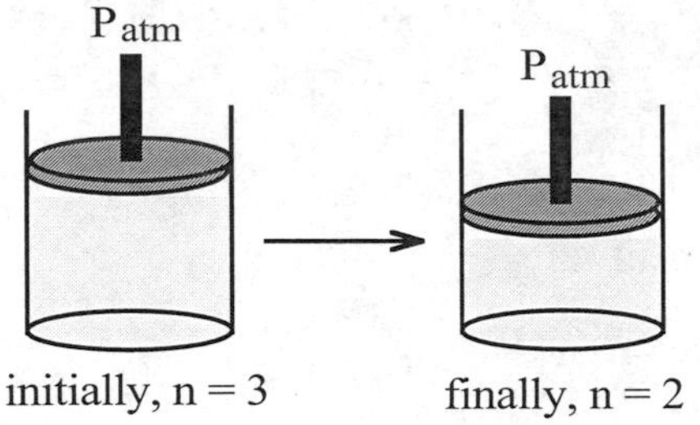

$\Delta n = 2 - 3 = -1$

Note: Volumes for liquids and solids are negligible compared to those of gases.

VII. **Enthalpy, ΔH**

Most chemical reactions are carried out in beakers or flasks that are open to the atmosphere (i.e., at constant pressure). As was mentioned previously, the heat transfer at constant pressure (q_p) is referred to as *enthalpy (ΔH)*. The enthalpy for a reaction, also known as the heat of reaction, is defined as:

$$\Delta H_{rxn} = H_{products} - H_{reactants}$$

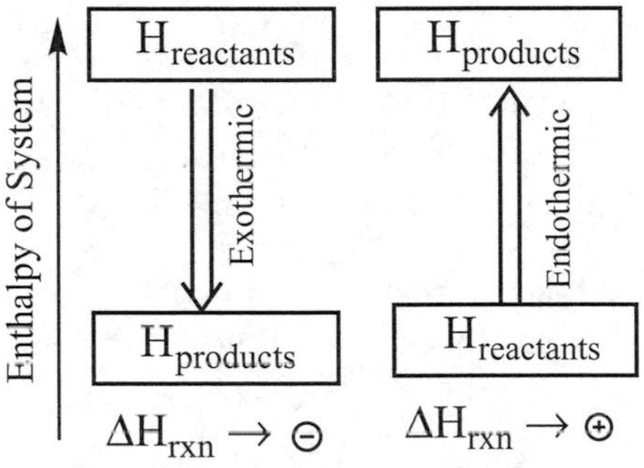

An exothermic process results in an enthalpy decrease and an endothermic process results in an enthalpy increase. (Refer to the figure to your right).

Although ΔH's for chemical reactions can in principle be directly determined by constant-pressure calorimetry, not all chemical reactions can be studied in practice this way. This is so because some reactions: may occur too slow, may not go to completion, or may yield side-products. Certainly, reactions that involve the consumption or production of gases can not be practically studied in open containers. Thus, indirect methods for the determination of ΔH's must be used.

The following indirect methods for determining ΔH's for chemical reactions can be used:

A. **ΔH's from Constant-Volume Calorimetry Data (ΔE's)**

Constant-volume calorimetry data can in part be used to obtain ΔH's. Remember that ΔE is the heat transfer under constant-volume conditions. The relationship that exists between ΔH and ΔE is as follows:

$$\Delta H = \Delta E + P\Delta V \qquad \text{(at constant T and P)}$$

As can be seen, the difference between ΔE and ΔH is the amount of PΔV work that is done by or on the system.

As we have seen previously (at constant temperature and pressure), $P\Delta V = \Delta nRT$

Thus, ΔH can also be defined as follows:

$$\Delta H = \Delta E + P\Delta V = \Delta E + \Delta nRT \qquad \text{(at constant T and P)}$$

$$R = 0.0821 \frac{L \cdot atm}{mol \cdot K} = 1.99 \times 10^{-3} \frac{kcal}{mol \cdot K} = 1.99 \frac{cal}{mol \cdot K} = 8.31 \times 10^{-3} \frac{kJ}{mol \cdot K} = 8.31 \frac{J}{mol \cdot K}$$

Example Problem:

1. When one mole of CH_4 (g) was combusted at 25°C in a bomb calorimeter, 212 kcal of energy were released. Given this information, what is the enthalpy change for this reaction?

   First you need to write the balance combustion reaction for CH_4 (g):

   $$CH_{4\,(g)} + 2\,O_{2\,(g)} \rightarrow CO_{2\,(g)} + 2\,H_2O_{\,(l)}$$

   NOTE: From bomb calorimetry data (constant volume) we get ΔE's

   $\Delta E = -212$ kcal (heat released → - sign)

   $R = 1.99 \times 10^{-3}$ kcal/mol·K

   $\Delta n = 1 - [(1 + 2)] = -2$ mol

   $$\Delta H = \Delta E + \Delta nRT \rightarrow -212 \text{ kcal} + (-2) \text{ mol}\left(1.99 \times 10^{-3} \frac{\text{kcal}}{\text{mol·K}}\right)(25 + 273) \text{ K} = -213 \text{ kcal}$$

B. **ΔH's from the Application of Hess's Law**

Hess's Law of heat summation was discovered empirically in 1840 by Germain H. Hess. According to Hess's Law, *if a reaction is carried out in a series of steps, ΔH for the reaction will be equal to the sum of the enthalpy changes for the individual steps*. This important fact permits us to use a relatively small number of experimental measurements to calculate ΔH for a vast number of different reactions. For example, the ΔH for the following reaction,

$$2\,C_{(graphite)} + O_{2\,(g)} \rightarrow 2\,CO_{(g)}$$

can not be measured by direct calorimetric measurement because once the carbon monoxide is formed, it is impossible to prevent it from reacting further to form CO_2 (g). Since we are not able to find the ΔH for the desired reaction in one step, then we must have available at our disposal at least two thermochemical equations that when they are summed together, they would yield the desired thermochemical equation. For example, consider the following two thermochemical equations:

a)	$C_{(graphite)} + O_{2\,(g)} \rightarrow CO_{2\,(g)}$	$\Delta H = -393.5$ kJ
b)	$2\,CO_{(g)} + O_{2\,(g)} \rightarrow 2\,CO_{2\,(g)}$	$\Delta H = -566.0$ kJ
Desired:	$2\,C_{(graphite)} + O_{2\,(g)} \rightarrow 2\,CO_{(g)}$	$\Delta H = ?$

The general approach is to multiply equations by a factor, perhaps reversing some, so that when all are added together the desired equation results. In this particular example, we will use the following approach:

1) Multiply equation a by 2 since we need 2 C (graphite) as a reactant:

   a) $2\,C_{(graphite)} + 2\,O_{2\,(g)} \rightarrow 2\,CO_{2\,(g)}$ $\Delta H = 2(-393.5)$ kJ $= -787.0$ kJ

2) Reverse equation b since we need CO (g) as the product:

   b) $2\,CO_{2\,(g)} \rightarrow 2\,CO_{(g)} + O_{2\,(g)}$ $\Delta H = -(-566.0)$ kJ

3) Summing the modified thermochemical equations a and b & elimination of common terms (1 O_2 (g) and 2 CO_2 (g) each appear on both sides of the chemical equation) yields the desired results:

a)	$2\,C_{(graphite)} + 2\,O_{2\,(g)} \rightarrow 2\,CO_{2\,(g)}$	$\Delta H = -787.0$ kJ
b)	$2\,CO_{2\,(g)} \rightarrow 2\,CO_{(g)} + O_{2\,(g)}$	$\Delta H = +566.0$ kJ
	$2\,C_{(graphite)} + O_{2\,(g)} \rightarrow 2\,CO_{(g)}$	$\Delta H = -221.0$ kJ

Example Problem:

1. Calculate the heat of reaction for the following reaction:

$W_{(s)} + C_{(graphite)} \rightarrow WC_{(s)}$ $\Delta H = ?$

given the following data:

a) $2\,W_{(s)} + 3\,O_{2\,(g)} \rightarrow 2\,WO_{3\,(s)}$ $\Delta H = -1680.6$ kJ

b) $C_{(graphite)} + O_{2\,(g)} \rightarrow CO_{2\,(g)}$ $\Delta H = -393.5$ kJ

c) $2\,WC_{(s)} + 5\,O_{2\,(g)} \rightarrow 2\,WO_{3\,(s)} + 2\,CO_{2\,(g)}$ $\Delta H = -2391.6$ kJ

To obtain the desired results, we shall use the following approach:

- Multiply equation a by $\frac{1}{2}$ since we need 1 $W_{(s)}$ as a reactant:

a) $\frac{2}{2}\,W_{(s)} + \frac{3}{2}\,O_{2\,(g)} \rightarrow \frac{2}{2}\,WO_{3\,(s)}$ $\Delta H = \frac{1}{2}(-1680.6)$ kJ

- Leave Equation b as is since it has the desired 1 $C_{(graphite)}$ as a reactant:

b) $C_{(graphite)} + O_{2\,(g)} \rightarrow CO_{2\,(g)}$ $\Delta H = -393.5$ kJ

- Equation c has to be reversed so that $WC_{(s)}$ is a product, and it also has to be multiplied by $\frac{1}{2}$ since we need only 1 $WC_{(s)}$:

c) $\frac{2}{2}\,WO_{3\,(s)} + \frac{2}{2}\,CO_{2\,(g)} \rightarrow \frac{2}{2}\,WC_{(s)} + \frac{5}{2}\,O_{2\,(g)}$ $\Delta H = \frac{1}{2}\,[-(-2391.6)]$ kJ

- Summing the modified thermochemical equations a, b, & c and the elimination of common terms ($\frac{5}{2}\,O_{2\,(g)}$, 1 $WO_{3\,(s)}$, and 1 $CO_{2\,(g)}$ each appear on both sides of the chemical equation) yields the desired results:

	ΔH, kJ
a) $W_{(s)} + \frac{3}{2}\,O_{2\,(g)} \rightarrow WO_{3\,(s)}$	-840.3
b) $C_{(graphite)} + O_{2\,(g)} \rightarrow CO_{2\,(g)}$	-393.5
c) $WO_{3\,(s)} + CO_{2\,(g)} \rightarrow WC_{(s)} + \frac{5}{2}\,O_{2\,(g)}$	1195.8
$W_{(s)} + C_{(graphite)} \rightarrow WC_{(s)}$	-38.0

C. ΔH's from Standard Molar Enthalpies of Formation, ΔH_f^o

By using Hess's Law, we can calculate the enthalpy changes for a great many reactions from a few tabulated values. To store such thermochemical information, a convenient method has been devised. This method involves storing the data as Standard Molar Enthalpies of Formation, given the symbol, ΔH_f^o (f stands for formation and ° stands for standard state). The thermochemical standard state for a substance is its most stable state at a standard pressure of 1 bar (since, a *bar* is practically equal to an *atm,* we will use atm instead; 1 bar = 0.987 atm) and at some specific temperature (25°C - unless otherwise specified). *Standard Molar Enthalpy of Formation* is defined as the heat change that results when *one mole* of compound is formed from its elements in their standard state. ΔH_f^o data is found in Appendix 1A.

By definition, the standard heat of formation of the most stable form of any element is zero (i.e., ΔH_f^o = 0 for elements in their standard state). Since the standard heat of formation for the most stable form of an element is zero, you will not find these elements listed in the table in Appendix 1A. Therefore, you will need to know in what physical state the elements are in while at standard state conditions. ***Most elements at 1 atm and 25°C commonly exist as monatomic solids and in only one allotropic form with the notable exceptions of:***

Monatomic Gases: $He_{(g)}$, $Ne_{(g)}$, $Ar_{(g)}$, $Kr_{(g)}$, $Xe_{(g)}$, $Rn_{(g)}$
Diatomic Gases: $H_{2(g)}$, $N_{2(g)}$, $O_{2(g)}$, $F_{2(g)}$, $Cl_{2(g)}$
Liquids: $Hg_{(l)}$ and $Br_{2(l)}$
Diatomic/Polyatomic Solids: $I_{2(s)}$, $P_{4(s)}$, $S_{8(s)}$*
Standard State Allotropes: $C_{(s, graphite)}$, $P_{4(s, white)}$, $S_{(s, rhombic)}$*, $O_{2(g)}$

Most elements exist as monatomic solids except for these elements. All have $\Delta H_f^o = 0$

* Due to complexities, S is used instead of S_8

The following is an example of the thermochemical equation that shows the standard state formation of (1 mol) $Na_2CO_{3(s)}$ from its elements.

$$2\,Na_{(s)} + C_{(graphite)} + \tfrac{3}{2}\,O_{2(g)} \rightarrow Na_2CO_{3(s)} \qquad \Delta H_f^o = -1130.9 \text{ kJ/mol } Na_2CO_{3(s)}$$

Determination of the standard enthalpy change for any reaction, ΔH^o_{rxn} or ΔH^o, is done by considering the balanced chemical equation and standard heat of formation data. ΔH^o_{rxn} for the following generalized chemical equation (where a, b, e, and f are stoichiometric coefficients)

$$a\,A + b\,B + \ldots \rightarrow e\,E + f\,F + \ldots$$

can be obtained as such:

$$\Delta H^o_{rxn} = [\,e\,\Delta H^o_{f,E} + f\,\Delta H^o_{f,F} + \ldots.] - [\,a\,\Delta H^o_{f,A} + b\,\Delta H^o_{f,B} + \ldots.]$$

The above equation can be generalized accordingly:

$$\Delta H^o_{rxn} = \sum n\,\Delta H^o_{f,\,products} - \sum m\,\Delta H^o_{f,\,reactants}$$

Σ (sigma) $\rightarrow$ "the sum of",
$n \rightarrow$ stoichiometric coefficient(s) for product(s)
$m \rightarrow$ stoichiometric coefficient(s) for reactant(s)

To find ΔH^o for the combustion of $C_2H_{4(g)}$ we first need a balanced chemical equation and then we can use ΔH_f^o data (see Appendix 1A) accordingly:

$$C_2H_{4(g)} + 3\,O_{2(g)} \rightarrow 2\,CO_{2(g)} + 2\,H_2O_{(l)} \qquad \Delta H^o = ?$$

$$\Delta H^o = [\,2\,\Delta H^o_{f,\,CO_2(g)} + 2\,\Delta H^o_{f,\,H_2O(l)}\,] - [\,\Delta H^o_{f,\,C_2H_4(g)} + 3\,\Delta H^o_{f,\,O_2(g)}\,]$$
$$= [\,2\,(-393.5 \text{ kJ}) + 2\,(-285.8 \text{ kJ})\,] - [\,1\,(52.47 \text{ kJ}) + 3\,(0 \text{ kJ})\,]$$
$$\Delta H^o = [\,-1359\,] - [\,52.47\,] = -1411 \text{ kJ}$$

Example Problems:

1. Write the thermochemical equation that shows how $HCN_{(g)}$ is formed from its elements under standard state conditions:

$$\tfrac{1}{2}\,H_{2(g)} + C_{(s, graphite)} + \tfrac{1}{2}\,N_{2(g)} \rightarrow HCN_{(g)} \qquad \Delta H_f^o = 135 \text{ kJ}$$

$\Delta H^o_{f,\,HCN(g)}$ was obtained from Appendix 1A.

2. From the following thermochemical equation:

$$C_3H_{8(g)} + 5\,O_{2(g)} \rightarrow 3\,CO_{2(g)} + 4\,H_2O_{(l)} \qquad \Delta H^o = -2220 \text{ kJ}$$

and the standard heats of formation given in Appendix 1A, calculate the standard heat of formation (in kJ) for $C_3H_{8(g)}$.

$$\Delta H^o = [\,3\,\Delta H^o_{f,\,CO_2(g)} + 4\,\Delta H^o_{f,\,H_2O(l)}\,] - [\,\Delta H^o_{f,\,C_3H_8(g)} + 5\,\Delta H^o_{f,\,O_2(g)}\,]$$
$$-2220 \text{ kJ} = [\,3\,(-393.5 \text{ kJ}) + 4\,(-285.8 \text{ kJ})\,] - [\,\Delta H^o_{f,\,C_3H_8(g)} + 5\,(0 \text{ kJ})\,]$$
$$-2220 \text{ kJ} = [\,-2324 \text{ kJ}\,] - [\,H^o_{f,\,C_3H_8(g)}\,]$$
$$\Delta H^o_{f,\,C_3H_8(g)} = -2324 \text{ kJ} + 2220 \text{ kJ} = -104 \text{ kJ}$$

D. **ΔH's from Bond Energies**

The Lewis theory of chemical bonding only depicts a covalent bond as the sharing of electrons between atoms; it however, does not indicate the relative strength of such a bond. A quantitative measure of the stability of a diatomic molecule is its bond dissociation energy. *Bond dissociation energy* is defined as the enthalpy change required to break a particular bond in 1 mole of gaseous diatomic molecules. The gaseous state is specified, because bond dissociation energies in solids and liquids are affected by neighboring molecules.

Bond dissociation involves homolytic bond cleavage (i.e., the bond, electron pair, is split in half). The bond dissociation energy of $H_{2\,(g)}$ is given as:

$$H_{2\,(g)} \rightarrow H^{\bullet}{}_{(g)} + {}^{\bullet}H_{(g)} \qquad \Delta H^{o}_{rxn} = \Delta H_{H\text{-}H} = 435 \text{ kJ}$$

[Note: To make it emphatic that this was a homolytic cleavage, the lone electron (i.e., free radical) on each H is shown; however, free radicals are usually not shown.]

The above thermochemical equation tells us that the dissociation of $H_{2\,(g)}$ is an endothermic process requiring 435 kJ of energy. It stands to reason that *the more energy that is required to break a bond, the stronger that bond is.*

Measuring the strength of covalent bonds becomes more complicated for polyatomic molecules due to the nature of the adjacent atom(s). For example, the C-H bond energy differs slightly from compound to compound, as in CH_4 (435 kJ) and CH_3F (452 kJ). Nevertheless, the C-H bond energy in various compounds is sufficiently constant to be useful. It is for this reason that we can only speak of an *average bond energy* when dealing with polyatomic molecules. The table in Appendix 1B, lists the bond energy for the dissociation of various bonds. Bond energies for double or triple bonds are not simply two or three times those for the corresponding single bonds. A single bond is a σ bond, whereas double and triple bonds involve a combination of σ and π bonding. Therefore, since the stability of σ and π bonds are different, it would stand to reason that a different amount of energy is required to break such bonds.

In order to obtain an estimate of how much energy is required to completely dissociate a particular molecule (that is in the gas phase) you must consider the following. For example, lets consider the complete dissociation of CH_3Cl (i.e., $CH_3Cl \rightarrow C_{(g)} + 3\,H_{(g)} + Cl_{(g)}$).

1) Draw the Lewis structure for the molecule.

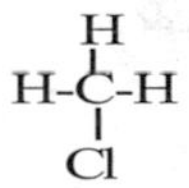

(Lone pairs have been omitted)

2) Look at what type of bonds need to be broken (dissociated).

3 C-H bonds and 1 C-Cl bond

3) From the table in Appendix 1B, add up all the bond energies (B.E.) to obtain an estimate of how much energy is required to dissociate the molecule in question.

3 (B.E.$_{C\text{-}H}$) = 3 (414) kJ	=	1242 kJ
1 (B.E.$_{C\text{-}Cl}$) = 1 (330) kJ	=	330 kJ
Dissociation of $CHCl_3$	=	1572 kJ

A special case of Hess's Law involves the use of bond energies (B.E.) to estimate heats of reactions. In general terms, ΔH^{o}_{rxn} is related to the bond energies of reactants (whose bonds are breaking) and products (whose bonds are forming) *in gas phase reactions* accordingly:

$$\Delta H^{o}_{rxn} = \sum \text{B.E.}_{\substack{\text{bonds broken} \\ \text{(in reactants)}}} - \sum \text{B.E.}_{\substack{\text{bonds formed} \\ \text{(in products)}}}$$ **(only for gas phase reactions)**

The above relationship allows us to estimate the ΔH^{o} for gas phase reactions when heat of formation data is not available.

Example Problems:

1. Use the bond energies listed in Appendix 1B to estimate the heat of reaction at 25°C for the following gas-phase reaction.

$$Br_{2\,(g)} + 3\,F_{2\,(g)} \rightarrow 2\,BrF_{3\,(g)} \qquad \Delta H^{o} = ?$$

Since we need to know what types of bonds are broken and formed we need to draw Lewis structures.

$$Br\text{-}Br + 3\ F\text{-}F \longrightarrow 2\ F\text{-}\underset{\underset{F}{|}}{Br}\text{-}F \qquad \text{(lone pairs not shown)}$$

Bonds broken for Br-Br: 1 (Br-Br)

Bonds broken for F-F: 1 (F-F), since 3 mol required → 3 (F-F) broken in total

Bonds formed for BrF_3: 3 (Br-F), since 2 mol formed → 6 (Br-F) formed in total

$$\Delta H^o_{rxn} = \sum B.E._{\substack{bonds\ broken \\ (in\ reactants)}} - \sum B.E._{\substack{bonds\ formed \\ (in\ products)}}$$

$$= [\ B.E._{Br\text{-}Br} + 3\ (B.E._{F\text{-}F})\ ] - [\ 6\ (B.E._{Br\text{-}F})\ ]$$

$$= [\ 192\ kJ + 3\ (159)\ kJ\ ] - [\ 6\ (197)\ kJ\ ] = -513\ kJ$$

2. Estimate the bond energy of the O=O bond, from the following data:

$$C_3H_8\ (g) + 5\ O_2\ (g) \rightarrow 3\ CO_2\ (g) + 4\ H_2O\ (g) \qquad \Delta H = -2.05 \times 10^3\ kJ$$

$$B.E. \rightarrow C\text{-}C\ (347\ kJ),\ C\text{-}H\ (414\ kJ),\ C\text{=}O\ (799\ kJ),\ O\text{-}H\ (464\ kJ)$$

Since we need to know what types of bonds are broken and formed we need to draw Lewis structures.

$$\underset{\underset{H}{|}}{\overset{\overset{H}{|}}{H\text{-}C}}\text{-}\underset{\underset{H}{|}}{\overset{\overset{H}{|}}{C}}\text{-}\underset{\underset{H}{|}}{\overset{\overset{H}{|}}{C}}\text{-}H + 5\ O\text{=}O \longrightarrow 3\ O\text{=}C\text{=}O + 4\ H\text{-}O\text{-}H \qquad \text{(lone pairs not shown)}$$

Bonds broken for C_3H_8: 8 (C-H) and 2 (C-C)

Bonds broken for O_2: 1 (O=O), since 5 mol required → 5 (O=O)

Bonds formed for CO_2: 2 C=O, since 3 mol produced → 6 (C=O)

Bonds formed for H_2O: 2 O-H, since 4 mol produced → 8 (O-H)

$$\Delta H^o_{rxn} = \sum B.E._{\substack{bonds\ broken \\ (in\ reactants)}} - \sum B.E._{\substack{bonds\ formed \\ (in\ products)}}$$

$$-2.05 \times 10^3 = [8\ (B.E._{C\text{-}H}) + 2\ (B.E._{C\text{-}C}) + 5\ (B.E._{O\text{=}O})] - [6\ (B.E._{C\text{=}O}) + 8\ (B.E._{O\text{-}H})]$$

$$-2.05 \times 10^3 = [8\ (414) + 2\ (347) + 5\ (B.E._{O\text{=}O})] - [6\ (799) + 8\ (464)]$$

$$-2.05 \times 10^3 = [3.31 \times 10^3 + 694 + 5\ (B.E._{O\text{=}O})] - [4.79 \times 10^3 + 3.71 \times 10^3]$$

$$-5\ (B.E._{O\text{=}O}) = 2.05 \times 10^3 + 3.31 \times 10^3 + 694 - 4.79 \times 10^3 - 3.71 \times 10^3$$

$$B.E._{O\text{=}O} = \frac{-2.11 \times 10^3}{-5} = 489.\ kJ$$

VIII. Heat of Solution and Dilution   [OPTIONAL]

In the vast majority of cases, dissolving a solute in a solvent produces measurable heat transfer. At constant pressures, the *Heat of Solution* (also known as *Enthalpy of Solution*), ΔH_{soln}, is the heat generated or absorbed when a certain amount of solute dissolves in a certain amount of solvent. Mathematically, ΔH_{soln} can be generally defined as:

$$\Delta H_{soln} = H_{soln} - H_{components}$$

The following example gives the thermochemical equation for the dissolution of NaCl:

$$NaCl\ (s) \rightarrow Na^+\ (aq) + Cl^-\ (aq) \qquad \Delta H_{soln} = 4\ kJ$$

Dissolving an ionic compound in water involves complex interactions among the solute & solvent. However, for the sake of energy analysis, we can represent the dissolution process as occuring in two steps:

1) The solid is separated into its respective ions in the *gas phase*. For example,

$$NaCl_{(s)} \rightarrow Na^{+}_{(g)} + Cl^{-}_{(g)}$$

The energy required for this process is called *Lattice Energy (U).*

2) The gaseous ions become hydrated. For example,

$$Na^{+}_{(g)} + Cl^{-}_{(g)} \rightarrow Na^{+}_{(aq)} + Cl^{-}_{(aq)}$$

The energy required for this process is called *Heat of Hydration* (ΔH_{hydr}).

Applying Hess's Law, it is possible to consider ΔH_{soln} as the sum of two related process: Lattice energy and heat of hydration:

$$NaCl_{(s)} \rightarrow Na^{+}_{(g)} + Cl^{-}_{(g)} \qquad U = 788\text{ kJ}$$

$$Na^{+}_{(g)} + Cl^{-}_{(g)} \rightarrow Na^{+}_{(aq)} + Cl^{-}_{(aq)} \qquad \Delta H_{hydr} = -784\text{ kJ}$$

$$NaCl_{(s)} \rightarrow Na^{+}_{(aq)} + Cl^{-}_{(aq)} \qquad \Delta H_{soln} = 4\text{ kJ}$$

When a previously prepared solution is diluted, additional heat is usually given off or absorbed. The heat change associated with the dilution process is called *heat of dilution*.

IX. Spontaneity (Thermodynamics) vs. Speed (Kinetics)

As mentioned previously, one of the uses of thermodynamics is to predict whether a particular process (i.e., physical change or chemical reaction) can occur under specified conditions without any continuing outside influences. However, while thermodynamics can predict the spontaneity of a process it can not be related to the speed at which that process occurs. The rate at which a process occurs will be addressed in a future module on Kinetics. In the sections to come we will discuss the factors that help us predict whether or not a particular process will occur spontaneously.

X. Second and Third Laws of Thermodynamics and ΔS

The *Second Law of Thermodynamics* states that in spontaneous changes, the universe tends toward a state of greater disorder. The thermodynamic state function **Entropy, S,** is used to measure disorder. $\Delta S_{universe}$ is equal to zero for processes carried out under reversible conditions and greater than zero for spontaneous processes.

The *Third Law of Thermodynamics* states that the entropy of a pure, perfect crystalline substance (perfectly ordered) is zero at absolute zero (0 K).

The following are examples of processes that result in predictable entropy changes:

a) Phase and Temperature Changes

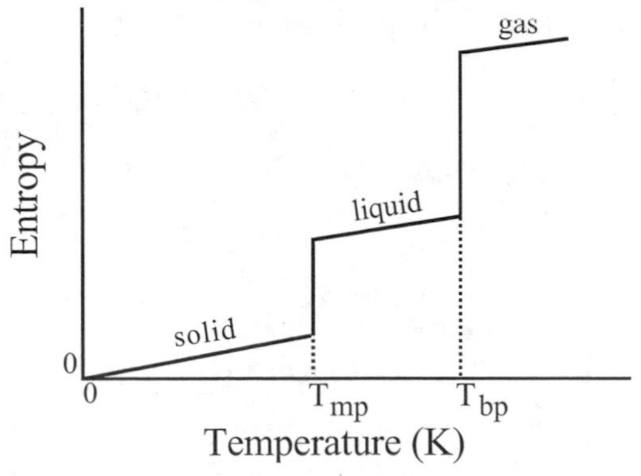

This figure shows how the entropy of a substance changes with temperature. Note that the entropy gradually increases as the temperature increases while the substance is in the same phase. But when there is a phase change, the entropy increases sharply. Note how the entropy change from liquid to gas is greater than that for the solid to liquid - this is because the gas phase is the phase that has the greatest entropy. Even though we see that entropy increases with increasing temperature while the substance is in the same phase, we are going to assume that this change is so small that for all practical purposes it is constant.

b) Volume Changes

When a gas occupies a larger volume, the gas molecules can occupy more positions, and hence are more randomly arranged and thus an increase in entropy occurs.

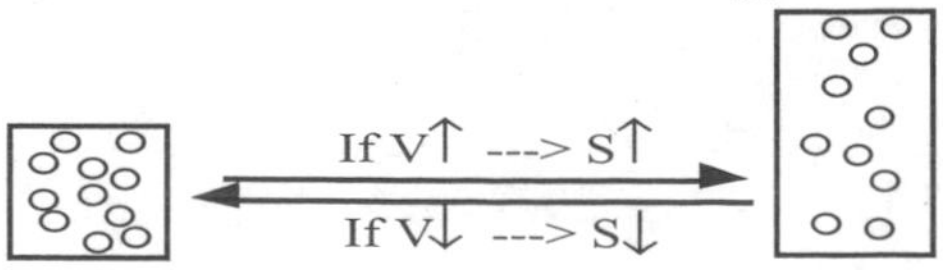

c) Mixing of Substances

Even without a chemical reaction occurring, situations in which molecules are more "mixed-up" (i.e., are more disordered) lead to a state of higher entropy.

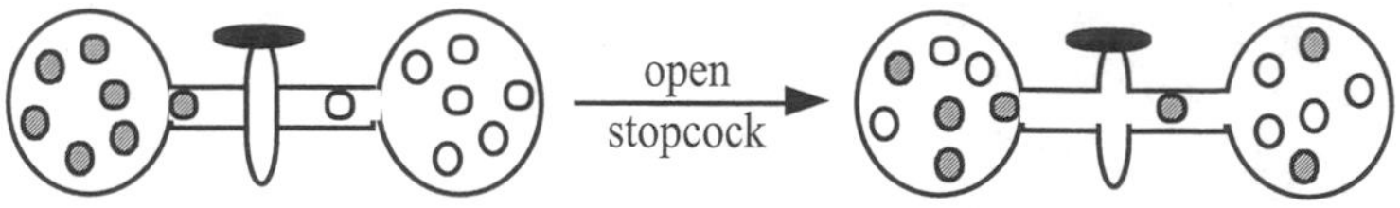

mixing occurs spontaneously because this leads to an increase in entropy

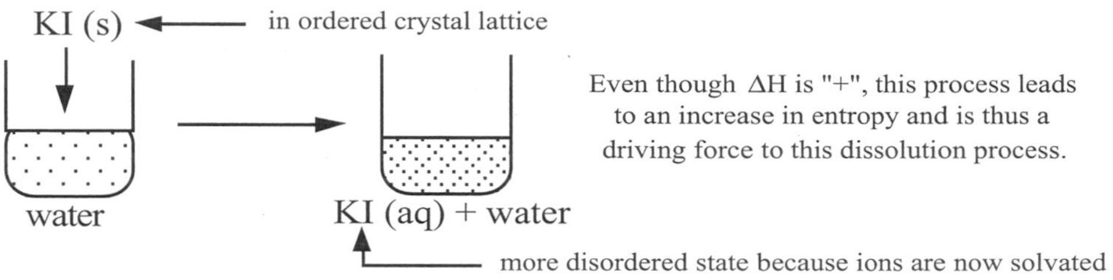

Even though ΔH is "+", this process leads to an increase in entropy and is thus a driving force to this dissolution process.

d) Changes in the Number of Moles of Gaseous Substances

Any process that leads to an increase in the number of moles of gaseous substances leads to an increase in entropy.

$$2\,H_2\,(g) + O_2\,(g) \underset{\text{S increases}}{\overset{\text{S decreases}}{\rightleftarrows}} 2\,H_2O\,(g)$$

3 moles of gaseous reactants — 2 moles of gaseous reactants

Product has less entropy, is less disordered, or is more ordered than reactants

The absolute entropy (also called standard molar entropy) of several substances have been tabulated in Appendix 1A at 298 K (25°C). The absolute entropy of a substance at 298 K is given the symbol S^o_{298} and has units of J/mol•K. Notice that S^o_{298} for all substances is a positive number (*this includes elements in their standard state*) - this is because at absolute zero S = 0 for a perfect crystalline substance and the higher the temperature the more entropy a substance has.

Just as with enthalpy changes (ΔH):

a) the standard entropy change, ΔS°, can be determined as follows for the following "reaction":

$$a\,A + b\,B + \ldots \rightarrow e\,E + f\,F + \ldots \qquad \text{(where a, b, e, f are coefficients)}$$

$$\Delta S^o_{rxn} = [\,e\,S^o_E + f\,S^o_F + \ldots] - [\,a\,S^o_A + b\,S^o_B + \ldots\,]$$

This above equation can be generalized accordingly:

$$\Delta S^o_{rxn} = \sum n\,S^o_{products} - \sum m\,S^o_{reactants}$$

Σ (sigma) → "the sum of",
n → stoichiometric coefficient(s) for product(s)
m → stoichiometric coefficient(s) for reactant(s)

b) ΔS is an extensive property.

c) ΔS changes sign when a process is reversed.

d) ΔS does not appreciably vary with temperature as long as substance is in the same physical state.

Example Problems:

1. Without looking at the values for the standard molar entropies in Appendix 1A, would you expect that the following reactions/processes to have a positive or negative entropy change?

   a) The sublimation of I_2.

   Sublimation of I_2 ($I_{2\,(s)} \rightarrow I_{2\,(g)}$). This process has a $+\Delta S$ because the gas state is more disordered than the solid state.

   b) The combustion of $CH_{4\,(g)}$.

   Before answering this question you need to have a completed and balanced combustion equation:

   $$CH_{4\,(g)} + 2\,O_{2\,(g)} \rightarrow CO_{2\,(g)} + 2\,H_2O_{(l)}$$

   This reaction has a $-\Delta S$ because there are less moles of gaseous products (i.e., 1) than gaseous reactants (i.e., 3).

   c) The condensation of water vapor.

   Condensation of water ($H_2O_{(g)} \rightarrow H_2O_{(l)}$). This process has a $-\Delta S$ because the liquid state is more ordered than the gas state.

   d) The formation of $C_6H_{6\,(l)}$ from its elements.

   Before answering this question you need to have a completed and balanced formation equation:

   $$6\,C_{(s,\ graphite)} + 3\,H_{2\,(g)} \rightarrow C_6H_{6\,(l)}$$

   This reaction has a $-\Delta S$ because there are less moles of gaseous products (i.e., 0) than gaseous reactants (i.e., 3).

2. Calculate the entropy change for the formation of sodium carbonate from its elements 25°C.

   S° (in J/mol•K) → $Na_{(s)}$ (51.0), $C_{(s,graphite)}$ (5.740), $O_{2(g)}$ (205.0), $Na_2CO_{3\,(s)}$ (136)

   Before answering this question you need to have a completed and balanced formation reaction:

   $$2\,Na_{(s)} + C_{(s,\ graphite)} + \tfrac{3}{2}\,O_{2\,(g)} \rightarrow Na_2CO_{3\,(s)}$$

   $$\Delta S^{o}_{rxn} = [\,1\,S^{o}_{Na_2CO_3\,(s)}\,] - [\,2\,S^{o}_{Na\,(s)} + 1\,S^{o}_{C\,(s,\ graphite)} + \tfrac{3}{2}\,S^{o}_{O_2\,(g)}\,]$$

   $$= [1(136)] - [2(51.0) + 1(5.740) + \tfrac{3}{2}(205.0)\,]\ \text{J/mol•K}$$

   $$= 136 - (102 + 5.740 + 307.5)$$

   $$= -279\ \text{J/mol•K}$$

3. If ΔS^{o}_{rxn} = -146.2 J/mol•K for 2 NO (g) + O_2 (g) → 2 NO_2 (g), then what is ΔS^{o}_{rxn} for the following reaction: 4 NO_2 (g) → 4 NO (g) + 2 O_2 (g)?

   This reaction is the reverse of the one shown (thus the sign is changed). In addition, the coefficients have been multiplied by 2, thus ΔS^{o}_{rxn} = 2(146.2) = 292.4 J/mol•K.

XI. Spontaneity and ΔG (Gibbs Free Energy)

J. Willard Gibbs formulated a relationship between enthalpy and entropy in terms of another state function that is called **Gibbs Free Energy (G)**. The Gibbs Free Energy change for a reaction / process is given by:

$$\Delta G = \Delta H - T\Delta S \quad \text{(at constant T and P)}$$

$T\Delta S$ → q_{rev} {heat transfer under isothermal reversible conditions}

ΔH → q_p {heat transfer under irreversible conditions at constant pressure}

ΔG → w_{max} { maximum amount of useful work }

For a process occurring at constant T and P, if:

$\Delta G < 0$ then the process is spontaneous (i.e., exergonic)

$\Delta G = 0$ then the process is at equilibrium

$\Delta G > 0$ then the process is non-spontaneous (i.e., endergonic)

ΔG varies with temperature; however, ΔH and ΔS do not appreciably vary with temperature.

The following table and graph show the relationship between the signs ΔH, ΔS& ΔG and spontaneity.

	ΔH	-	T	ΔS	=	ΔG	Spontaneity of Process
a)	−	-	+	−		− or +	there is a temperature above which process is non-spontaneous
b)	−	-	+	+		−	always spontaneous
c)	+	-	+	−		+	always non-spontaneous
d)	+	-	+	+		− or +	there is a temperature below which process is non-spontaneous

$$\Delta G = -\Delta S\,T + \Delta H$$
$$y = m\,x + b$$

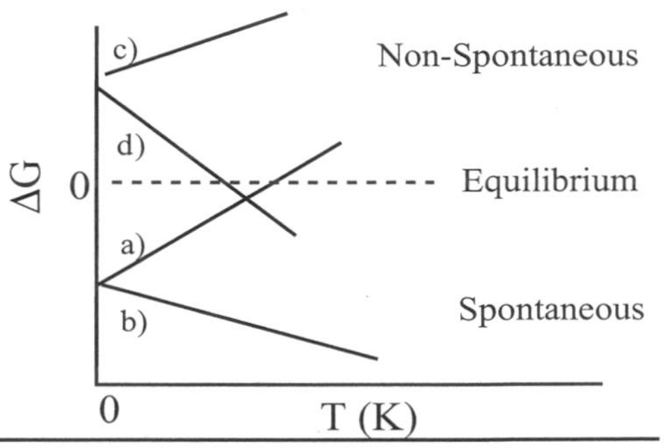

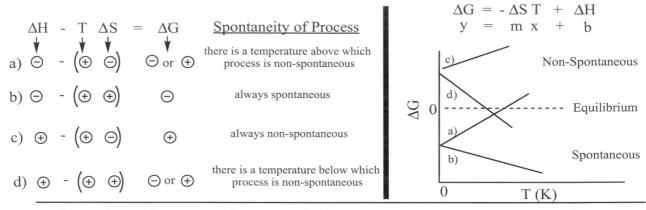

T is always + because it is expressed in K and 0 K is the lowest temperature possible.

Given that $q_{rev} = T\Delta S$ (at constant T and P) then:

$$\Delta S = \frac{q_{rev}}{T}$$

During a phase change that occurs at constant pressure, the temperature is constant. At this time the process is at equilibrium (i.e., $\Delta G = 0$; therefore, $\Delta H = T\Delta S$) and the process is reversible as well, thus at a substance's:

$$\text{boiling point:} \quad q_{rev} = q_p = \Delta H_{vap} \rightarrow \Delta S_{vap} = \frac{\Delta H_{vap}}{T}$$

$$\text{melting point:} \quad q_{rev} = q_p = \Delta H_{fus} \rightarrow \Delta S_{fus} = \frac{\Delta H_{fus}}{T}$$

XII. Standard Free Energy Change, $\Delta G°$

Just as with enthalpy:

a) ΔG is an extensive property.

b) the *Standard Gibbs Free Energy of Formation* (ΔG_f^o) is defined as the free energy change that results when *one mole* of compound is formed from its elements in their standard state. ΔG_f^o data is found in Appendix 1A and is for substances at 1 atm and 298 K (25°C). ***By definition, the standard Gibbs Free Energy of formation of the most stable form of any element is zero (i.e., $\Delta G_f^o = 0$ for elements in their standard state).*** Earlier in this module we discussed what the standard state was for all elements at 25°C.

c) ΔG changes sign when a process is reversed.

d) ΔG° for a reaction can be generalized as:

$$\Delta G^\circ_{rxn} = \sum n \, \Delta G^\circ_f \text{, products} - \sum m \, \Delta G^\circ_f \text{, reactants}$$

Σ (sigma) $\rightarrow$ "the sum of",
$n \rightarrow$ stoichiometric coefficient(s) for product(s)
$m \rightarrow$ stoichiometric coefficient(s) for reactant(s)

ΔG° for a reaction can be obtained either by using ΔG°_f for "products - reactants" given in Appendix 1A (only when the reaction is run at 25°C) or by using the equation:

$$\Delta G^\circ = \Delta H^\circ - T\Delta S^\circ$$

It should be noted that ΔG is temperature dependent, while ΔH and ΔS are temperature independent (as long as the substance is in the same physical state).

ΔS° can either be given or obtained from S°_{298} data in Appendix 1A as previously seen.

ΔH°can either be given or obtained from ΔH°_f data in Appendix 1A or it can be obtained from ΔE° as previously seen:

$$\Delta H = \Delta E + P\Delta V = \Delta E + (\Delta n)RT \qquad \text{(at constant T and P)}$$

($\Delta E \rightarrow q_V$) {heat transfer under irreversible conditions at constant volume}

Also, you may want to note that:

$$\Delta E = q + w$$

	Sign	Process
heat (q)	+	heat absorbed by the system from the surroundings (endothermic process)
	-	heat released by the system to the surroundings (exothermic process)
work (w)	+	work done on the system by the surroundings
	-	work done by the system on the surroundings

$$w = -P\Delta V = -(\Delta n)RT \qquad \text{(at constant T and P)}$$

($w \rightarrow$ pressure-volume work)

<u>Example Problems</u>:

1. The enthalpy of vaporization for benzene is 30.8 kJ at its boiling point of 80.1°C. What is the entropy change (in kJ/K) for benzene as it undergoes a transition from vapor to liquid at 80.1°C.

   During a phase change occurring at a substances' bp: $\Delta S_{vap} = \dfrac{\Delta H_{vap}}{T}$

   When we reverse a process [boiling ($l \rightarrow g$) to condensation ($g \rightarrow l$)], the value for ΔH and ΔS changes (i.e, $\Delta H_{vap} = -\Delta H_{cond}$ and $\Delta S_{vap} = -\Delta S_{cond}$) ; thus, in this particular case:

   $$\Delta S_{vap} = \frac{\Delta H_{vap}}{T} = \frac{30.8 \text{ kJ}}{(80.1 + 273) \text{ K}} = 0.0872 \frac{\text{kJ}}{\text{K}} \rightarrow \Delta S_{cond} = -0.0872 \frac{\text{kJ}}{\text{K}}$$

2. For a given reaction, $\Delta H = -22.6$ kJ and $\Delta S = -45.2$ J/K. If ΔH and ΔS are constant with changes in temperature (in K), for what temperature range would the reaction be spontaneous?

   For a spontaneous reaction, $\Delta G < 0$. Remember that $\Delta G = \Delta H - T\Delta S$. Solve for T while making $\Delta H - T\Delta S$ (which is ΔG) less than zero.

$\Delta H - T\Delta S < 0$

$-22.6 \text{ kJ} - T(-45.2 \times 10^{-3} \text{ kJ/K}) < 0$

$T < \dfrac{(0 + 22.6)}{-(-45.2 \times 10^{-3})}$

$T < 500 \text{ K}$ [The rxn is spontaneous at temperatures below 500 K]

3. Consider the following fictitious thermochemical equation : 2 A (s) → B (g) $\Delta H^\circ = -45.0$ kJ. Assuming that no change in state occurs as the temperature is changed and that ΔH° remains constant, will this reaction be spontaneous at all temperatures?

   ΔH° is negative. ΔS° is positive because there are more moles of gaseous products than reactants; thus, $T\Delta S^\circ$ will always be positive. This being the case, this reaction is spontaneous at all temperatures because ΔG° would always be a negative number no matter what the temperature was [$\Delta H^\circ - T\Delta S^\circ \rightarrow -45 - (+?) = -??$].

4. For the reaction, 2 Ag (s) + Cl_2 (g) → 2 AgCl (s), at 25°C and 1.0 atm, $\Delta H^{o}_{rxn} = -254.05$ kJ and $\Delta S^{o}_{rxn} = -116.32$ J/K.

   a) If this reaction was carried out in a constant volume bomb calorimeter, how much energy (in kJ) is transferred at 25°C?

   The energy transferred under constant volume → ΔE°. To find ΔE° use:

   $\Delta H^\circ = \Delta E^\circ + (\Delta n)RT$

   $-254.05 \text{ kJ} = \Delta E^\circ + (0 - 1)(8.31 \times 10^{-3} \text{ kJ})(25 + 273 \text{ K})$

   $\Delta E^\circ = -254.05 + 2.48 = -251.57$ kJ [This reaction is exothermic by convention a negative sign for heat indicates that the heat was released.]

   b) If this reaction was carried out in a beaker at 25°C, how much energy (in kJ) was transferred?

   Since the reaction was performed in an open container it was performed under constant pressure conditions. ΔH° is the energy transferred under constant pressure. The given ΔH° for the reaction is -254.05 kJ; therefore, this is the energy transferred when the reaction is carried out in a beaker.

   c) What is the standard enthalpy of formation (in kJ) for AgCl (s)?

   The formation reaction for AgCl is: Ag (s) + $\frac{1}{2}$ Cl_2 (g) → AgCl (s). Therefore, the standard enthalpy for the formation of AgCl (s) is (-254.05/2) = -127.02 kJ

   d) How much pressure-volume work (in kJ) is done at 25°C?

   $w = -(\Delta n)RT = -(0 - 1)(8.31 \times 10^{-3} \text{ kJ})(25 + 273 \text{ K}) = 2.48$ kJ (since w is positive, this represents that the work was done on the system).

   e) Are the products more or less ordered than the reactants?

   More ordered because the given ΔS^{o}_{rxn} is negative (-116.32 J/K), but without this information, there are less moles of gaseous products than reactants; therefore, we would have been able to predict that the products are more ordered than the reactants.

   f) What is ΔG° (in kJ) at 25°C ?

   $\Delta G^\circ = \Delta H^\circ - T\Delta S^\circ$

   $= (-254.05 \text{ kJ}) - (25{+}273 \text{ K})(-116.32 \times 10^{-3} \text{ kJ/K})$

   $= (-254.05 \text{ kJ}) - (-34.66 \text{ kJ}) = -219.39$ kJ (since ΔG° is - this reaction is spontaneous at 25°C)

   g) What is the heat flow (in kJ) if this process is carried out reversibly at 25°C?

   $q_{rev} = T\Delta S^\circ = (25{+}273 \text{ K})(-116.32 \times 10^{-3} \text{ kJ}) = -34.66$ kJ

h) What is the maximum amount of useful work (in kJ) that can be obtained for this reaction at 25°C if 45.0 g of AgCl (MM = 143.4) were obtained?

$w_{max} = \Delta G^\circ \quad \rightarrow \quad -219.39\text{ kJ}$ (this is for the reaction as written)

$$? \text{ kJ} = 45.0 \text{ g AgCl}\left(\frac{1 \text{ mol AgCl}}{143.4 \text{ g AgCl}}\right)\left(\frac{-219.39 \text{ kJ}}{2 \text{ mol AgCl}}\right) = -34.4 \text{ kJ}$$

i) At what temperature (in K) will this reaction be at equilibrium?

At equilibrium ΔG is equal to 0.

$\Delta G = \Delta H - T\Delta S$

$0 = (-254.05 \text{ kJ}) - T(-116.32 \times 10^{-3} \text{ kJ/K})$

$$\frac{0 + 254.05}{-(-116.32 \times 10^{-3})} = T = 2184 \text{ K}$$

j) Assuming that ΔH and ΔS are temperature independent, what is ΔG° (in kJ) at 45°C?

$\Delta G^\circ = \Delta H^\circ - T\Delta S^\circ$

$\Delta G^\circ = (-254.05 \text{ kJ}) - (45+273 \text{ K})(-116.32 \times 10^{-3} \text{ kJ/K})$

$\Delta G^\circ = -254.05 \text{ kJ} + 36.99 \text{ kJ} = -217.06 \text{ kJ}$

5. Considering just the following reaction and information:

$$2\, C_2H_{6\,(g)} + 7\, O_{2\,(g)} \rightarrow 4\, CO_{2\,(g)} + 6\, H_2O_{\,(l)}$$

Substance	ΔG_f^o (kJ)	S^o_{298} (J/K)
$C_2H_{6\,(g)}$	-32.90	229.5
$CO_{2\,(g)}$	-394.4	213.6
$H_2O_{\,(l)}$	-237.2	69.90
$O_{2\,(g)}$	0	205.0

a) What is ΔG° (in kJ) at 25°C?

$$\begin{aligned}\Delta G^o &= [\,4\,\Delta G_f^o, CO_{2\,(g)} + 6\,\Delta G_f^o, H_2O_{\,(l)}\,] - [\,2\,\Delta G_f^o, C_2H_{6\,(g)} + 7\,\Delta G_f^o, O_{2\,(g)}\,] \\ &= [\,4(-394.4 \text{ kJ}) + 6(-237.2 \text{ kJ})\,] - [\,2(-32.90 \text{ kJ}) + 7(0 \text{ kJ})\,] \\ &= [\,-1577.6 - 1423.2\,] - [\,-65.8\,] \\ &= -2935.0 \text{ kJ}\end{aligned}$$

b) What is ΔH° (in kJ) at 25°C?

From just the information given, we'll need to use $\Delta G^\circ = \Delta H^\circ - T\Delta S^\circ$ to find ΔH°. However, we first need to find ΔS° from the information given in the above table.

$$\begin{aligned}\Delta S^o &= [\,4\,S^o_{298}\ CO_{2\,(g)} + 6\,S^o_{298}, H_2O_{\,(l)}\,] - [\,2\,S^o_{298}, C_2H_{6\,(g)} + 7\,S^o_{298}, O_{2\,(g)}\,] \\ &= [\,4(213.6 \text{ J/K}) + 6(69.90 \text{ J/K})\,] - [\,2(229.5 \text{ J/K}) + 7(205.0 \text{ J/K})\,] \\ &= [\,854.4 + 419.4\,] - [\,459.0 + 1435.\,] \\ &= -620.2 \text{ J/K} = -620.2 \times 10^{-3} \text{ kJ/K}\end{aligned}$$

$\Delta G^\circ = \Delta H^\circ - T\Delta S^\circ$

$-2935.0 \text{ kJ} = \Delta H^\circ - (25+273 \text{ K})(-620.2 \times 10^{-3} \text{ kJ/K})$

$\Delta H^\circ = -2935.0 - 184.8 = -3119.8 \text{ kJ}$

EXERCISES

Calorimetry

Unless otherwise noted, assume that $q_{cal} = 0$.

1. How much heat (in cal) is necessary to heat 27.0 mL of octane ($s = 0.526 \frac{cal}{g\ °C}$; d = 0.703 g/mL) from 50.6°C to 67.2°C?

2. How many grams of water (s = 1.00 cal/g · °C) will release 1367 J of heat when cooled from 45.2°C to 36.2°C?

3. What will the final temperature (in °C) be, if 82.0 cal of heat are added to 32.0 g of carbon tetrachloride
(s = 0.210 cal/g · °C) at 33.0°C?

4. By how many °C will the temperature of 23.67 g of a liquid (s = 0.590 cal/g · °C) at 25.3°C be raised if 1794 J of heat are added to the liquid?

5. A 46.33 g sample of an unknown metal at 95.0°C is dropped into 36.30 g of water at 24.6°C. The final temperature reached, was 35.5°C. What is the specific heat (in cal/g · °C) of the unknown metal? (s_{water} = 1.00 cal/g · °C)

6. A 45.0 g sample of a substance at 55.0°C (s = 1.66 cal/g · °C) was placed into a coffee-cup calorimeter (C = 4.20 cal/°C) which contained 50.0 g of ethyl alcohol at 25.0°C (s = 0.590 cal/g·°C). What is the resulting final temperature (in °C)?

7. What mass (in g) of a substance at 95.0°C with a specific heat of 0.601 J/g · °C is required to raise the temperature of 36.3 g of water (s = 1.00 cal/g · °C) at 24.6°C to 35.5°C?

8. An alloy at 10.0°C weighing 100.0 g was dropped into a coffee-cup calorimeter (C = 8.20 cal/°C) which contained 50.0 g of water at 45.0°C the resulting final temperature was 30.0°C. What is the specific heat (in cal/g · °C) of the alloy? (s_{water} = 1.00 cal/g · °C)

9. A 25.0 g sample of a substance at 55.0°C (s = 0.660 cal/g · °C) was placed into 50.0 g of water at 25.0°C (s = 1.00 cal/g · °C). What is the resulting final temperature (in °C)?

10. What mass (in g) of a substance at 85.0°C with a specific heat of 0.55 cal/g · °C is required to raise the temperature of 25.0 g of water (s = 1.00 cal/g · °C) at 30.0°C to 35.0°C?

11. a) When a 50.0 mL sample of 0.400 M $CuSO_4$ at 23.35°C is mixed with 50.0 mL of 0.600 M NaOH at 23.35°C in a coffee-cup calorimeter (C = 24.0 J/°C) the temperature rises to 26.65°C. If the density of the final solution is 1.02 g/mL and its specific heat is 4.184 J/g·°C, calculate the amount of heat evolved in J.

    b) Determine ΔH (in J/mol NaOH).

12. When a sample contained inside a bomb calorimeter which is immersed in 2000. mL of water (d = 1.00 g/mL, s = 1.00 cal/g·°C) was burned, 2.294 kcal of heat were released. As a result, the temperature rose by 0.89°C. Given this information, what is the heat capacity (in kcal/°C) of the bomb calorimeter?

13. a) When 0.562 g of $C_{(graphite)}$ was burned in a bomb calorimeter (C = 12.3 kJ/°C), which was immersed in 2000. g of water (s = 4.184 J/g·°C) at 25.00°C, the temperature rose to 25.89°C. Given this information, how many kJ of heat were released?

    b) Calculate the heat given off by the reaction in kJ/mol $C_{(graphite)}$.

    c) Calculate ΔE for the combustion of $C_{(graphite)}$ in kJ/mol.

14. When a 2.00 g sample of N_2H_4 (MM = 32.0) was burned in a bomb calorimeter (C = 3.76 kJ/°C) that was surrounded by 6400 g of water (s = 4.184 J/g·°C) the temperature increased from 25.00°C to 26.17°C. Given this information, calculate ΔE for the combustion of N_2H_4 in a) kJ/g and b) kJ/mol.

Thermochemical Equations and Stoichiometry of Reaction Heats

15. When 1 mol of N_2 (g) completely reacts with 3 mol of H_2 (g), 2 mol of NH_3 (g) are produced. As a result of such a reaction, 91.8 kJ of heat are released under constant pressure conditions. Given this information,
    a) Write the thermochemical equation for this reaction.
    b) Is the reaction endothermic or exothermic?
    c) Write the thermochemical equation for the reverse reaction.
    d) If 5 mol of N_2 (g) are used instead of one, write the corresponding thermochemical equation.

16. How many Joules per gram of sulfur (J/g S_8) are evolved when sulfur is burned according to the following thermochemical equation: $S_{8\,(s)} + 8\ O_{2\,(g)} \rightarrow 8\ SO_{2\,(g)}$ $\Delta H = -2374$ kJ

17. Given the following information: $H_3PO_{4\,(aq)} \rightarrow \frac{1}{4}\ P_4O_{10\,(s)} + \frac{3}{2}\ H_2O_{(l)}$ $\Delta H = -108$ kJ
What is ΔH for the following reaction? $P_4O_{10\,(s)} + 6\ H_2O_{(l)} \rightarrow 4\ H_3PO_{4\,(aq)}$

18. What is the heat transfer (in kJ) when 27.0 g of CH_4 (g) (MM = 16.0) are burned according to the following thermochemical equation?

$$CH_{4\,(g)} + 2\ O_{2\,(g)} \rightarrow CO_{2\,(g)} + 2\ H_2O_{(l)} \qquad \Delta H = -213 \text{ kcal}$$

19. Consider the following thermochemical equation:

$$CH_3OH_{(g)} + 1.5\ O_{2\,(g)} \rightarrow CO_{2\,(g)} + 2\ H_2O_{(l)} \qquad \Delta H = -76.2 \text{ kJ}$$

    a) What is the heat transfer (in kJ) when 30.0 g of CH_3OH (g) (MM = 32.0) are burned?
    b) What mass (in g) of O_2 (MM = 32.0) is consumed when 950 kJ of heat are released?
    c) How many grams of CH_3OH (g) must be burned in order to obtain 18.2 kcal of heat energy?

Internal Energy and Changes in Internal Energy (ΔE)

20. What happens to the internal energy of a system during a process in which $q < 0$ and $w < 0$?

21. During the isothermal (constant temperature) expansion of a gas, ΔE = 0 kJ. If a gas is allowed to expand isothermally from 1.00 L to 3.00 L at a constant external pressure of 975 torr until equilibrium is reached, calculate q and w (in cal)?

22. When a gas was expanded, 200 J of work were released. During this process 500 J of heat energy were released. Given this information, calculate ΔE (in J).

23. If a system performs 70.50 L·atm of pressure-volume work on its surroundings and absorbs 6000 J of heat from its surroundings, what is the change in internal energy (in J)?

24. If 2.00 L of a gas contained in a cylinder fitted with a weightless movable piston was compressed to 1.50 L under an external pressure of 1.75 atm, calculate the work (in kcal) associated with this process.

25. If 5000 J of work were required to compress 54.0 L of a gas contained in a cylinder fitted with a weightless movable piston under an external pressure of 745 torr, then what is its final volume?

26. For each of the following chemical or physical processes carried out at a constant pressure indicate whether: a) work was done on the system, b) work was done by the system, or c) no work was done.
    a) $0.5\ N_{2\,(g)} + 1.5\ H_{2\,(g)} \rightarrow NH_{3\,(g)}$
    b) $CH_3OH_{(s)} \rightarrow CH_3OH_{(g)}$
    c) $3\ H_2S_{(g)} + 2\ HNO_{3\,(g)} \rightarrow 2\ NO_{(g)} + 4\ H_2O_{(l)} + 3\ S_{(s)}$

27. If the combustion of 2 mol of CH_4 (g) (MM = 16.0) conducted at constant pressure conditions and 25.0°C liberated 426 kcal of heat energy, then:
   a) Write down the corresponding thermochemical equation.
   b) Calculate ΔH for the combustion of CH_4 (g) in kcal/mol.
   c) How much work (in kcal) was done on or by the system?

28. If the combustion of 1 mol of C_2H_4 (g) (MM = 28.0) is conducted at 760 torr in a cylinder fitted with a weightless movable piston at 25.0°C, then:
   a) Write down the balanced chemical equation for this process.
   b) How much pressure-volume work (in kcal) was done?
   c) Was work done by the system or by the surroundings?
   d) Would the piston move up, down, or remain stationary?

Enthalpy and Changes in Enthalpy (ΔH)

29. What is the difference between enthalpy and internal energy?

30. What is the difference between: ΔH, ΔH^o, and ΔH_f^o

31. When 500 J of heat are added to a gas contained in a cylinder fitted with a weightless movable piston, it expands and does 200 J of work on the surroundings. Given this information,
   a) Calculate ΔE (in J).
   b) Calculate ΔH (in J).

32. Given the following thermochemical equation, calculate ΔE (in kJ) at 30.0°C.

$$2\,N_{2\,(g)} + O_{2\,(g)} \rightarrow 2\,N_2O_{(g)} \qquad \Delta H = +163.2\text{ kJ}$$

33. When one mol of C_8H_{18} (*l*) was combusted at 25.0°C in a bomb calorimeter, 5450 kJ of energy were released. Given this information, calculate the heat of reaction (i.e., enthalpy change) in kJ for the following reaction.

$$C_8H_{18\,(l)} + 12.5\,O_{2\,(g)} \rightarrow 8\,CO_{2\,(g)} + 9\,H_2O_{(l)}$$

34. Calculate the heat of reaction (in kJ) for the following reaction:

$$CH_{4\,(g)} + 2\,O_{2\,(g)} \rightarrow CO_{2\,(g)} + 2\,H_2O_{(l)} \qquad \Delta H = ?$$

given the following data:

   a) $CH_{4\,(g)} + 2\,O_{2\,(g)} \rightarrow CO_{2\,(g)} + H_2O_{(g)}$ $\Delta H = -802$ kJ
   b) $H_2O_{(g)} \rightarrow H_2O_{(l)}$ $\Delta H = -44$ kJ

35. Calculate the heat of reaction (in kJ) for the following reaction:

$$C_{(s,\ graphite)} + 0.5\,O_{2\,(g)} \rightarrow CO_{(g)} \qquad \Delta H = ?$$

given the following data:

   a) $C_{(s,\ graphite)} + O_{2\,(g)} \rightarrow CO_{2\,(g)}$ $\Delta H = -393.5$ kJ
   b) $2\,CO_{(g)} + O_{2\,(g)} \rightarrow 2\,CO_{2\,(g)}$ $\Delta H = -566.0$ kJ

36. Calculate the heat of reaction (in kJ) for the following reaction:

$$2\,C_{(s,\ graphite)} + H_{2\,(g)} \rightarrow C_2H_{2\,(g)} \qquad \Delta H = ?$$

given the following data:

   a) $C_{(s,\ graphite)} + O_{2\,(g)} \rightarrow CO_{2\,(g)}$ $\Delta H = -393.5$ kJ
   b) $H_{2\,(g)} + 0.5\,O_{2\,(g)} \rightarrow H_2O_{(l)}$ $\Delta H = -285.9$ kJ
   c) $C_2H_{2\,(g)} + 2.5\,O_{2\,(g)} \rightarrow 2\,CO_{2\,(g)} + H_2O_{(l)}$ $\Delta H = -1299.6$ kJ

37. Calculate the heat of reaction (in kJ) for the following reaction:

$$NO_{(g)} + O_{(g)} \rightarrow NO_{2\,(g)} \qquad \Delta H = ?$$

given the following data:

a) $NO_{(g)} + O_{3\,(g)} \rightarrow NO_{2\,(g)} + O_{2\,(g)}$ $\Delta H = -198.9$ kJ

b) $O_{2\,(g)} \rightarrow 2\,O_{(g)}$ $\Delta H = 495.0$ kJ

c) $O_{3\,(g)} \rightarrow 1.5\ O_{2\,(g)}$ $\Delta H = -142.3$ kJ

38. What is ΔH_f^o (in kJ) for each of the following? *(Appendix 1A contains ΔH_f^o data)*

a) $C_{(s,\ graphite)}$ b) $N_{2\,(g)}$ c) $O_{(g)}$

d) $S_{(s,\ rhombic)}$ e) $H_{(g)}$ f) $I_{2\,(s)}$

39. Write the corresponding thermochemical equation that shows the standard state formation for each of the following compounds from its elements.

a) $CCl_{4\,(l)}$ b) $NH_4Cl_{(s)}$

40. Using standard heat of formation data, calculate the enthalpy change (in kJ) for each of the following:

a) $C_2H_5OH_{(l)} + 3\,O_{2\,(g)} \rightarrow 2\,CO_{2\,(g)} + 3\,H_2O_{(l)}$

b) $C_6H_{6\,(l)} + 7.5\,O_{2\,(g)} \rightarrow 6\,CO_{2\,(g)} + 3\,H_2O_{(l)}$

c) $C_{(diamond)} + 2\,H_{2\,(g)} \rightarrow CH_{4\,(g)}$

d) $H_{2\,(g)} + 0.5\,O_{2\,(g)} \rightarrow H_2O_{(l)}$

e) $C_2H_{4\,(g)} + H_{2\,(g)} \rightarrow C_2H_{6\,(g)}$

41. From each of the following thermochemical equations and standard heat of formation data given in Appendix 1A, calculate the standard heat of formation (in kJ) for each boldfaced compound.

a) $CH_{4\,(g)} + 2\,\mathbf{S_{2\,(g)}} \rightarrow CS_{2\,(g)} + 2\,H_2S_{(g)}$ $\Delta H^o = -106$ kJ

b) $CH_{4\,(g)} + 2\,Cl_{2\,(g)} \rightarrow \mathbf{CH_2Cl_{2\,(l)}} + 2\,HCl_{(g)}$ $\Delta H^o = -226$ kJ

c) $P_{4\,(white)} + 6\,Cl_{2\,(g)} \rightarrow 4\,\mathbf{PCl_{3\,(l)}}$ $\Delta H^o = -1279$ kJ

d) $3\,CO_{2\,(g)} + 4\,H_2O_{(l)} \rightarrow \mathbf{C_3H_{8\,(g)}} + 5\,O_{2\,(g)}$ $\Delta H^o = 2220$ kJ

Bond Energies

42. Use the bond energies listed in Appendix 1B to estimate the heat of reaction (in kJ) at 25°C for each of the following *gas-phase* reactions.

a) $HCN + 3\,H_2 \rightarrow CH_4 + NH_3$

b) 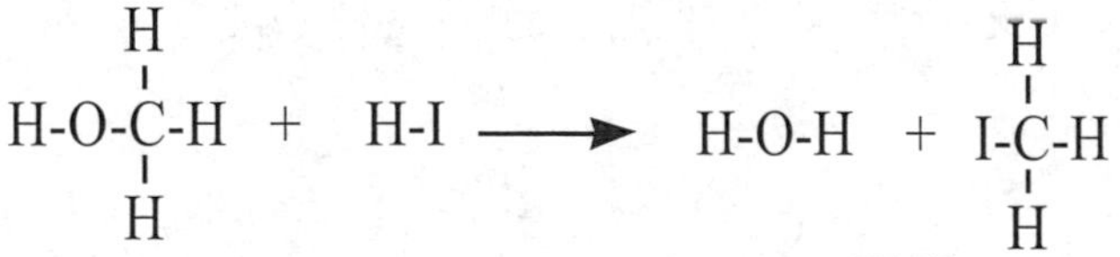

c) 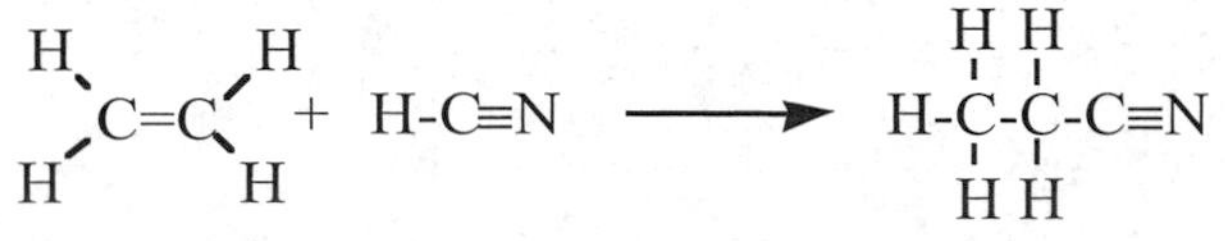

d) 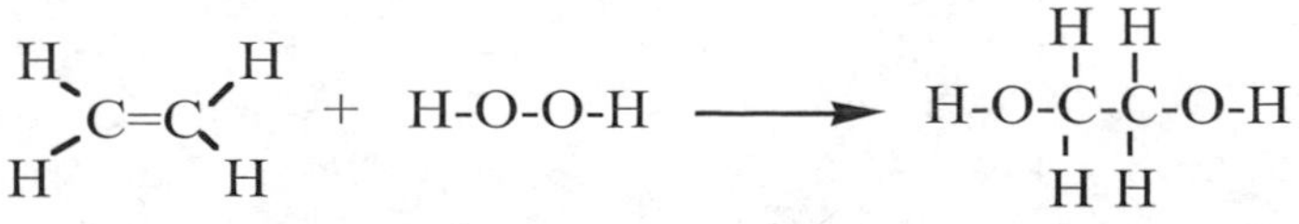

43. Estimate the bond energy (in kJ) of the C-N bond, given the following gas phase reaction and data:

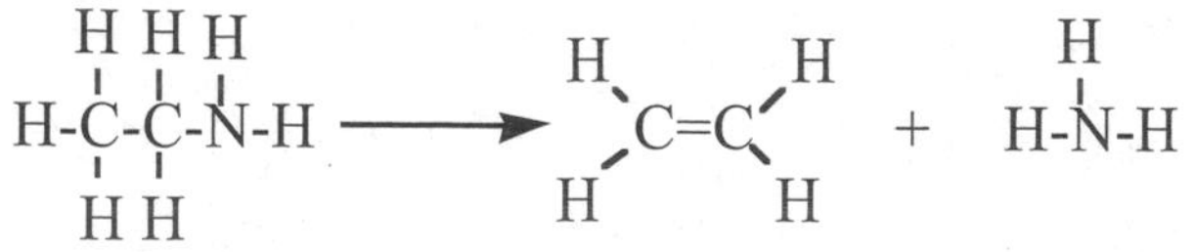

$\Delta H = 54.68$ kJ

Average Bond Energies: C-H (414 kJ), C-C (347 kJ), C=C (611 kJ), N-H (389 kJ)44. Given the data in Appendix 1B, which of the following has the strongest bond? EXPLAIN.

1) H - H 2) H - F 3) F - F 4) Cl - Cl 5) I – I

Spontaneity, Entropy (ΔS), and Gibbs Free Energy (ΔG)

45. Predict the sign for $\Delta S°$, if possible, for each of the following processes. If it is not possible to predict $\Delta S°$ state why not.

a) C_2H_2 (g) + 2 H_2 (g) → C_2H_6 (g)

b) N_2 (g) + O_2 (g) → 2 NO (g)

c) 2 C (s, graphite) + O_2 (g) → 2 CO (g)

d) H_2O (g) → H_2O (*l*)

e) Evaporation of a liquid

f) NaCl (s) → NaCl (aq)

g) messy room → clean room

h) Standard formation reaction of N_2O (g)

46. Diethyl ether ($C_4H_{10}O_2$, MM = 90.1) has a boiling point of 35.6°C and a heat of vaporization of 26.7 kJ/mol. Given this information:

a) What is the change in entropy (in kJ/K • mol diethyl ether) for 1 mol of diethyl ether at 35.6°C for the liquid → vapor transition?

b) What is the change in entropy (in kJ/K • mol diethyl ether) for 1 mol of diethyl ether at 35.6°C for the vapor → liquid transition?

c) What is the change in entropy (in kJ/K) when 2.7 g of diethyl ether at 35.6°C vaporizes at its boiling point?

47. Without referring to the table in Appendix 1A which of the following have $\Delta G_f^o = 0$ kJ?

a) C $_{(s, graphite)}$ b) $Br_{2\,(g)}$ c) $N_{(g)}$ d) $Na^+_{(aq)}$ e) $Na_{(s)}$

48. At what temperatures (in K) would a reaction with a ΔH = -11.7 kJ and ΔS = -105 J/K be spontaneous? Assume ΔH and ΔS are temperature independent.

49. Calculate $\Delta S°$ (in J/K), $\Delta G°$ (in kJ), and $\Delta H°$ (in kJ) for each of the following reactions using the given information in the problem.

a)

	SO_2 (g)	+	NO_2 (g)	→	SO_3 (g)	+	NO (g)
S° (J/K)	248.5		240.5		256.2		210.6
ΔG_f^o (kJ)	-300.2		51		-371		86.6

b)

	2 Na (s)	+	Cl_2 (g)	→	2 NaCl (s)
S° (J/K)	51.4		223		72.1
ΔG_f^o (kJ)	0		0		-384

50. For each of the reactions in the previous problem, answer the following questions. (You'll need the information given and calculated to answer these questions.)

A. What is the heat transfer (in kJ) under reversible conditions at 25°C?

B. How much pressure-volume work (in kJ) was done at 25°C?

C. At 25°C, which occurs: work done on the system, work done by the system, or no work done by the system?

D. What is the change in internal energy (in kJ) at 25°C?

E. What is the heat transfer (in kJ) at 25°C under constant volume conditions?

F. What is the heat transfer (in kJ) at 25°C under constant pressure conditions?

G. At what temperature (in K) would equilibrium be reached? Assume that no change in state is occurring and that ΔS and ΔH are temperature independent.

H. Find ΔG° (in kJ) at 45°C. Assume that no change in state is occurring and that ΔS and ΔH are temperature independent.

I. Is the reaction spontaneous at 45°C?

J. What is the maximum amount of useful work (in kJ) that can be obtained at 45°C?

51. A certain reaction is spontaneous at 75°C. If the enthalpy change for the reaction is 20 kJ, for what values of ΔS (in kJ/K) will the reaction be spontaneous?

52. ΔG^{o}_{rxn} = 1139 kJ for the reaction: 2 MgO (s) → 2 Mg (s) + O_2 (g). What is the maximum amount of useful work (in kJ) that would be transferred when 45.0 g of MgO (MM = 40.3) is reacted?

MULTIPLE CHOICE PRACTICE EXAM FOR MODULE 3

1. A 100. g sample of water absorbs how many Joules of energy as its temperature is changed from 35.0°C to 60.0°C? (s_{water} = 4.184 J/g · °C)
   1) 1.05×10^4 2) 1.46×10^4 3) 2.51×10^4 4) 2.50×10^3 5) 4.18×10^2

2. When a 50.0 gram sample of a metal at 90.0°C was placed into 100. mL of water at 25.0°C, the resulting temperature was 35.0°C. Given this information, calculate the specific heat (in J/g · °C) of the metal. (s_{water} = 4.184 J/g · °C, d_{water} = 1.00 g/mL)
   1) 0.572 2) 1.09 3) 0.364 4) 27.5 5) 1.52

3. When 0.7521 g of benzoic acid was burned in a bomb calorimeter surrounded by 1000. g of water at 22.50°C, the temperature rose to 26.10°C. If the heat of combustion of benzoic acid is 26.42 kJ/g, then calculate the heat capacity (in kJ/°C) of the calorimeter.
   1) 1.34 2) 752.1 3) 5.52 4) 15.87 5) 4.18

For questions 4 - 5, consider the following thermochemical equation:

$$2\ SO_{2\,(g)} + O_{2\,(g)} \rightarrow 2\ SO_{3\,(g)} \qquad \Delta H = -198\ kJ$$

4. How much heat (in kJ) is released when 60.0 g of $SO_{2\,(g)}$ (MM = 64.1) is reacted with excess O_2?
   1) 0.546 2) 186 3) 5940 4) 92.7 5) 371

5. What is the heat transfer (in kJ) when 2.00 g of $SO_{3\,(g)}$ (MM = 80.0) undergoes decomposition?
   1) -2.48 2) 2.48 3) -4.95 4) -1.24 5) 4.95

6. Which of the following are state functions?
   a. T b. P c. H d. q
   1) only c 2) only a & c 3) only c & d 4) only a, c, & d 5) only a, b, & c

7. Calculate the internal energy change (in kJ) for a system that releases 200. kJ of heat as it does 300. kJ of work on its surroundings.
   1) 500 2) -100 3) 100 4) 300 5) -500

8. If a gas releases 300. cal of heat as it is compressed from 15.0 L to 5.0 L by an opposing pressure of 2.00 atm, then calculate ΔE (in cal).
   1) 784 2) 320 3) 184 4) -184 5) -784

9. For which of the following chemical or physical processes carried out at constant pressure will there be work done on the system.
   a. $H_2O_{(s)} \rightarrow H_2O_{(l)}$
   b. $2\ SO_{3\,(g)} \rightarrow 2\ SO_{2\,(g)} + O_{2\,(g)}$
   c. $CH_{4\,(g)} + 2\ Cl_{2\,(g)} \rightarrow CH_2Cl_{2\,(l)} + 2\ HCl_{(g)}$
   d. $P_{4\,(s,\ white)} + 6\ Cl_{2\,(g)} \rightarrow 4\ PCl_{3\,(l)}$
   1) only a 2) only b 3) only c 4) only c & d 5) only b, c, & d

10. Calculate ΔE (in kJ) for the following reaction

$$2\ SO_{2\,(g)} + O_{2\,(g)} \rightarrow 2\ SO_{3\,(g)}$$

given that when 100. g $SO_{2\,(g)}$ (MM = 64.1) were reacted with excess $O_{2\,(g)}$ to produce $SO_{3\,(g)}$ at a pressure of 760 torr and 25.0°C, 154.4 kJ of heat were released.
   1) -200 2) 200 3) -198 4) -196 5) 198

11. For the decomposition reaction

$$2\ SO_{3\ (g)} \rightarrow 2\ SO_{2\ (g)} + O_{2\ (g)}$$

$\Delta E = 196$ kJ and $\Delta H = 198$ kJ. If 1.00 mol of $SO_{2\ (g)}$ were to undergo a combination reaction with excess oxygen to yield $SO_{3\ (g)}$ in a bomb calorimeter, then what would be the expected heat transfer (in kJ)?

1) -196 2) 99 3) -198 4) -98 5) 198

12. The combustion of 0.100 g of $C_2H_{4\ (g)}$ (MM = 28.0) caused the temperature of the 1000. g of water surrounding the bomb calorimeter to rise by 1.00°C. If the heat capacity of the calorimeter is 200 cal/°C, then what is ΔE in kcal/mol of C_2H_4? $s_{water} = 1.00$ cal/g·°C

1) -336 2) -0.0600 3) 1.20 4) -1.20 5) -33.6

13. When two moles of $SO_{2\ (g)}$ were reacted with one mol of oxygen to produce two moles $SO_{3\ (g)}$ at 25.0°C in a bomb calorimeter, 196 kJ of heat were released. Given this information, what is the enthalpy change (in kJ) for the following reaction?

$$2\ SO_{2\ (g)} + O_{2\ (g)} \rightarrow 2\ SO_{3\ (g)}$$

1) -194 2) 194 3) -198 4) -196 5) 198

14. Calculate the heat of reaction (in kJ) for the following reaction

$$2\ SO_{2\ (g)} + O_{2\ (g)} + 2\ H_2O_{\ (l)} \rightarrow 2\ H_2SO_{4\ (l)}$$

given the following thermochemical equations:

$$2\ SO_{2\ (g)} + O_{2\ (g)} \rightarrow 2\ SO_{3\ (g)} \qquad \Delta H = -196.7\ \text{kJ}$$

$$SO_{3\ (g)} + H_2O_{\ (l)} \rightarrow H_2SO_{4\ (l)} \qquad \Delta H = -130.1\ \text{kJ}$$

1) -456.9 2) 66.6 3) 326.7 4) -326.7 5) 456.9

15. Which of the following equations constitutes the standard state formation reaction for $NH_4Br_{\ (s)}$?

1) $N_{\ (g)} + 2\ H_{2\ (g)} + 0.5\ Br_{2\ (s)} \rightarrow NH_4Br_{\ (s)}$
2) $0.5\ N_{2\ (g)} + 2\ H_{2\ (g)} + 0.5\ Br_{2\ (l)} \rightarrow NH_4Br_{\ (s)}$
3) $0.5\ N_{2\ (g)} + 2\ H_{2\ (g)} + 0.5\ Br_{2\ (g)} \rightarrow NH_4Br_{\ (g)}$
4) $0.5\ N_{2\ (g)} + 2\ H_{2\ (g)} + 0.5\ Br_{2\ (s)} \rightarrow NH_4Br_{\ (g)}$
5) $N_{\ (g)} + 4\ H_{\ (g)} + Br_{\ (g)} \rightarrow NH_4Br_{\ (g)}$

16. Which of the following have standard molar enthalpies and Gibb's Free Energy of formation equal to zero?

a. $Au_{(s)}$ b. $Hg_{\ (l)}$ c. $Br_{2\ (l)}$

1) only a 2) only b 3) only c 4) only a & b 5) a, b, & c

17. From the following thermochemical equation:

$$C_3H_{6\ (g)} + 4.5\ O_{2\ (g)} \rightarrow 3\ CO_{2\ (g)} + 3\ H_2O_{\ (l)} \qquad \Delta H^o = -2061\ \text{kJ}$$

and the standard heats of formation given in Appendix 1A, calculate the standard heat of formation (in kJ) for $C_3H_{6\ (g)}$.

1) -4099 2) 23 3) -23 4) 1382 5) 155

18. Using the data in Appendix 1A, calculate the heat of reaction (in kJ) for the combustion of 1 mol of $C_2H_{4\ (g)}$.

$$C_2H_{4\ (g)} + 3\ O_{2\ (g)} \rightarrow 2\ CO_{2\ (g)} + 2\ H_2O_{\ (l)}$$

1) -1411 2) 731.4 3) 1411 4) -1307 5) 1307

19. From the following thermochemical equation, $2\ Al_{(s)} + 1.5\ O_{2\ (g)} \rightarrow Al_2O_{3\ (s)}$ $\Delta H = -400$ kcal, determine ΔH (in kcal) for the reaction: $2\ Al_2O_{3\ (s)} \rightarrow 4\ Al_{(s)} + 3\ O_{2\ (g)}$

1) -400 2) 400 3) 200 4) -200 5) 800

20. When 2.00 g of $Mg_{(s)}$ were reacted with a stoichiometric amount of $O_{2(g)}$ under standard state conditions to produce $MgO_{(s)}$, 49.6 kJ of heat energy were liberated. Given this information, calculate the standard enthalpy for the formation of $MgO_{(s)}$ in kJ/mol. (MM: MgO = 40.3, Mg = 24.3, O_2 = 32.0)

1) -24.8 2) 603 3) -603 4) -999 5) 999

21. From the bond energies given in Appendix 1B, estimate the enthalpy change (in kJ) for the following gas-phase reaction: $C_2H_{2\ (g)} + \frac{5}{2}\ O_{2\ (g)} \rightarrow 2\ CO_{2\ (g)} + H_2O_{(g)}$

1) -1214 2) -982 3) 642 4) 2240 5) -384

22. For which of the following chemical or physical processes carried out at constant pressure will ΔS for sure be positive.

a. $H_2O_{(s)} \rightarrow H_2O_{(l)}$

b. $2\ SO_{3\ (g)} \rightarrow 2\ SO_{2\ (g)} + O_{2\ (g)}$

c. $CH_{4\ (g)} + 2\ Cl_{2\ (g)} \rightarrow CH_2Cl_{2\ (l)} + 2\ HCl_{(g)}$

d. $P_{4\ (s,\ white)} + 6\ Cl_{2\ (g)} \rightarrow 4\ PCl_{3\ (l)}$

1) only a 2) only b 3) only c 4) only c and d 5) only a & b

For questions 23- 30, consider the following information:

For the fictitious reaction [5 A (g) → 1 B (s) + 4 C (g)] occurring at 59.0°C, the enthalpy change is -143.0 kJ and the Gibbs free energy change is -93.5 kJ.

23 What is the heat transfer (in kJ) under reversible conditions at 59.0°C?

1) -143.0 2) -192.5 3) -0.149 4) -8.79 5) -49.5

24. What is the maximum amount of useful work (in kJ) that can be obtained during this process at 59.0°C?

1) -143.0 2) -93.5 3) -0.149 4) 2.76 5) 49.5

25. What is the change in entropy (in kJ/K) for this reaction at 59.0°C?

1) -143.0 2) -192.5 3) -0.149 4) -8.79 5) -49.5

26. How much pressure-volume work (in kJ) was done at 59.0°C?

1) -2.76 2) 2.76 3) -93.5 4) 93.5 5) -143.0

27. What is the change in internal energy (in kJ) for this reaction at 59.0°C?

1) -140.2 2) -145.8 3) -142.8 4) -143.0 5) -236.5

28. If this reaction was carried out in a bomb calorimeter at 59.0°C, then how much heat (in kJ) was transferred?

1) -140.2 2) -145.8 3) -142.8 4) -143.0 5) -236.5

29. What is the Gibbs free energy change (in kJ) for this reaction at 25°C? (Assume that ΔH and ΔS are temperature independent and no change in state is occurring.)

1) -146.7 2) -139.2 3) -93.5 4) -187.4 5) -98.6

30. At what temperature (in K) would this reaction be at equilibrium? (Assume that ΔH and ΔS are temperature independent and no change in state is occurring.)

1) 960 2) 687 3) 1233 4) 143 5) 59.0

31. For a process, the enthalpy change is 100.0 kJ and the entropy change is 0.4770 kJ/K. Assuming that the change in enthalpy and entropy are temperature independent and that no change in state is occurring, this process is ___________.
   1) spontaneous at all temperatures
   2) spontaneous only if the temperature is less than 209.6 K
   3) spontaneous only if the temperature is equal to 209.6 K
   4) spontaneous only if the temperature is greater than 209.6 K
   5) non-spontaneous at all temperatures

32. The normal boiling point for compound A is 37°C and its freezing point is -20°C. Given the following thermochemical equation:

$$A_{(s)} \rightarrow A_{(l)} \qquad \Delta H = 50.8 \text{ kJ}$$

What is the change in entropy (in kJ/K) for the following process $A_{(l)} \rightarrow A_{(s)}$ at 1 atm?

1) 0.201 2) -0.201 3) 2.54 4) -2.54 5) 50.8

33. As a result of a spontaneous process, which of the following always occurs?
   1) The entropy of the system increases.
   2) The entropy of the universe increases.
   3) The entropy of the universe decreases.
   4) The free energy of the system is greater than zero.
   5) More than one of the above choices is corrrect.

34. For a reaction which occurs at 27.0°C, the enthalpy change is 14.5 kJ and the entropy change is 0.0784 kJ/K. Which of the following statements would be true?
   1) If the reaction is allowed to occur under constant pressure, heat would be evolved.
   2) The products are more ordered than the reactants.
   3) The reaction is not spontaneous.
   4) More than one of the above statements is correct.
   5) None of the above statements is correct.

35. A chemical reaction will always be spontaneous if:
   1) The sign of ΔH is positive and that of ΔS is negative.
   2) The sign of ΔG is positive.
   3) The sign of ΔH is negative and that of ΔS is positive.
   4) More than one of the above statements is correct.
   5) None of the above statements is correct.

36. For an isothermal reversible process, the heat transfer is given by:

1) $T\Delta S$ 2) ΔG 3) ΔH 4) ΔE 5) $(\Delta n)RT$

37. If ΔS for a reaction is negative, then:
   1) the products are more ordered than the reactants.
   2) the reactants have less entropy than the products.
   3) the reaction will always be spontaneous.
   4) q_{rev} will be positive.
   5) More than one of the above statements is correct.

38. Given the data in Appendix 1B, which of the following has the strongest bond?

1) H - F 2) H - H 3) F - F 4) Cl - Cl 5) I - I

39. Given that the normal freezing point for compound A is 30°C. Predict the sign for ΔH, ΔS, and ΔG for $A_{(l)} \rightarrow A_{(s)}$ at 25°C and 1 atm.

	ΔH	ΔS	ΔG
1)	-	-	0
2)	-	+	-
3)	+	-	+
4)	+	+	0
5)	-	-	-

40. Given that the absolute entropy (at 25 °C) for $N_{2\,(g)}$ = 198.6 J/K, $O_{2\,(g)}$ = 205.0 J/K, $NO_{2\,(g)}$ = 240.1 J/K, calculate the change in entropy (in J/K) for the following reaction:

$$N_{2\,(g)} + 2\,O_{2\,(g)} \rightarrow 2\,NO_{2\,(g)}$$

1) 1088.8 2) -128.4 3) 691.6 4) 128.4 5) -691.6

Consider the following information for questions 41 and 42.

Compound	$NO_{2\,(g)}$	$NO_{(g)}$	$CO_{2\,(g)}$	$CO_{(g)}$
ΔG_f^o (kcal/mol)	12.3	20.7	-94.5	-32.8
ΔH_f^o (kcal/mol)	7.9	21.6	-94.1	-26.4

41. Which of the following reactions would be spontaneous under standard conditions?

1) $N_{2\,(g)} + 2\,O_{2\,(g)} \rightarrow 2\,NO_{2\,(g)}$
2) $C_{(s,\ graphite)} + O_{2\,(g)} \rightarrow CO_{2\,(g)}$
3) $NO_{2\,(g)} + CO_{(g)} \rightarrow NO_{(g)} + CO_{2\,(g)}$
4) Two of the above reactions are spontaneous.
5) There is not enough information to answer the question.

42. Which of the following reactions would be endothermic under standard conditions?

1) $N_{2\,(g)} + 2\,O_{2\,(g)} \rightarrow 2\,NO_{2\,(g)}$
2) $C_{(s,\ graphite)} + O_{2\,(g)} \rightarrow CO_{2\,(g)}$
3) $NO_{2\,(g)} + CO_{(g)} \rightarrow NO_{(g)} + CO_{2\,(g)}$
4) Two of the above reactions are endothermic.
5) There is not enough information to answer the question.

43. Which of the following is ***false***?

1) When a gas is allowed to expand, its entropy increases.
2) The standard formation reaction for $NO_{2\,(g)}$ has a negative ΔS.
3) $S^o_{NaCl\,(s)} < S^o_{NaCl\,(aq)}$
4) $S^o_{Ne\,(g)} = 0$ kJ/K
5) There is not enough information to answer the question.

MODULE 3 - ANSWERS

1. 166 cal
2. 36. g
3. 45.2°C
4. 30.7°C
5. 0.144 cal/g · °C
6. 45.7 °C
7. 46.3 g
8. 0.436 cal/g · °C
9. 32.4°C
10. 4.5 g
11. a) 1.49×10^3 J b) -4.96×10^4 J/mol NaOH
12. 0.578 kcal/°C
13. a) 18.4 kJ b) 3.9×10^2 kJ/mol C c) -3.9×10^2 kJ/mol
14. a) -17.9 kJ/g b) -572 kJ/mol
15. a) $N_{2\,(g)} + 3\,H_{2\,(g)} \rightarrow 2\,NH_{3\,(g)}$ $\Delta H = -91.8$ kJ b) exothermic
    c) $2\,NH_{3\,(g)} \rightarrow N_{2\,(g)} + 3\,H_{2\,(g)}$ $\Delta H = 91.8$ kJ d) $5\,N_{2\,(g)} + 15\,H_{2\,(g)} \rightarrow 10\,NH_{3\,(g)}$ $\Delta H = -459$ kJ
16. 9.245×10^3 J/g S_8
17. 432 kJ
18. -1504. kJ
19. a) -71.4 kJ b) 598 g c) 32.0 g
20. becomes more negative
21. w = -62.1 cal q = 62.1 cal
22. -700 J
23. -1144 J
24. 0.0212 kcal
25. 3.7 L
26. a) work done on system b) work done by system c) work done on system
27. a) $2\,CH_{4\,(g)} + 4\,O_{2\,(g)} \rightarrow 2\,CO_{2\,(g)} + 4\,H_2O_{(l)}$ $\Delta H = -426$ kcal b) -213 kcal/mol c) 2.37 kcal
28. a) $C_2H_{4\,(g)} + 3\,O_{2\,(g)} \rightarrow 2\,CO_{2\,(g)} + 2\,H_2O_{(l)}$ b) 1.19 kcal
    c) work done by surroundings d) move down
29. Enthalpy is the heat released or absorbed by a system at constant pressure
    Internal Energy is the heat released or absorbed by a system at constant volume
30. ΔH is the change is enthalpy for a reaction or physical process at non-standard state conditions
    ΔH^o is the change is enthalpy for a reaction or physical process at standard state conditions (P = 1 atm and T = 25°C - unless otherwise specified)
    ΔH_f^o is the standard enthalpy of formation for 1 mol of substance from its elements at standard state conditions
31. a) 300 J b) 500 J
32. 166 kJ
33. -5461 kJ
34. -890 kJ
35. -110.5 kJ
36. 226.7 kJ
37. -304.1 kJ
38. a) 0 kJ b) 0 kJ c) 249.2 kJ d) 0 kJ e) 218.0 kJ f) 0 kJ
39. a) $C_{(graphite)} + 2\,Cl_{2\,(g)} \rightarrow CCl_{4\,(l)}$ $\Delta H_f^o = -139$ kJ
    b) $\frac{1}{2}\,N_{2\,(g)} + 2\,H_{2\,(g)} + \frac{1}{2}\,Cl_{2\,(g)} \rightarrow NH_4Cl_{(s)}$ $\Delta H_f^o = -315.4$ kJ
40. a) -1366.7 kJ b) -3267 kJ c) -76.77 kJ d) -285.8 kJ e) -137.2 kJ
41. a) 128 kJ b) -117 kJ c) -319.8 kJ d) -103.9 kJ
42. a) -213 kJ b) -54 kJ c) -83 kJ d) -300 kJ
43. 294 kJ

44. The bond that takes the most energy to break is the strongest bond, therefore, H - F has the strongest bond.
45. a) - b) ? because same # of gas mol of products and reactants c) + d) - e) + f) + g) - h) -
46. a) 0.0865 kJ/K • mol diethyl ether b) -0.0865 kJ/K • mol diethyl ether c) 0.00259 kJ/K
47. a and e
48. below 111 K
49. a) $\Delta S° = -22.2$ J/K, $\Delta G° = -35.2$ kJ, $\Delta H° = -41.8$ kJ
    b) $\Delta S° = -181.6$ J/K, $\Delta G° = -768.0$ kJ, $\Delta H° = -822.1$ kJ

50. A. a) -6.6 kJ b) -54.1 kJ
    B. a) 0 kJ b) 2.5 kJ
    C. a) no work b) on the system
    D. a) -41.8 kJ b) -820 kJ
    E. a) -41.8 kJ b) -820 kJ
    F. a) -41.8 kJ b) -822 kJ
    G. a) 1884 K b) 4527 K
    H. a) -34.8 kJ b) -764.4 kJ
    I. a) yes b) yes
    J. a) -34.8 kJ b) -764.4 kJ
51. $\Delta S > 0.057$ kJ/K
52. 636 kJ

ANSWERS TO MULTIPLE CHOICE PRACTICE EXAM

1	2	3	4	5	6	7	8	9	10	11	12	13	14	15	16	17	18	19	20
1	5	1	4	2	5	5	3	4	4	4	1	3	1	2	5	2	1	5	3

21	22	23	24	25	26	27	28	29	30	31	32	33	34	35	36	37	38	39	40
1	5	5	2	3	2	1	1	5	1	4	2	2	5	3	1	1	1	5	2

41	42	43
4	1	4

MODULE 4. Chemical Kinetics

I. Reaction Rates and Chemical Kinetics

In the previous module we learned how chemical thermodynamics can be used to assess whether a particular reaction was favorable. For example, the reaction of diamond with oxygen is spontaneous;

$$C_{(s,\ diamond)} + O_{2\ (g)} \rightarrow CO_{2\ (g)} \qquad \Delta G° = -397 \text{ kJ/mol}$$

however, we know from experience that this does not happen even over a long period of time. While thermodynamics tells us that a particular reaction (or process) may be favorable, it does not tell us how fast that reaction will occur. In this module we will discuss reaction rates and chemical kinetics.

Reaction rates describe how fast reactants are used up and products are formed. Chemical kinetics is the study of rates of chemical reactions and the mechanism (i.e., the series of steps) by which reactions occur.

The following graph shows the change in concentration of the reactant and product in the hypothetical chemical reaction, A $\rightarrow$ B, as a function of time.

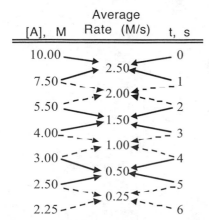

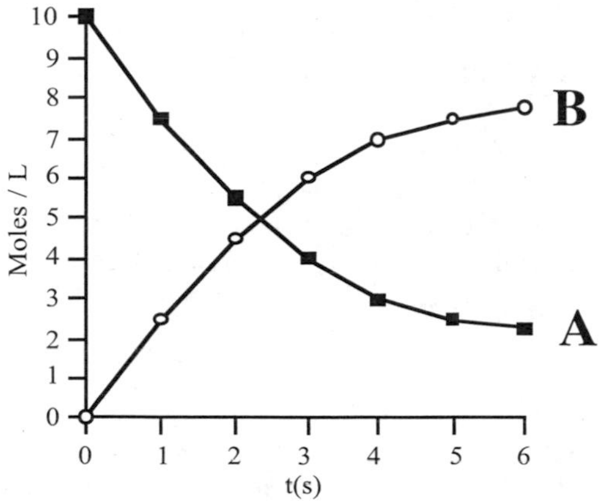

Initially (t = 0 s), there are 10 mol/L of A present and 0 mol/L of B.

As the reaction progresses, A disappears and B appears. For example, at 1 s, 2.5 mol/L of B have formed and 7.5 mol/L of A remain (i.e., from the initial 10 mol/L of A that were present, 2.5 mol/L of A have reacted to form 2.5 mol/L of B; thus, 7.5 mol/L of A are left unreacted).

Also note from this graph that the rate of disappearance of A slows down with time; for that matter, the rate of appearance of B slows down with time as well. Thus, the rate of a reaction, almost always, varies with time.

The average rate of the reaction <u>can</u> be defined as the change in reactant concentration (i.e., molarity = M = moles/L) over a certain *small* time interval. The average rate for the reaction of A $\rightarrow$ B can be defined as:

always has a positive value (reaction rate) — change in concentration of A over time ($\Delta[A]$)

$$\text{reaction rate}_{av} = -\frac{[A]_2 - [A]_1}{t_2 - t_1} = -\frac{\Delta[A]}{\Delta t}$$

A negative sign is indicative that A is disappearing with time.
A negative sign is also used so that the average reaction rate will be a positive number.

From the following table, we can calculate the average reaction rate (i.e., rate_{av}) for A $\rightarrow$ B.

[A], M	Average Rate (M/s)	t, s
10.00		0
	2.50	
7.50		1
	2.00	
5.50		2
	1.50	
4.00		3
	1.00	
3.00		4
	0.50	
2.50		5
	0.25	
2.25		6

The average rate of 2.50 M/s for the time interval from t = 0 to t = 1 sec was obtained as follows:

$$\text{rate}_{av} = -\frac{[A]_2 - [A]_1}{t_2 - t_1} = -\frac{(7.50 - 10.00)\text{ M}}{(1 - 0)\text{ s}} = 2.50\,\frac{\text{M}}{\text{s}}$$

Again note from the data to your left how the average reaction rate is not constant and how it decreases with time.

The average rate has the disadvantage of not telling us the rate at a specific time, but rather the rate between two time intervals. To find the rate at a specific time: 1) we need to make a plot of concentration vs. time, 2) we need to draw a line that is tangent (i.e., perpendicular) to the curve at that point in time that we want to find the rate of, 3) then from the slope of the tangent line, the rate of the reaction, which the *instantaneous rate*, can then be obtained.

For example, the instantaneous rate for the reaction of A $\rightarrow$ B at 3 seconds can be obtained as follows:

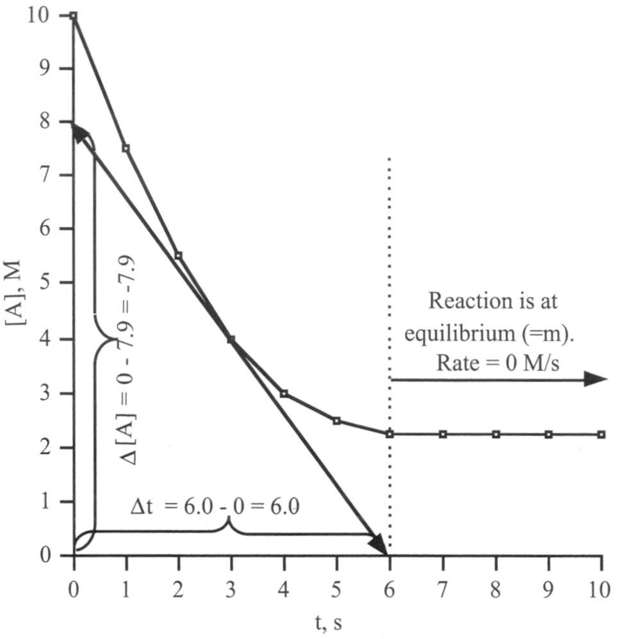

The line that is tangent to the curve at 3 seconds is represented by the line with the double arrowheads. The slope of the "tangent line" is:

$$\text{slope} = \frac{\Delta y}{\Delta x} = \frac{\Delta A}{\Delta t} = \frac{-7.9\ \text{M}}{6.0\ \text{s}} = -1.3\ \frac{\text{M}}{\text{s}}$$

Thus, the *instantaneous rate for the disappearance* of A at 3 seconds is 1.3 M/s.

Also note that the reaction reaches equilibrium at ~ 6 s. The rate of the reaction at this time and beyond is equal to 0 M/s.

The reaction of A $\rightarrow$ B does not go to completion (~ 2.3 mol/L of A remain unreacted when the reaction reaches equilibrium). Thus, of the initial 10 mol/L of A that we started with ~7.7 mol/L reacted to produce ~7.7 mol/L of B).

In general, we try to measure the *initial rate of the reaction* (i.e., the rate of reaction when the reactants are initially brought together). The initial reaction rate is obtained by drawing a line tangent to the curve at t = 0. As the reaction progresses, it is possible that the products will react to form something else in the reaction mixture or revert back to form reactants; either way, the presence of products can alter the reaction rate and lead to very different and even confusing results. Therefore, for the remainder of this module when we give reaction rates, it will be initial reaction rates that will quoted (unless otherwise noted).

So far we have only discussed the simple reaction of A $\rightarrow$ B. For more complicated reactions, such as:

$$a\,A + b\,B \rightarrow c\,C + d\,D$$ (where a, b, c, and d are the stoichiometric coefficients)

the average rate with respect to each of the reactants and products is given by:

reactants (⊖ ⊖) products (⊕ ⊕)

$$\text{reaction rate} = -\frac{1}{a}\frac{\Delta[A]}{\Delta t} = -\frac{1}{b}\frac{\Delta[B]}{\Delta t} = +\frac{1}{c}\frac{\Delta[C]}{\Delta t} = +\frac{1}{d}\frac{\Delta[D]}{\Delta t}$$

negative sign indicates disappearance of substance

change in concentration (of A) with change in time

stoichiometric coefficient

positive sign indicates appearnace of substance

Since the concentration unit that is used is molarity (mol/L), the units for reaction rate are:

$$\frac{\text{mol}}{\text{L}\bullet\text{time}} = \frac{\text{M}}{\text{time}} = \text{M} \bullet \text{time}^{-1}$$

Example Problems:

1. Consider the reaction: $2\ K + L \rightarrow 4\ M$. Given the following data,

[K], M	Time, s
1.37	0
0.45	10

a) What is the average rate of change in concentration of K (in M/s) during the time interval given (t = 0 to t = 10 sec)?

$$\text{rate of change in [K]} = \frac{[K]_2 - [K]_1}{t_2 - t_1} = \frac{\Delta[K]}{\Delta t} = \frac{(0.45 - 1.37)\ M}{(10 - 0)\ s} = -9.2 \times 10^{-2}\ \frac{M}{s}$$

[NOTE: A negative sign indicates that K is disappearing with time.]

b) What is the average rate of disappearance (in M/s) with respect to L?

In Problem 1a (above) we calculated the average rate of change in [K] over time is:

$$\frac{\Delta[K]}{\Delta t} = -9.2 \times 10^{-2}\ \frac{M}{s}$$

$$\text{For this reaction, } \text{rate}_{av} = -\frac{1}{1}\frac{\Delta[L]}{\Delta t} = -\frac{1}{2}\frac{\Delta[K]}{\Delta t}$$

$$\text{reaction rate}_{av} = -\frac{1}{1}\frac{\Delta[L]}{\Delta t} = -\frac{1}{2}\left(-9.2 \times 10^{-2}\ \frac{M}{s}\right)$$

$$\frac{\Delta[L]}{\Delta t} = \frac{1}{2}\left(-9.2 \times 10^{-2}\ \frac{M}{s}\right) = -4.6 \times 10^{-2}\ \frac{M}{s}$$

The sign is used to indicate that L is disappearing with time.

The average rate of *disappearance* with respect to L $= 4.6 \times 10^{-2}\ \frac{M}{s}$

As expected, K disappears 2x as fast as L.

c) What is the average rate of appearance (in M/s) with respect to M?

$$\text{For this reaction, } \text{rate}_{av} = +\frac{1}{4}\frac{\Delta[M]}{\Delta t} = -\frac{1}{2}\frac{\Delta[K]}{\Delta t}$$

$$+\frac{1}{4}\frac{\Delta[M]}{\Delta t} = -\frac{1}{2}\left(-9.2 \times 10^{-2}\ \frac{M}{s}\right)$$

$$\frac{\Delta[M]}{\Delta t} = \frac{4}{2}\left(9.2 \times 10^{-2}\ \frac{M}{s}\right) = 1.84 \times 10^{-1}\ \frac{M}{s}$$

The average rate of appearance of M $= \frac{\Delta[M]}{\Delta t} = 1.84 \times 10^{-1}\ \frac{M}{s}$

As expected, M appears 2x as fast as K and 4x as fast as L.

NOTE: When the average rate of the reaction is expressed relative to the average rate of change in concentration of the various reactants/products, all are equal.

$$\text{reaction rate}_{av} = -\frac{1}{2}\frac{\Delta[K]}{\Delta t} = -\frac{1}{1}\frac{\Delta[L]}{\Delta t} = +\frac{1}{4}\frac{\Delta[M]}{\Delta t}$$

$$\text{reaction rate}_{av} = -\frac{1}{2}\left(-9.2 \times 10^{-2}\ \frac{M}{s}\right) = -\frac{1}{1}\left(-4.6 \times 10^{-2}\ \frac{M}{s}\right) = +\frac{1}{4}\left(1.84 \times 10^{-1}\ \frac{M}{s}\right) = 4.6 \times 10^{-2}\ \frac{M}{s}$$

2. Consider the reaction: 2 A + 4 B → 4 D + 3 E. If a graph of [B] vs. time (min) has a slope of -0.0706 at t = 10 min, what is the instantaneous rate of the reaction at 10 min?

$$\text{reaction rate} = -\frac{1}{4}\frac{\Delta[B]}{\Delta t} = -\frac{1}{4}(-0.0706\ \text{M/min}) = 0.0177\ \text{M/min}$$

II. Factors that Affect Reaction Rates

The following four factors influence the rate at which a chemical reaction proceeds: A) the nature of the reactants, B) the concentration of the reactants, C) the temperature at which the reaction takes place, and D) the presence of a catalyst or inhibitor.

A. The Nature of Reactants and Rate of Reaction

The physical state of the reactants can have a profound effect on the rate of the reaction; for example:

- Homogenous reaction mixtures react faster than non-homogenous reaction mixtures.
- One allotropic form of a chemical can react faster than another form.
- Metals that have been finely ground react faster than a chunk of metal. In this particular case the finely ground metal has a larger surface area.
- Reactions occur faster in gas, liquid, or solution phase than in the solid phase.

B. The Concentration of Reactants and Rate of Reaction

As the concentration of any of the reactants change (at constant temperature), the rate of the reaction changes.

a) Rate Law, Rate Constant, and Reaction Order - Relationship between Concentration and Rate

The *differerential rate law* or simply the *rate law* for the reaction describes how the rate of the reaction depends on concentration. Thus for a reaction:

$$a\,A + b\,B \rightarrow \text{Products}$$

$$\text{rate} = k\,[A]^x\,[B]^y$$

where, k is called the **rate constant** at a particular temperature. **The exponents, x and y, and the rate constant, k, bear <u>no necessary</u> relationship to the coefficients of the balanced chemical equation - they must be determined experimentally.** The exponents are usually positive integers or zero, but they can occasionally be a fraction or a negative number. For the above rate law,

$x \rightarrow$ *order* of the reaction with respect to A

$y \rightarrow$ *order* of the reaction with respect to B

Overall order of the reaction (sum of exponents) $\rightarrow x + y$

Only if you know that the reaction occurs in a one-step mechanism, that you can then relate the order of the reaction to the stoichiometric coefficients (e.g., if the reaction, <u>a</u> A + <u>b</u> B → Products, had a one step mechanism, then its rate law would be: rate = k $[A]^a[B]^b$).

The following are specific points about the rate constant, k:

- Its value is for a specific reaction only.
- Its units depend on the overall reaction order.
- Its value does not change with concentration.
- Its value does not change with time.
- Its value is temperature dependent (if the temperature is increased, k will increase).
- Its value depends on the presence of a catalyst (a catalyst causes an increase in k) or an inhibitor (an inhibitor causes k to decrease).

Example Problems:

1. The reaction: $2\ NO\ (g) + 2\ H_2\ (g) \rightarrow N_2\ (g) + 2\ H_2O\ (g)$, is second order in NO (g) and first order in H_2 (g). Given this information,

   a) What are the units of the rate constant, k? (Assume that the time is in seconds.)

   $$\text{rate} = k\,[NO]^2\,[H_2]^1$$

   Using mol/L

   $$\frac{mol}{L \bullet s} = k\left(\frac{mol}{L}\right)^2\left(\frac{mol}{L}\right)^1$$

   $$\frac{mol}{L \bullet s} = k\left(\frac{mol}{L}\right)^3$$

   $$k = \left(\frac{mol}{L \bullet s}\right)\left(\frac{L}{mol}\right)^3 = \frac{L^2}{mol^2 \bullet s}$$

   or

   Using M

   $$\frac{M}{s} = k\,(M)^2\,(M)^1$$

   $$\frac{M}{s} = k\,(M)^3$$

   $$k = \frac{M}{M^3 \bullet s} = \frac{1}{M^2 \bullet s} = M^{-2} \bullet s^{-1}$$

   b) Write the rate expression that shows the rate law as a function of the rate of change of N_2.

   $$\text{Rate} = +\frac{1}{1}\frac{\Delta[N_2]}{\Delta t} = \frac{\Delta[N_2]}{\Delta t} = k\,[NO]^2\,[H_2]^1$$

   c) Write the rate expression that shows the rate law as a function of the rate of change of NO.

   $$\text{Rate} = -\frac{1}{2}\frac{\Delta[NO]}{\Delta t} = k\,[NO]^2\,[H_2]^1$$

   d) What is the overall order of the reaction?

   The overall order = sum of exponents $\rightarrow$ $2 + 1 = 3$

2. Consider the following reaction, $2\ A + 2\ B \rightarrow C$. If the reaction is zero order in A and second order in B, then:

   a) What is the rate law?

   $\text{Rate} = k\,[A]^0\,[B]^2 = k\,[B]^2$

   b) What happens to the rate if the initial concentration of A is increased by a factor of 2 and that of B is changed so that it's concentration is a factor of 3 times smaller?

   Since the reaction is zero order in A, changing the concentration of A does not affect the reaction rate. Since the reaction is second order in B, if the concentration of B is decreased so it is three times smaller, then the reaction rate decreases by a factor of 9 (i.e., $3^2 = [B]^2$) or the rate changes so that it is $^1/_9$ the original rate.

3. If the following reaction has a one-step mechanism: $2\ A\ (g) + B\ (g) \rightarrow C\ (g)$. If the 8.00 mol of A and 3.00 mol of B are mixed in a 10.0 L container and if $k = 1.00\ M^{-2} \bullet hr^{-1}$, then

   a) What is the rate law?

   Since the reaction occurs in a one-step mechanism, then the order of the reaction can be related to the stoichiometric coefficients. Therefore, the rate law is:

   $\text{Rate} = k\,[A]^2\,[B]$

   b) What is the initial rate (in $M \bullet hr^{-}$)?

   $$\text{Rate} = k\,[A]^2\,[B] = 1.00\ M^{-2} \bullet hr^{-1}\left(\frac{8.00\ mol}{10.0\ L}\right)^2\left(\frac{3.00\ mol}{10.0\ L}\right)$$

   $$= (1.00\ M^{-2} \bullet hr^{-1})\,(0.800\ M)^2\,(0.300\ M) = 0.192\ \frac{M}{hr}$$

c) What is the rate (in M/hr) if $^1/_4$ of the original amount of B has been consumed?

If $\frac{1}{4}$ of B has been consumed, $\frac{3}{4}$ remain unreacted; therefore $\frac{3}{4}$(3.00 mol) = 2.25 mol are still present.

	2 A	+ B	→ C	
mol_0	8.00	3.00	0	← Given initial moles
mol_{change}	- 2x	- x	+ x	← Relative change in moles is dependent on stoichiometric coefficients
mol_t	8.00 - 2x	3.00 - x (2.25 mol)	x	← moles present at desired time interval is obtained from mol_i and mol_{change}

To get the number of moles of A that are still present, we need to solve for x:

$$2.25 = 3.00 - x \quad \text{therefore,} \quad x = 3.00 - 2.25 = 0.75$$

$$\text{mol of A still present:} \quad 8.00 - 2x = 8.00 - 2(0.75) = 6.50$$

$$\text{Rate} = k\,[A]^2\,[B] = 1.00\ M^{-2} \bullet hr^{-1} \left(\frac{6.50\ mol}{10.0\ L}\right)^2 \left(\frac{2.25\ mol}{10.0\ L}\right) = 0.0951\ \frac{M}{hr}$$

d) What is the rate (in M/hr) at the point in the reaction where 3.00 mol of A remain unreacted?

	2 A	+ B	→ C	
mol_0	8.00	3.00	0	← Given initial moles
mol_{change}	- 2x	- x	+ x	← Relative change in moles is dependent on stoichiometric coefficients
mol_t	8.00 - 2x (3.00 mol)	3.00 - x	x	← moles present at desired time interval is obtained from mol_i and mol_{change}

To get the number of moles of B that are still present, we need to solve for x:

$$3.00 = 8.00 - 2x \quad \text{therefore,} \quad x = \frac{3.00 - 8.00}{-2} = 2.50$$

$$\text{mol of B still present:} \quad 3.00 - x = 3.00 - 2.50 = 0.50$$

$$\text{Rate} = k\,[A]^2\,[B] = 1.00\ M^{-2} \bullet hr^{-1} \left(\frac{3.00\ mol}{10.0\ L}\right)^2 \left(\frac{0.50\ mol}{10.0\ L}\right) = 0.0045\ \frac{M}{hr}$$

As was mentioned previously, the order of the reaction with respect to each reactant must be determined experimentally.

The following is an example of one of the ways that can be used to find the order of a reaction:

Consider the reaction, $A + 2B \rightarrow AB_2$. The initial rate of reaction (at a specific temperature) as a function of concentration is tabulated below for a series of experiments:

Experiment	$[A]_{initial}$	$[B]_{initial}$	Initial Rate (M/s)
1	0.32	0.21	3.15×10^{-4}
2	0.32	0.42	8.92×10^{-4}
3	0.64	0.21	2.52×10^{-3}

Because the same reaction is being performed, the only variable is that the concentration of one of the reactants is being changed, the rate law has the same form:

$$\text{rate} = k\,[A]^x\,[B]^y$$

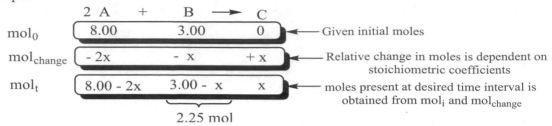

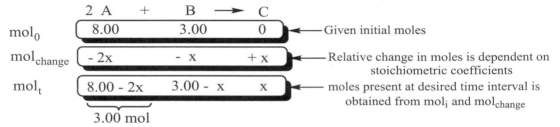

Experiments 1 and 2 have $[A]_{initial}$ being the same while $[B]_{initial}$ is doubled. Thus any change in the rate of the reaction would be due to an increase in $[B]_{initial}$. To find y (in this case):

$$\frac{rate_2}{rate_1} = \frac{8.92 \times 10^{-4}}{3.15 \times 10^{-4}} = \frac{k\,[0.32]^x\,[0.42]^y}{k\,[0.32]^x\,[0.21]^y}$$

$$2.83 = (2)^y$$

to solve for y, take log of both sides:

$$\log(2.83) = \log[(2)^y] \rightarrow \log(2.83) = y \log(2)$$

$$y = \frac{\log(2.83)}{\log(2)} = \frac{0.452}{0.301} = 1.5 \text{ or } \frac{3}{2}$$

Experiments 1 and 3 have $[B]_{initial}$ being the same while $[A]_{initial}$ is doubled. Thus any change in the rate of the reaction would be due to an increase in $[A]_{initial}$. To find x (in this case):

$$\frac{rate_3}{rate_1} = \frac{2.52 \times 10^{-3}}{3.15 \times 10^{-4}} = \frac{k\,[0.64]^x\,[0.21]^y}{k\,[0.32]^x\,[0.21]^y}$$

$$8 = (2)^x$$

to solve for y, take log of both sides:

$$\log(8) = \log[(2)^x] \rightarrow \log(8) = x \log(2)$$

$$x = \frac{\log(8)}{\log(2)} = \frac{0.903}{0.301} = 3$$

The rate law for this particular reaction is then:

$$rate = k\,[A]^3\,[B]^{1.5}$$

The rate constant can be obtained by substituting the data from any of the experiments into the above the equation (in this particular case we'll use experiment 1):

$$3.15 \times 10^{-4} = k\,[0.32]^3\,[0.21]^{1.5} \rightarrow 3.15 \times 10^{-4} = k\,(0.0328)\,(0.0962)$$

$$k = \frac{3.15 \times 10^{-4}}{(0.0328)\,(0.0962)} = 9.98 \times 10^{-2} \frac{L^{3.5}}{mol^{3.5} \bullet s} = 9.98 \times 10^{-2}\ M^{-3.5} \bullet s^{-1}$$

b) **Integrated Rate Equation and Half-life - Relationship between Concentration and t**

We saw how the rate law told us how the rate of a reaction depends on reactant concentration at a particular moment. However, we often would like to have a mathematical relationship showing how a reactant concentration varies over a period of time. Using calculus, we can transform the differential rate law (which gives a relationship between concentration and rate) to an *integrated rate equation or law* (which gives a relationship between concentration and time).

The table on the next page gives the various relationships / formulas that can be used for the reaction:

$$a\,A \rightarrow \text{products}$$

having the following general rate form:

$$rate = k\,[A]^x \qquad x = 0, 1, \text{ or } 2$$

The above rate law tells us that the rate is just dependent on one substance, A, and can be either zero, first, or second order with respect to that substance, as well as, being zero, first, or second order overall.

All the integrated rate expressions have been rearranged into linear equations (see below). To find the order of a reaction various plots must be made. The order can be attained by seeing which type of plot gives a straight line (e.g., if a plot of [A] vs. t gives a straight line, then the reaction is zero order). The table below gives which plots are needed to decide whether a reaction is zero, first or second order.

From the integrated rate equation, we can also obtain the time it takes for one-half of the sample to react. This is called the **half-life** ($t_{1/2}$). The half-life equation for each order reaction can be simply obtained by replacing [A] with $\frac{1}{2}[A]_o$. Subsequent manipulation and simplification yields the half-life equation shown below for each order reaction. Note that only first-order reactions are independent of the initial concentration of reactant (i.e., the half-life is the same during any stage of the reaction). The same can not be said for zero and second order reactions. As can be seen from the graphs below (where the concentration vs. time for three half-lives are plotted) the half-life for zero order reactions gets shorter with decreasing concentration of reactant, while the opposite is true for second order reactions.

Plots of concentration vs. time for zero, first, and second order reactions where $[A]_o$ = 10.0 M and k = 0.1. After the initial starting point, each data point indicates the passage of a half-life.

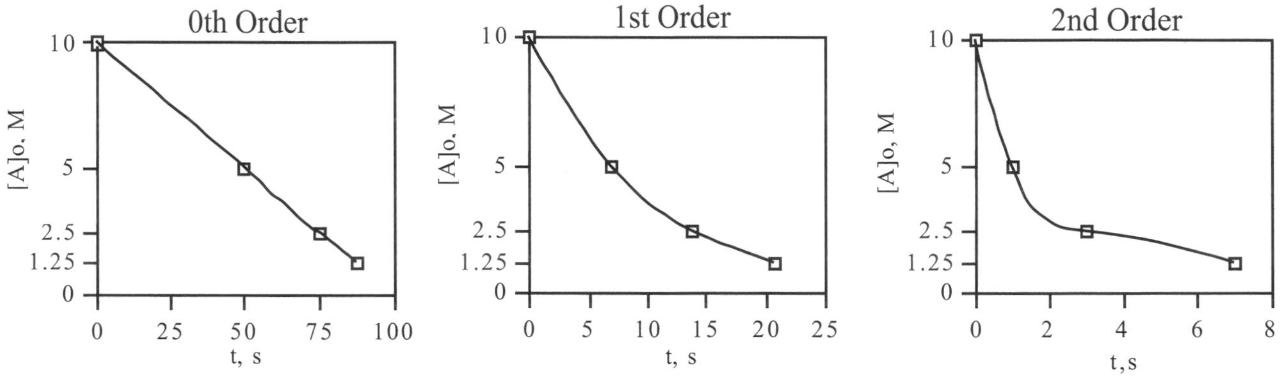

Summary of Relationships for Various Reaction Orders*

a A → Products	zero order	first order	second order
Rate Law / Rate Equation	$-\frac{\Delta[A]}{\Delta t} = k[A]^0 = k$	$-\frac{\Delta[A]}{\Delta t} = k[A]^1$	$-\frac{\Delta[A]}{\Delta t} = k[A]^2$
Integrated Rate Equation (all are linear equations) y = mx + b	$[A] = -kt + [A]_o$	$\ln[A] = -kt + \ln[A]_o$ †	$\frac{1}{[A]} = kt + \frac{1}{[A]_o}$
Half-life ($t_{1/2}$) - The time it takes for one-half of the sample to react	$t_{1/2} = \frac{[A]_o}{2k}$	$t_{1/2} = \frac{0.693}{k}$	$t_{1/2} = \frac{1}{k[A]_o}$
To find the order of reaction, the following three plots must be done. Only one will be a straight line.	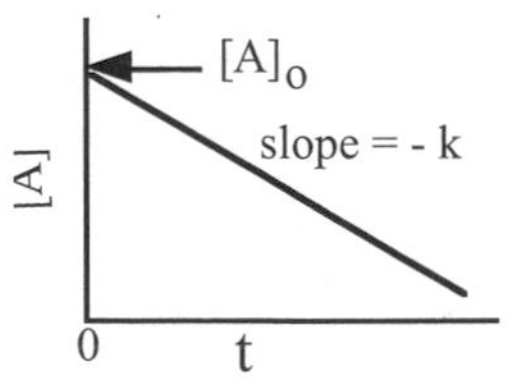	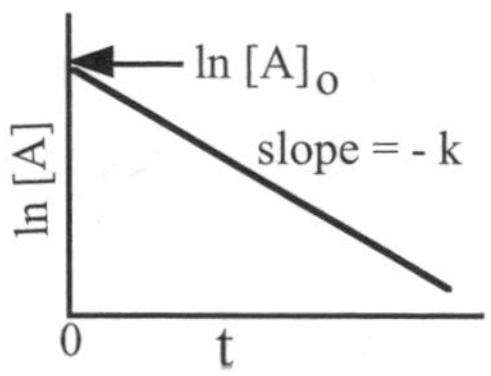	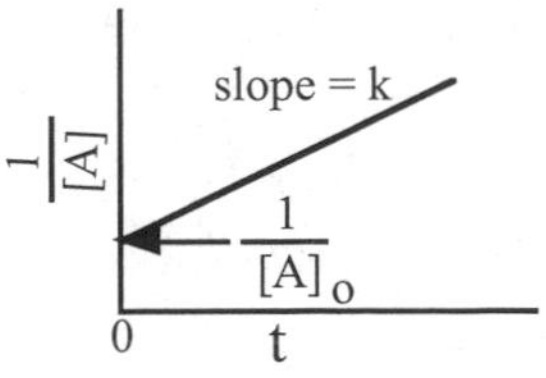

* Technically, the rate constant, *k*, shown in the above table has been multiplied by the stoichiometric coefficient, *a*; thus, k = ak' (where k' is the rate constant carried on from the rate law to the integrated rate equation). Since *a* is a constant, it will be incorporated into the value of *k* without any further ado.

† The exponential form of this equation $-\frac{[A]}{[A]_o} = e^{-kt}$ - is also often used.

NOTE: A reaction in which the rate law is dependent on more than one reactant can be manipulated into behaving like one in which the rate law is dependent on only one reactant. This is done by making the concentration of one of the reactants very small in comparison to the other reactants that affect the rate. If such is the case, the concentration of those reactants present in large concentrations will not change significantly and can be regarded as constant. Thus, the change in concentration with time of that reactant whose concentration was very small can be used to determine the order of the reaction with respect to that reactant.

$$\underbrace{\text{Rate} = k\,[A]^x\,[B]^y\,[C]^z}_{\substack{\text{Complicated rate law can be} \\ \text{simplified by making concentration} \\ \text{of all but one reactant very large.}}} \xrightarrow[\substack{\text{[B] and [C] very large} \\ \text{The rate law will now} \\ \text{be pseudo-dependent on} \\ \text{only one reactant.}}]{\substack{\text{Study reaction when} \\ \text{[A] very small}}} \begin{array}{c} \text{Rate} = k'\,[A]^x \\[4pt] \text{where } k' = k\,[B]^y\,[C]^z \end{array}$$

Example Problems:

1. The reaction: $2\,NO_2\,(g) \rightarrow 2\,NO\,(g) + O_2\,(g)$ has a rate law:

rate = $(1.40 \times 10^{-10}\ M^{-1} \cdot s^{-1})\,[NO_2]^2$. If the initial molarity of $NO_2 = 3.0$ mol/L, then:

a) Calculate the half-life in seconds.

For a second order reaction:

$$t_{1/2} = \frac{1}{k\,[A]_o} = \frac{1}{(1.40 \times 10^{-10}\ M^{-1} \cdot s^{-1})\,(3.00\ M)} = 2.4 \times 10^9\ s$$

b) How many sec does it take for the molarity of NO_2 to be 2.75 M?

For a second order reaction:

$$\frac{1}{[A]} = kt + \frac{1}{[A]_o} \quad \rightarrow \quad \frac{1}{2.75\ M} = \left(1.40 \times 10^{-10}\ \frac{1}{M \cdot s}\right) t + \frac{1}{3.0\ M}$$

$$0.364\ M^{-1} = 1.40 \times 10^{-10}\ M^{-1} \cdot s^{-1}\ t + 0.333\ M^{-1}$$

$$t = \left(\frac{(0.364 - 0.333)\ M^{-1}}{1.40 \times 10^{-10}\ M^{-1} \cdot s^{-1}}\right) = 2.21 \times 10^8\ s$$

c) Calculate the molarity of NO_2 that remains after 150 yrs.

For a second order reaction:

$$\frac{1}{[A]} = kt + \frac{1}{[A]_o}$$

$$\frac{1}{[A]} = \left(1.40 \times 10^{-10}\ \frac{1}{M \cdot s}\right)\left(150\ yr\left(\frac{365\ days}{1\ yr}\right)\left(\frac{24\ hr}{1\ day}\right)\left(\frac{3600\ s}{1\ hr}\right)\right) + \frac{1}{3.0\ M}$$

$$\frac{1}{[A]} = 0.662\ M^{-1} + 0.333\ M^{-1} = 0.995\ M^{-1} \quad \rightarrow \quad [A] = \frac{1}{0.995\ M^{-1}} = 1.0\ M$$

Therefore, after 150 years, out of the original 3.0 mol/L of NO_2 that were originally present, 1.0 mol/L remains unreacted while 2.0 mol/L (i.e., 3.0 - 1.0 mol/L) have reacted.

d) Calculate the molarity of NO and O_2 that have formed after 150 yrs.

This problem requires that we remember that as a chemical reaction proceeds, the stoichiometric coefficients give us either the mol or molar ratio at which reactants and products *change*. The following setup gives us a reaction summary (in terms of mol/L) that is most useful at solving this problem:

	$2\ NO_2 \rightarrow$	$2\ NO$ +	O_2	
$[\ ]_0$	3.0	0	0	← Given initial concentrations
$[\ ]_{change}$	- 2x	+ 2x	+ x	← Relative change in concentration is dependent on stoichiometric coefficients
$[\ ]_t$	3.0 - 2x	2x	x	← Concentration present at desired time interval is obtained from $[\ ]_i$ and $[\ ]_{change}$

↑ From the previous problem, we found that after 150 yr (i.e., the desired time interval), that $[NO_2] = 1.0$ M. Using this information, we can solve for x, so that we can obtain the [NO] and $[O_2]$ that have formed after this time interval.

Since $[NO_2]_{t = 150\ yr} = 1.0 = 3.0 - 2x \rightarrow x = 1.0$ M. Therefore,

$[NO]_{t = 150\ yr} = 2x = 2(1.0) = 2.0$ M and $[O_2]_{t = 150\ yr} = x = 1.0$ M

2. Consider the reaction, $A \rightarrow B$, which occurs in one step. If the half-life of the reaction is 1.99 hr and the initial molarity of A is equal to 0.866 M, then

a) What is the rate constant (in hr^{-})?

Since this reaction occurs in one step each reactant stoichiometric coefficient is equal to the order with respect to that reactant; thus, this reaction is first order in A.

$$t_{1/2} = \frac{0.693}{k} \rightarrow 1.99\ hr = \frac{0.693}{k} \rightarrow k = \frac{0.693}{1.99\ hr} = 0.348\ hr^{-}$$

b) How many hours will it take for the molarity of A to equal 0.0161 M?

For first order reactions:

$$\ln [A] = -kt + \ln [A]_o \rightarrow \ln [0.0161] = -0.348\ t + \ln [0.866]$$

$$-4.13 = -0.348\ t + (-0.144) \rightarrow t = \frac{-4.13 + 0.144}{-0.348} = \frac{-3.99}{-0.348} = 11.5\ hr$$

c) What percentage of A remains unreacted after 4 hr?

To solve this problem, the exponential form of the integrated rate equation will be used.

$\frac{[A]}{[A]_o} = e^{-kt}$ where, $\frac{[A]}{[A]_o}$ represents the fraction of A that remains unreacted.

$$\%\ A_{unreacted} = \frac{[A]}{[A]_o} \times 100 \rightarrow e^{-(0.348\ hr^{-})(4\ hr)} \times 100 = 25\%$$

3. The reaction, $A \rightarrow B$, is zero order in A and has a rate constant of 0.170 M/hr. Given this information, calculate how many hours it would take for 25% of a 1.0 M solution of A to react?

If 25% of A has reacted, then 75% is still present and remains to react.

Thus, if $[A]_o = 1.0$ M then $[A] = 0.75$ M (75% of $[A]_o$)

For zero order reactions: $[A] = -kt + [A]_o$

$$(0.75\ M) = -(0.170\ M/hr)\ t + 1.0\ M$$

$$t = \frac{(0.75 - 1.0)\ M}{-0.170\ M/hr} = 1.5\ hr$$

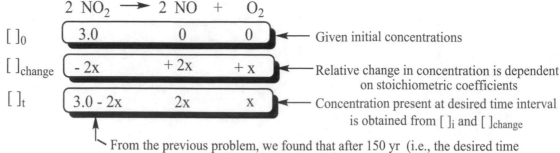

C. Temperature and Rate of Reactions

Basically, in order for a chemical reaction to occur, molecules must undergo effective collisions with the necessary energy (i.e., called the *activation energy* or *energy of activation*) for the reaction to take place.

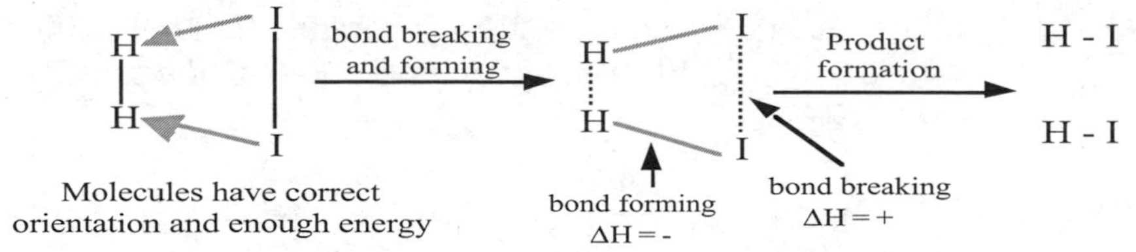

It is theorized that reactants pass through a short-lived, unstable high-energy state, called a *transition state,* before they are converted into products. For example,

$$\underset{\text{reactants}}{A + B\text{-}B} \rightarrow \underset{\text{transition state}}{A\text{---}B\text{---}B} \rightarrow \underset{\text{products}}{A\text{-}B + B}$$

Each of the following energy diagram (potential energy vs. reaction coordinate) is typical for a one-step exothermic and endothermic reaction, respectively. Both diagrams show an "energy hill", which constitutes the energy of activation (E_a). The higher the energy of activation, the slower the reaction; conversely, the lower the energy of activation the faster the reaction. At the top of the hill is the transition state, where bond breaking and bond forming is taking place.

The differences between an exothermic and endothermic potential energy (PE) diagram are:

Exothermic $\rightarrow$ PE for reactants is greater than that for the products

Endothermic $\rightarrow$ PE for products is greater than that for the reactants

Typical E nergy Diagram for a One-Step Reaction

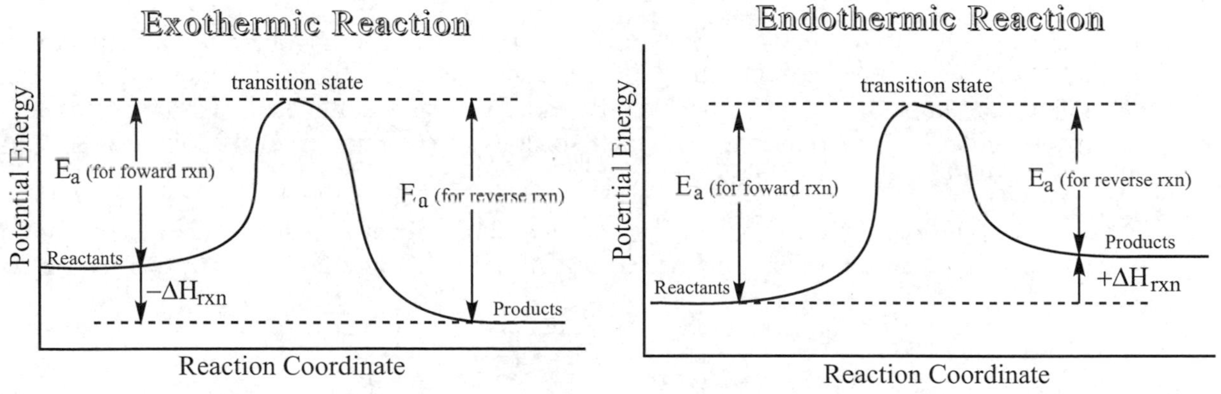

The Maxwell-Boltzman distribution, shown below, shows the effect of temperature on the kinetic energy of molecules.

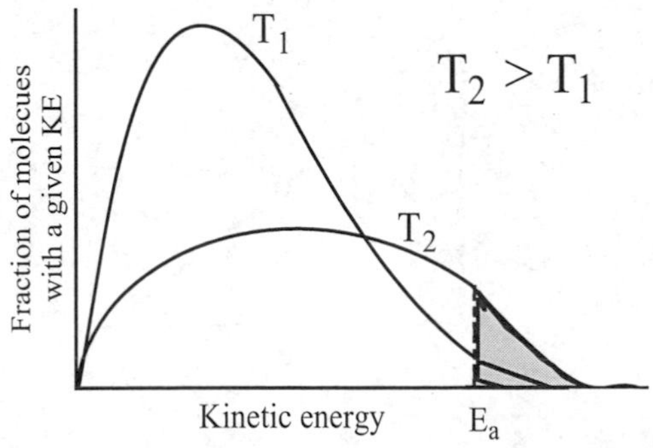

When the temperature increases, not only is the average speed of molecules greater, but there is also a different distribution of speeds. The figure to the left shows that the fraction of molecules with kinetic energies (KE) greater than E_a increases with increasing temperature. The shaded area under each of the two temperature curves represents the total number of molecules with KE > E_a. This increase in temperarture causes the number of effective collisions to increase as well. *It is this increase in the number of effective collisions that is mainly responsible for the sharp increase in the reaction rate as the temperature is increased.*

From experimental observations, S. Arrhenius, developed a mathematical equation that relates the rate constant to T (in K). The Arrhenius equation is:

$$k = A\, e^{-E_a/RT}$$

where, A is called the frequency factor, T is the temperature (in K), R is the gas constant, and E_a is the energy of activation. [NOTE: The energy units for R (i.e., the units on top) must match those for E_a.]

$$R = 0.0821 \frac{\text{L·atm}}{\text{mol·K}} = 1.99 \times 10^{-3} \frac{\text{kcal}}{\text{mol·K}} = 1.99 \frac{\text{cal}}{\text{mol·K}} = 8.31 \times 10^{-3} \frac{\text{kJ}}{\text{mol·K}} = 8.31 \frac{\text{J}}{\text{mol·K}}$$

The frequency factor, A, has the same units as the rate constant, k, and is constant for a given reaction (though it can change when the reaction is catalyzed). The *frequency factor* depends on the frequency of collisions and the fraction of these collisions whose molecules undergoing a reaction have the correct geometry or orientation. Consider the following reaction:

$$CH_3I + Br^- \longrightarrow CH_3Br + I^-$$

where the colliding molecules have proper and improper orientation.

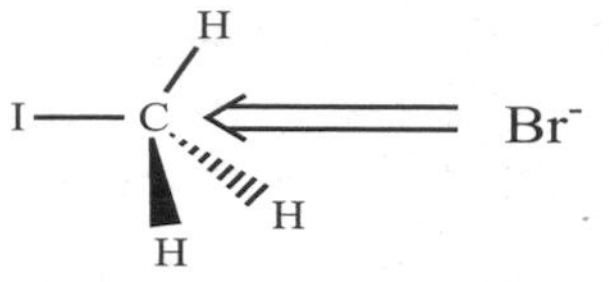

Reactants have proper orientation and possess the minimum amount of energy for chemical reaction to occur.

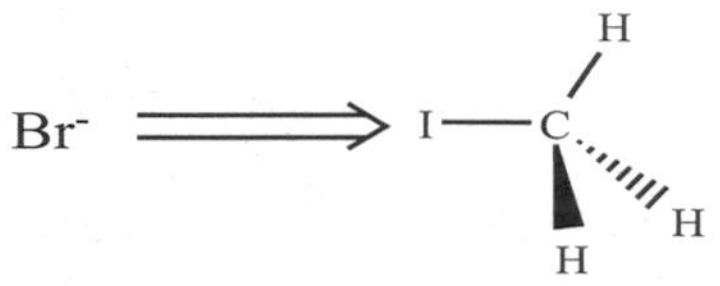

Reactants have improper orientation for chemical reaction to occur.

Thus, for a first order reaction (B $\rightarrow$ C) the rate law can be written as:

$$\text{Rate} = k\,[B] = (A\, e^{-E_a/RT})\,[B]$$

We see from the above equation how the rate of a reaction is not only affected by reactant concentration, but how it is affected by the E_a, T, and A as well. The frequency factor is something that is hard to manipulate directly; however, E_a and T can be manipulated. If E_a decreases (because a catalyst is added), k increases and as such so does the reaction rate. If T increases, k increases and as such so does the reaction rate.

Conversion of the Arrhenius equation into its logarithmic form and subsequent manipulation leads to the following equation which can be used to find E_a when rate constants at two temperatures are known:

$$\ln \frac{k_2}{k_1} = \frac{E_a}{R}\left(\frac{1}{T_1} - \frac{1}{T_2}\right)$$

[NOTE: The energy units for R (i.e., the units on top) must match those for E_a.]

In addition to the above equation, a graphical approach (used when k's for 3 or more temperatures are obtained) can be used to find E_a. This graphical approach again involves using the logarithmic form of the Arrhenius equation, which yields a straight line.

$$\begin{array}{ccccccc} \ln k & = & -\left(\frac{E_a}{R}\right) & \frac{1}{T} & + & \ln A \\ \downarrow & & \downarrow & \downarrow & & \downarrow \\ y & = & (\text{slope}) & x & + & \text{y-intercept} \end{array}$$

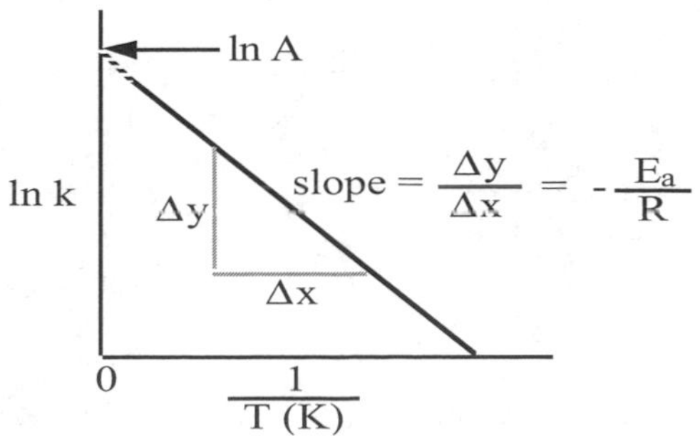

Thus, from a plot of ln k vs. $\frac{1}{T}$, the energy of activation can be obtained.

Example Problems:

1. If a first order reaction has a frequency factor of $3.98 \times 10^{13}\ s^{-1}$ and an E_a of 160 kJ, then calculate the rate constant at 25°C.

$$k = A\, e^{-Ea/RT}$$

$$k = (3.98 \times 10^{13}\ s^{-1})\ e^{-160\ kJ\ /\ (8.31 \times 10^{-3}\ kJ/mol\cdot K)\ (25 + 273\ K)}$$

$$k = (3.98 \times 10^{13})\ e^{-64.61} = (3.98 \times 10^{13})\ (8.71 \times 10^{-29}) = 3.47 \times 10^{-15}\ s^{-1}$$

(k and A have same units)

2. The E_a for a reaction is 72.4 kJ/mol. If the rate constant for the reaction at 298 K is $7.50 \times 10^{-5}\ s^{-1}$, then calculate the rate constant at 323 K.

$$\ln\frac{k_2}{k_1} = \frac{E_a}{R}\left(\frac{1}{T_1} - \frac{1}{T_2}\right)$$

$$\ln\frac{k_2}{7.50 \times 10^{-5}} = \frac{72.4\ kJ/mol}{8.31 \times 10^{-3}\ kJ/mol\cdot K}\left(\frac{1}{298\ K} - \frac{1}{323\ K}\right)$$

$$\ln k_2 - \ln(7.50 \times 10^{-5}) = -(8.71 \times 10^{3})(3.36 \times 10^{-3} - 3.10 \times 10^{-3})$$

$$\ln k_2 - (-9.50) = (8.71 \times 10^{3})(2.60 \times 10^{-4})$$

$$\ln k_2 = 2.26 - 9.50$$

$$\ln k_2 = -7.24$$

$$k_2 = e^{-7.24} = 7.2 \times 10^{-4}\ s^{-1}$$

3. Given the graph to the right for a second order reaction:

a) Calculate the frequency factor.

y-intercept = ln A

0.569 = ln A

$A = e^{0.569} = 1.77\ M^{-1}\ t^{-1}$

NOTE: Since this is a second order reaction, A has the same units as k for a second order reaction.

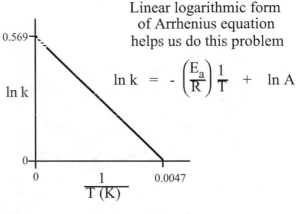

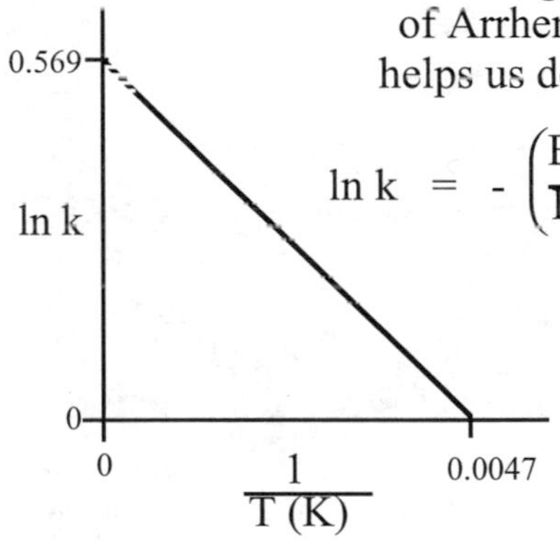

Linear logarithmic form of Arrhenius equation helps us do this problem

$$\ln k = -\left(\frac{E_a}{R}\right)\frac{1}{T} + \ln A$$

b) Calculate the energy of activation (in J/mol).

$$\text{slope} = -\left(\frac{E_a}{R}\right)$$

$$\left(\frac{0 - 0.569}{0.0047 - 0}\right) = -\frac{E_a}{8.31\ J/mol \bullet K} \quad \rightarrow \quad Ea = 1.0 \times 10^{3}\ J/mol$$

4. A reaction has an E_a of 48.0 kJ. If you have a measured rate at 298 K, then at what temperature would you observe a doubling of the rate?

This problem wants us to find T_2 when $k_2 = 2\,k_1$, thus:

$$\ln\frac{k_2}{k_1} = \frac{E_a}{R}\left(\frac{1}{T_1} - \frac{1}{T_2}\right)$$

$$\ln\left(\frac{2\,k_1}{k_1}\right) = \frac{48.0}{8.31 \times 10^{-3}}\left(\frac{1}{298} - \frac{1}{T_2}\right) \rightarrow \ln 2 = (5.78 \times 10^3)\left(3.36 \times 10^{-3} - \frac{1}{T_2}\right)$$

$$0.693 = \left(19.4 - \frac{5.78 \times 10^3}{T_2}\right) \rightarrow 0.693 - 19.4 = -\frac{5.78 \times 10^3}{T_2}$$

$$T_2 = -\frac{5.78 \times 10^3}{0.693 - 19.4} = 309 \text{ K}$$

Rule of thumb: From this problem, we can conclude that for either a 10°C or 10 K rise in T, the rate of the reaction doubles provided that the $E_a \sim 50$ kJ.

Catalysts and Rate of Reactions

A catalyst is a substance that speeds up a reaction by causing the reaction to occur via a "speedier" alternative pathway. This alternative pathway, route, or mechanism by which the reaction proceeds has a lower energy of activation, thereby, allowing more collisions to have KE > E_a.

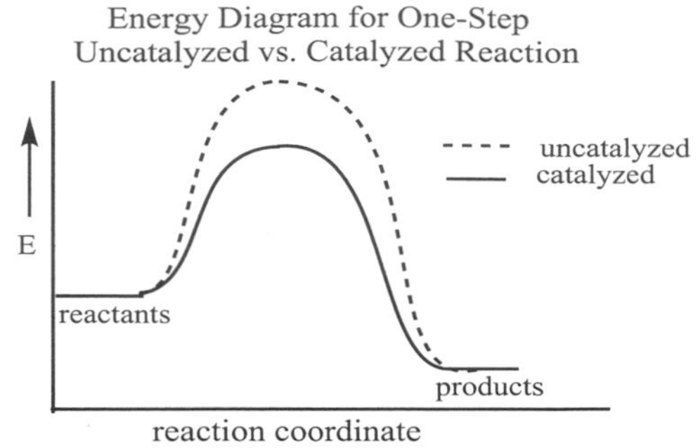

While catalysts can be consumed in one of the steps of the reaction, in another step they are regenerated; thus, catalysts are not consumed during the overall chemical reaction. A catalyst can not make a non-spontaneous reaction take place. Also, for a reaction at equilibrium, if a catalyst causes a two-fold increase in the forward reaction, the reverse reaction will also experience a two-fold increase in rate.

Catalysts can be either homogenous or heterogeneous.

Enzymes are biological catalysts.

III. Reaction Mechanisms

A *reaction mechanism* is a proposed step-by-step pathway by which a reaction can occur. Some reactions take place in a single step, most reactions however, occur in a series of *elementary steps.*

For each of these elementary steps:

- The order for a particular reactant in any single elementary step is equal to the sum of reactant coefficients.
- There is an elementary step that is much slower than the others. This slow step is called the *rate-determining step.* The speed at which the rate-determining step occurs limits the rate at which the overall reaction takes place. Fast steps occurring after the rate determining step have no effect on the rate law.
- Species that are formed and that are consumed are called *intermediates.*

  The following energy diagram is that of an exothermic reaction that occurs in three steps.

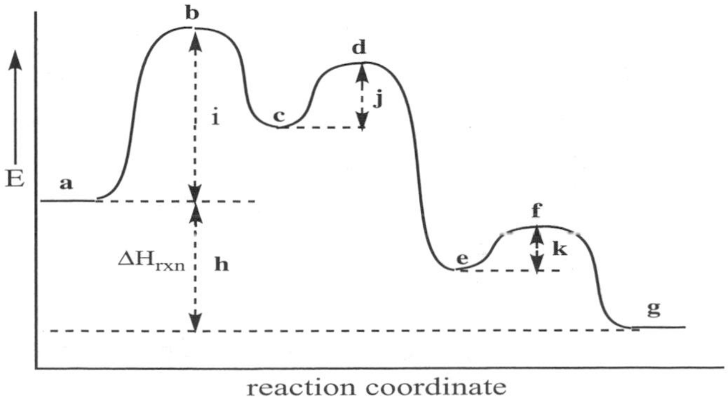

The *transition states* are located at energy maxima (*b, d, and f*), while the *intermediates* are located at the following energy minima - c and e.

Each step has an E_a (*i, j, and k*). Since the first step of the reaction has the largest energy of activation (i), it is the *slow* or *rate-determining step.*

The overall energy difference between starting materials (i.e., reactants) (*a*) and products (*g*) is equal to $\Delta H_{rxn} = h$. In this particular energy diagram, since the products (*g*) have a lower energy (i.e., enthalpy) than the reactants (*a*), the overall reaction is exothermic.

- The sum of all the elementary steps is equal to the balanced equation for the overall reaction.
- The term that describes the number of molecules reacting is called the *molecularity* of a reaction. Most elementary steps are *unimolecular* (only one reactant or intermediate participates) or *bimolecular* (two reactants and/or intermediates collide). There are very few termolecular (3 reactants and/or intermediates collide) reactions.

NOTE: As mentioned previously, the rate law exponents are not necessarily the same as those of the coefficients of the overall balanced equation.

Certain elementary steps are said to be *equilibrium steps* - in such cases - the rate of its forward reaction step is equal to rate of its reverse reaction step. Equilibrium steps in a reaction are represented with a double headed arrow ($\rightleftharpoons$). Consider the fictitious reaction:

$$2\ AB + B_2 \longrightarrow 2\ AB_2 \qquad \Delta H = -47\ kJ/mol$$

that proceeds via the following proposed two step mechanism in which the first step is a fast equilibrium step and the second step is a slow (or rate-determining) step.

A_2B_2 is an intermediate

$$2\ AB \underset{k_{1r}}{\overset{k_{1f}}{\rightleftharpoons}} A_2B_2 \qquad A_2B_2 + B_2 \xrightarrow{k_2} 2\ AB_2$$

step 1: a fast equilibrium bimolecular step

$rate_f = rate_r \rightarrow k\,[AB]^2 = k\,[A_2B_2]$

step 2: a slow bimolecular step

$rate = k\,[A_2B_2]\,[B_2]$

Because the 1st elementary step is a fast equilibrium step, a dynamic equilibrium can be established before the second step significantly occurs.

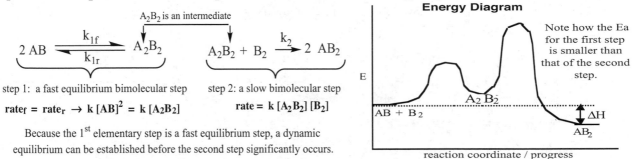

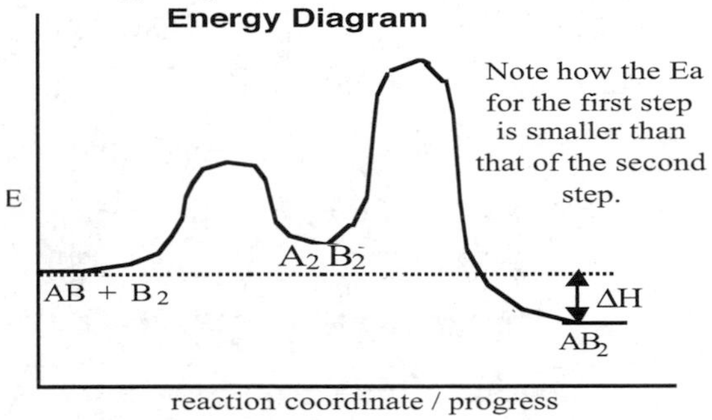

The first step involves the collision of two AB molecules to produce the *intermediate* A_2B_2. A_2B_2 can quickly decompose to reform AB or it can eventually combine with B_2 to produce AB_2. Note how the sum of both of the above elementary steps is equal to the overall balanced equation. From the given information, the energy diagram that graphically represents the relative energies for all species in the reaction is depicted in the above diagram.

A. Determination of the Reaction Mechanism

We can postulate a reaction mechanism by using experimental data coupled with chemical intuition. Proof that a postulated mechanism is correct is not possible; all we can do is postulate a mechanism that is consistent with the data. It is possible that more than one mechanism may satisfy the experimental rate law. If this is the case, then one must try to detect an intermediate species that would help support or invalidate the mechanism.

The reaction: $H_2\,(g) + I_2\,(g) \rightarrow 2\,HI\,(g)$, has been found to have the following rate law:

$$Rate = k\,[H_2]\,[I_2]$$

The following are two mechanisms that support the rate law.

a) A one-step mechanism that involves the collision of single molecules of H_2 and I_2:

$H_2 + I_2 \rightarrow 2\,HI$

Since this is a one-step mechanism, the coefficients can be used as exponents.

$Rate = k\,[H_2]\,[I_2]$

b) A three-step mechanism:

$I_2 \rightleftharpoons 2\,I$	(step 1: fast, equilibrium)	$k_{1f}\,[I_2] = k_{1r}\,[I]^2$
$I + H_2 \rightleftharpoons H_2I$	(step 2: fast, equilibrium)	$k_{2f}\,[I]\,[H_2] = k_{2r}\,[H_2I]$
$H_2I + I \longrightarrow 2\,HI$	(step 3: slow - rate determining)	$k_3\,[H_2I]\,[I]$
$H_2 + I_2 \longrightarrow 2\,HI$	(overall)	

To get the overall rate law from each of the individual steps to match that which was obtained experimentally, we need to manipulate equation 1 to solve for [I] and equation 2 to solve for $[H_2I]$. Then we need to put these two manipulated equations into equation 3.

eq. 1: $k_{1f}[I_2] = k_{1r}[I]^2 \rightarrow$ solving for [I] $\rightarrow [I] = \frac{k_{1f}}{k_{1r}}\left(\frac{[I_2]}{[I]}\right)$

eq. 2: $k_{2f}[I][H_2] = k_{2r}[H_2I] \rightarrow$ solving for $[H_2I] \rightarrow [H_2I] = \frac{k_{2f}}{k_{2r}}[I][H_2]$

eq. 3: $k_3[H_2I][I]$ = k_3 **Error!**) = $k[H_2][I_2]$

where $k = \frac{k_3\, k_{2f}\, k_{1f}}{k_{2r}\, k_{1r}}$

Since both mechanisms a and b are supported by the rate law, one would try to detect the presence or absence of the intermediates (I and H_2I) in mechanism b.

The following reaction: $2\,NO\,(g) + Br_2\,(g) \rightarrow 2\,NOBr\,(g)$, has been found to have the following rate law $\rightarrow$ Rate $= k[NO]^2[Br_2]$

Two mechanisms that support the above rate law are:

a) A one-step mechanism that involves a termolecular reaction (i.e., three-body collision of 2 NO molecules and 1 Br_2) is not likely.

$2\,NO + Br_2 \rightarrow 2\,NOBr$

Since this is a one-step mechanism, the coefficients can be used as exponents so:

Rate = $k[NO]^2[Br_2]$

b) A two-step mechanism is more likely.

$NO + Br_2 \rightleftharpoons NOBr_2$	(step 1: fast, equilibrium)	$k_{1f}[NO][Br_2] = k_{1r}[NOBr_2]$
$NOBr_2 + NO \longrightarrow 2\,NOBr$	(step 2: slow - rate determining)	$k_2[NOBr_2][NO]$
$2\,NO + Br_2 \longrightarrow 2\,NOBr$	(overall)	

To get the overall rate law from each of the individual steps to match that which was obtained experimentally, we need to manipulate equation 1 to solve for $[NOBr_2]$. Then we need to put this manipulated equation into equation 2.

eq. 1: $k_{1f}[NO][Br_2] = k_{1r}[NOBr_2] \rightarrow$ solving for $[NOBr_2] \rightarrow [NOBr_2] = \frac{k_{1f}}{k_{1r}}[NO][Br_2]$

eq. 2: $k_2[NOBr_2][NO] = k_2\left(\frac{k_{1f}}{k_{1r}}[NO][Br_2]\right)[NO] = k[NO]^2[Br_2]$

where $k = \frac{k_2\, k_{1f}}{k_{1r}}$

To determine whether or not this mechanism was probable, one would try to detect the presence of the intermediate, $NOBr_2$.

Example Problems:

1. The following are steps in a proposed mechanism:

$Cl_2 \longrightarrow Cl^+ + Cl^-$	(step 1: slow)
$Cl^- + H_2S \longrightarrow HCl + HS^-$	(step 2: fast)
$Cl^+ + HS^- \longrightarrow HCl + S$	(step 3: fast)

a) What is the the overall reaction?

$$Cl_2 + H_2S \longrightarrow 2\,HCl + S$$

b) What is the rate law for the overall reaction?

Rate = k $[Cl_2]$ Since the first step is the slow rate-determining step, the other fast steps <u>afterwards</u> have basically no effect on the rate of the reaction.

c) What is the molecularity of step 1?

Step 1 is unimolecular because only one reactant is present.

d) Which species are reaction intermediates?

Cl^+, Cl^-, HS^-

2. *Chlorofluorocarbons (CFCs)* are used in many industrial processes (e.g., they are excellent coolants for air conditioners and refrigerators). Freon-12 (CCl_2F_2) is an example of a CFC which has been linked to ozone depletion.

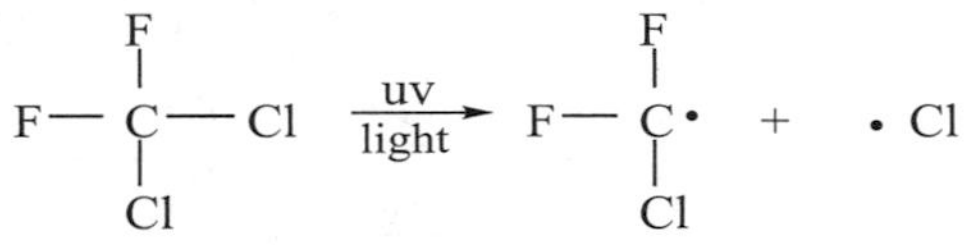

(lone pairs are not shown)

When CFCs are exposed to uv light/radiation in the *stratosphere* (layer of the atmosphere where the ozone layer is found), they break down to form chlorine radicals (Cl•). The formation of these very reactive chlorine radicals is what is believed cause ozone (O_3) depletion. A simplified representation of the proposed mechanism for this ozone depletion has been proposed to occur via a two step mechanism. Given the first step and the overall reaction, what is the missing second step of the mechanism?

$Cl\bullet + O_3 \rightarrow Cl\text{-}O\bullet + O_2$	(step 1)
?	(step 2)
$O_3 + O\bullet \rightarrow 2\,O_2$	(overall reaction)

The sum of step 1 and 2 must give you the overall reaction, therefore, the missing second step is:

$$Cl\text{-}O\bullet + O\bullet \rightarrow Cl\bullet + O_2$$

Note that the chlorine radical that initiates this reaction's first step is regenerated in the second step, therefore, a single chlorine radical can act as a catalyst that depletes many thousands of O_3 molecules.

IV. Kinetics and Equilibrium

While the concept of equilibrium will be discussed in detail in the next couple of modules, we will give you a brief introduction on how kinetics and equilibrium are interrelated. Most chemical reactions do not go to completion (i.e., reactants do not get completely converted into products), but instead reach a state called *equilibrium,* in which:

$$\text{Rate}_{\text{forward reaction}} = \text{Rate}_{\text{reverse reaction}}$$

A reaction that is at equilibrium is also called a *reversible reaction.*

Let's consider the following ***elementary step*** in a mechanism that is in equilibrium:

$$A + B \underset{k_r}{\overset{k_f}{\rightleftharpoons}} 2\,C$$

$$\text{Rate}_{\text{forward}} = \text{Rate}_{\text{reverse}}$$

$$k_f[A]\,[B] = k_r\,[C]^2$$

Solving for k_f/k_r we have

$$\frac{k_f}{k_r} = \frac{[C]^2}{[A]\,[B]} = K$$

rate constants → k_f, k_r; equilibrium constant → K

V. Kinetics Data Acquisition in a Nutshell

A. Two Reactant System

The following schematic gives the steps necessary in order to obtain items such as: initial rates, reaction order, the rate constant, and the energy of activation for a reaction such as:

$$a\ A + b\ B \longrightarrow \text{Products}$$

Obtain and plot concentration vs. time data

↓ Determine the slope of the line that is tangent to the curve at t = 0 for each plot.

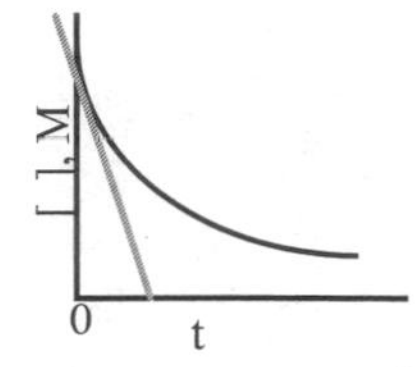

Initial Rate (Units M/t)

↓ Compare initial rates when [A] is changed while [B] is held constant, then vice-versa.

$$\frac{\text{rate 2}}{\text{rate 1}} = \frac{k\,[A]^x\,[B]^y}{k\,[A]^x\,[B]^y}$$

Reaction Order

↓ Substitute
1) initial rate
2) concentrations
3) orders
into rate law
rate = k $[A]^x\,[B]^y$

Rate Constant

Units
0th order ---> M/t
1st order ---> 1/t
2nd order ----> 1/M • t
3rd order ----> $1/M^2$ • t

↓ Determine k at different temperatures

Energy of Activation

$$\ln\frac{k_2}{k_1} = \frac{E_a}{R}\left(\frac{1}{T_1} - \frac{1}{T_2}\right)$$

or

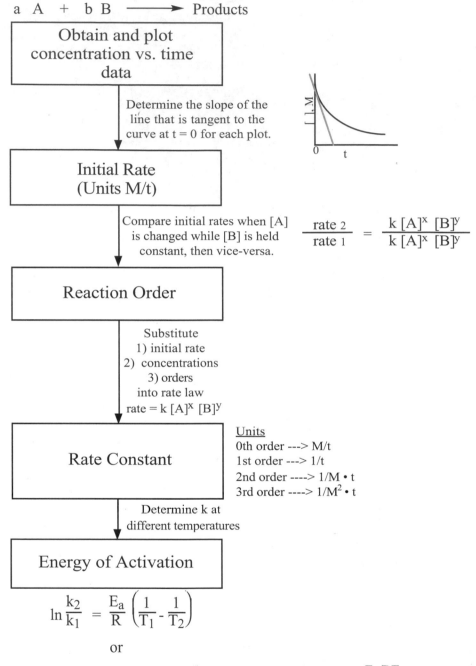

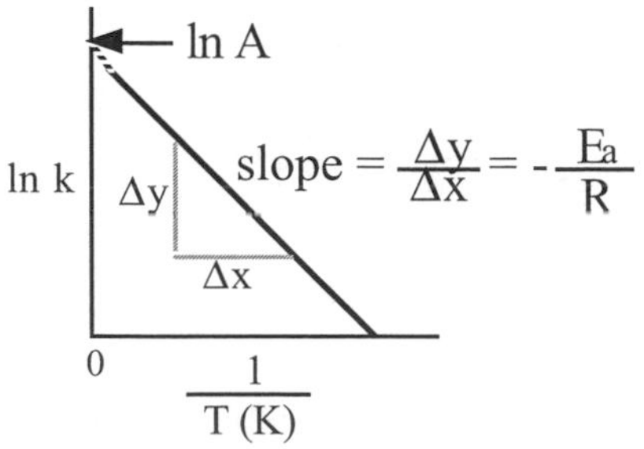

Arrhenius Equation: $k = A\,e^{-Ea/RT}$

Logarithmic form of Arrhenius Equation:

$$\ln k = -\left(\frac{E_a}{R}\right)\frac{1}{T} + \ln A$$

$$\downarrow \qquad \downarrow \quad \downarrow \qquad \downarrow$$

$$y = (\text{slope})\ x + \text{y-intercept}$$

B. **One Reactant System**

The following schematic gives the steps necessary in order to obtain items such as: initial rates, reaction orders, the rate constant, the energy of activation, and concentration vs. time relationships for a reaction such as:

$$a\ A \longrightarrow \text{Products}$$

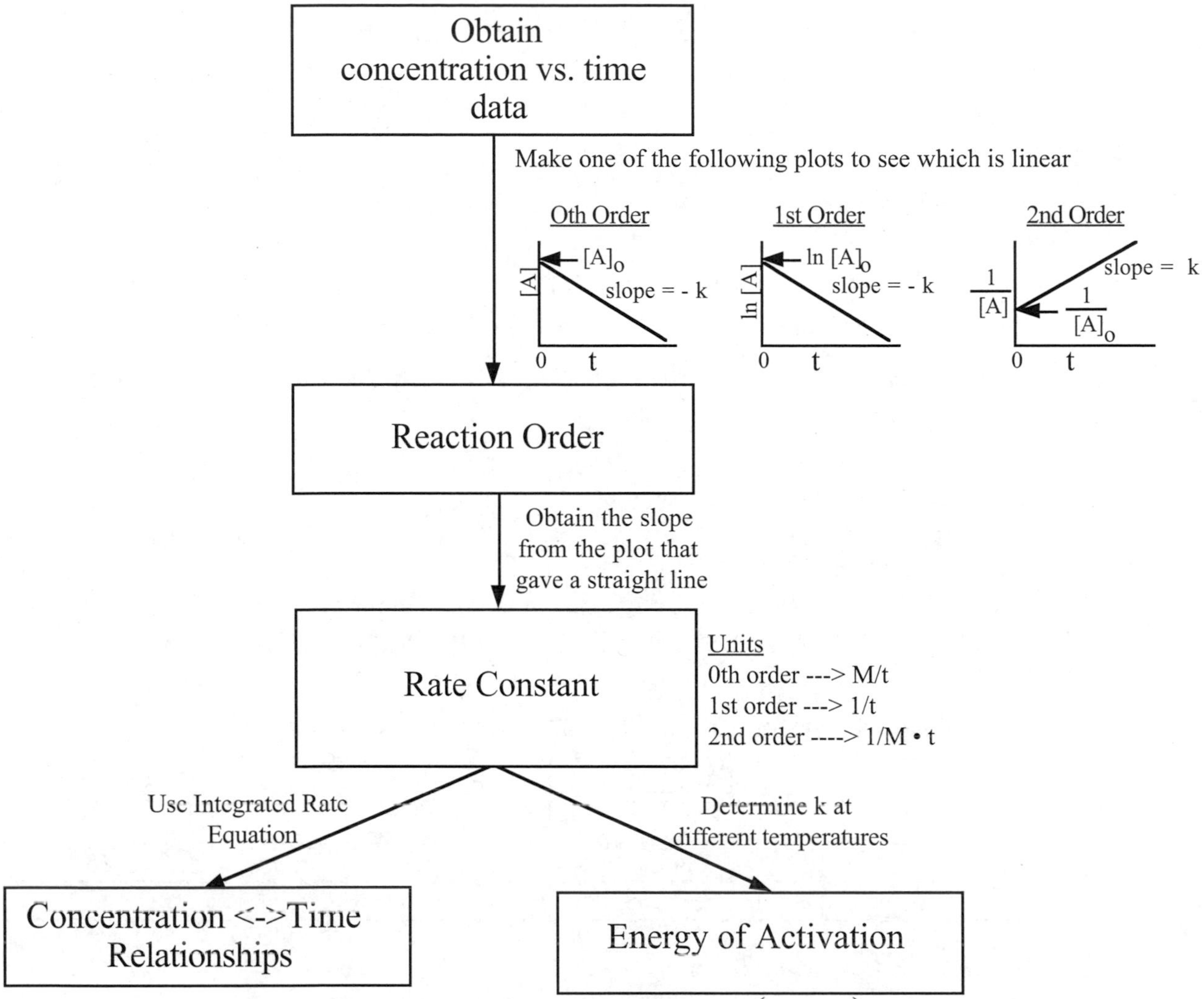

0th order --> $[A] = -kt + [A]_o$

1st order --> $\ln [A] = -kt + \ln [A]_o$

2nd order --> $\dfrac{1}{[A]} = kt + \dfrac{1}{[A]_o}$

0th order --> $t_{1/2} = \dfrac{[A]_o}{2k}$

1st order --> $t_{1/2} = \dfrac{0.693}{k}$

2nd order --> $t_{1/2} = \dfrac{1}{k[A]_o}$

$$\ln \frac{k_2}{k_1} = \frac{E_a}{R}\left(\frac{1}{T_1} - \frac{1}{T_2}\right)$$

or

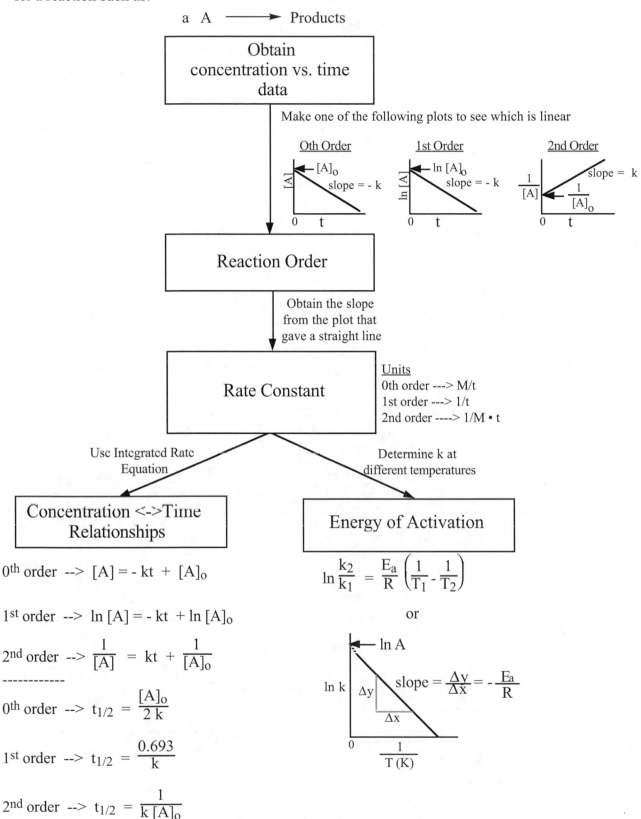

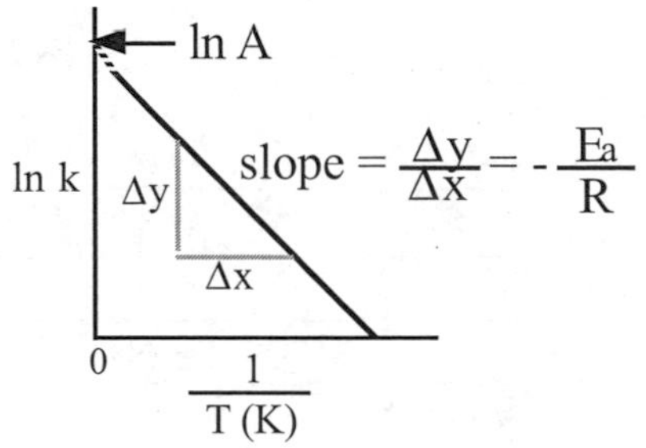

EXERCISES

Reaction Rates and Rate Laws

1. Consider the reaction, $2\ A + 3\ B \rightarrow C + 2\ D$. If the rate of disappearance for **A** at a particular point in time is 0.250 M/s, then:
   a) What is the rate of disappearance (in M/s) of **B** during this same period of time?
   b) What is the rate of appearance (in M/s) of **C** during this period of time?

2. What are the general units of k for a:
   a) Zero order reaction?
   b) First order reaction?
   c) Second order reaction?
   d) Third order reaction?
   e) Reaction that has the following rate law: Rate = k $[A]^{-1}$
   f) Reaction that has the following rate law: Rate = k $[A]^{1/2}$ [B]

3. Consider the reaction: $2\ A + 3\ B \rightarrow$ Products. The reaction is zero order in A and first order in B and the rate constant is 0.0610 min^{-1}.
   a) What is the rate law?
   b) What is the overall order of the reaction?
   c) If the [A] is decreased so that it is smaller by a factor of 2 and [B] is increased by a factor of 2, then what will happen to the rate of the reaction?
   d) If $[A]_o$ = 0.820 M and $[B]_o$ = 0.620 M and if the reaction proceeds until the molarity of A is 0.670 M, then what is the rate of the reaction (in M/min) at this point? [Hint: The molarity of B is also decreasing.]

4. Consider the reaction: $2\ A + 2\ B \rightarrow$ Products. Given the following data:

Experiment	$[A]_{initial}$	$[B]_{initial}$	Initial Rate (M/s)
1	0.22	0.22	0.816
2	0.44	0.22	3.26
3	0.22	0.44	1.63

   a) What is the rate law?
   b) What is the order of the reaction with respect to **A**?
   c) What is the order of the reaction with respect to **B**?
   d) What is the order of the overall reaction?
   e) What is the value for the rate constant?

5. Consider the reaction: $A + 2\ B \rightarrow$ Products. Given the following data:

Experiment	$[A]_{initial}$	$[B]_{initial}$	Initial Rate (M/s)
1	0.52	0.46	2.24
2	0.52	0.70	2.24
3	0.68	0.73	3.83

   a) What is the rate law?
   b) What is the order of the reaction with respect to **A**?
   c) What is the order of the reaction with respect to **B**?
   d) What is the order of the overall reaction?
   e) What is the value for the rate constant?

6. At high temperatures, the decomposition of N_2O is first order with $k = 3.4 \times 10^{-5}\ s^{-1}$. Given this information, what percentage of N_2O has reacted after the reaction has been allowed to proceed for 3600 s?
7. The decomposition of a gas is first order and has a rate constant of $0.100\ s^{-1}$ at 660 K. If the initial pressure of the gas is 10 atm, then what will its pressure (in atm) at 20.8 s into the reaction be? [HINT: For gases $P \propto M$]
8. The following reaction has a one-step mechanism: $2\ A\ (g) + B\ (g) \rightarrow C\ (g)$. If 8.0 mol of A and 3.0 mol of B are mixed in a 10. L container and $k = 0.20\ M^{-2} \bullet s^{-1}$, then
   a) What is rate law?
   b) What is the rate (in M/s) after 1/4 of A has been consumed?
   c) What is the rate (in M/s) when only 1.0 mol of B remains?
9. Consider the following reaction: $2\ A \rightarrow$ Products. The initial concentration of A is 0.440 M and the rate constant is 0.255. [NOTE: The time units for k are in hr.]
   a) What is $t_{1/2}$ (in hr) if the reaction was zero order?
   b) What is $t_{1/2}$ (in hr) if the reaction was first order?
   c) What is $t_{1/2}$ (in hr) if the reaction was second order?
   d) How many hours will it take for the concentration of A to reach 0.150 M if the reaction was zero order?
   e) How many hours will it take for the concentration of A to reach 0.150 M if the reaction was first order?
   f) How many hours will it take for the concentration of A to reach 0.150 M if the reaction was second order?
   g) How many hours will it take for the reaction to be 25% complete if the reaction was zero order?
   h) How many hours will it take for the reaction to be 25% complete if the reaction was first order?
   i) How many hours will it take for the reaction to be 25% complete if the reaction was second order?
10. Consider the following reaction: $A \rightarrow$ Products. If the initial concentration of A was 0.800 M and the half-life was 0.200 hr:
    a) What is k (in M/hr) if the reaction was zero order?
    b) What is k (in hr^{-1}) if the reaction was first order?
    c) What is k (in $M^{-1} \bullet hr^{-1}$) if the reaction was second order?

Temperature and Catalysts in Relation to Rates of Reactions

11. Consider the following reaction: $A + B \rightarrow C$. What happens to the rate of the reaction if:
    a) The concentration of B is increased and the reaction is zero order in A and first order in B.
    b) The concentration of A is increased and the reaction is zero order in A and first order in B.
    c) The temperature is increased.
    d) A catalyst is added.
12. Consider the following one-step reaction: $A + B \rightarrow 2\ C$. If the energy of activation for the forward reaction is 37 kJ/mol and that of the backward reaction is 25 kJ/mol, what is ΔH (in kJ/mol) for the reaction?
13. If the rate constant at 303 K is $0.0237\ hr^{-1}$ and that at 343 K is $0.0551\ hr^{-1}$, then calculate the energy of activation (in kJ/mol) for this reaction?
14. The energy of activation for a reaction is 32.5 kJ/mol. If the rate constant at 40°C is 0.237 M/hr, then calculate the rate constant (in M/hr) at 80°C?

15. The E_a for a reaction is 54.5 kJ/mol. If the rate constant at 293 K is 7.50 x 10^{-5} hr^{-1}, then calculate at what temperature (in K) will the reaction be when the rate constant is 6.00 x 10^{-4} hr^{-1}?

16. A plot of ln k vs $\frac{1}{T\ (K)}$ for a first order reaction has a slope of -1.21 x 10^2 and a y-intercept of 0.569 s^{-1}.
   a) What is the frequency factor (in s^{-1})?
   b) What is the energy of activation (in kJ/mol)?

17. Complete the following sentences with the words increase(s), decrease(s), greater, or less.
   a) An increase in temperature causes the rate of the reaction to __________.
   b) An increase in the number of effective collisions causes a(n) __________ in the rate of the reaction.
   c) When the temperature of a reaction is increased, the average speed of molecules __________, this causes the number of molecules with kinetic energies __________ than the energy of activation to __________.
   d) If the energy of activation for a reaction is lowered, the rate of the reaction __________ because there is a(n) __________ in the number of effective collisions.

18. In a potential energy diagram, where is the transition state found?

19. The potential energy diagram for the one-step reaction: X + Y → P is given to your right. a = 100 kJ and d = 25 kJ.
   a) What is the energy of activation for the forward reaction?
   b) Is the forward reaction endothermic or exothermic?
   c) What is the change in enthalpy (ΔH) for the forward reaction?
   d) What is the energy of activation for the reverse reaction?
   e) The energy of the transition state is represented by what point in the diagram?

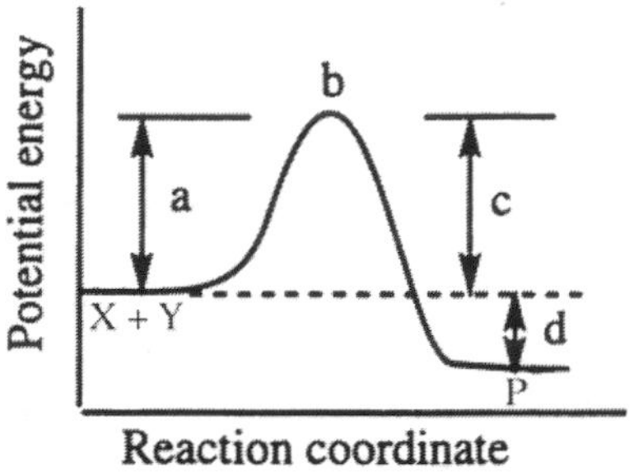

Reaction Mechanisms

20. The following elementary steps, constitute a proposed mechanism for a reaction.

Step Number	Elementary Step	
1	$Cl_2 \rightleftharpoons 2\,Cl$	fast
2	$Cl + CO \rightleftharpoons COCl$	fast
3	$COCl + Cl \longrightarrow COCl_2$	slow

   a) What is the overall reaction?
   b) What is the molecularity of the second step?
   c) What intermediates are present?
   d) What is the rate law for the second elementary step?
   e) What is the rate determining step?
   f) What is the overall rate law?
   g) Given the above mechanism and given that the overall reaction is exothermic, could the energy diagram to your right be a possible energy diagram for the overall reaction? EXPLAIN.

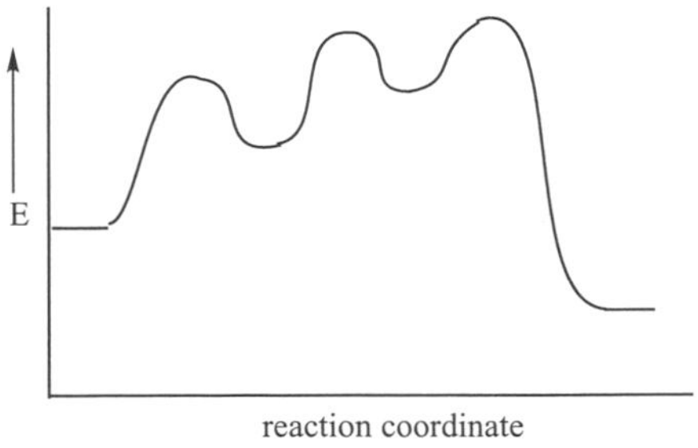

21. Would you expect that the following reaction --- $C_2H_4 + 3\,O_2 \rightarrow 2\,CO_2 + 2\,H_2O$ --- to proceed via a one-step mechanism?

MULTIPLE CHOICE PRACTICE EXAM FOR MODULE 4

Consider the following balanced equation and data when answering questions 1 - 4

$$2\ A + 4\ B \rightarrow 3\ C + 5\ D$$

[A], M	time, s
4.00	0
3.00	5.00

1. What is the average rate for the disappearance of A (in M/s) during the time interval of 0 to 5 seconds?
   1) 0.200 2) 5.00 3) 0.600 4) 1.00 5) 2.00

2. What is the average rate for the appearance of C (in M/s) during the time interval of 0 to 5 seconds?
   1) 0.133 2) 0.833 3) 0.300 4) 3.00 5) 6.00

3. The rate of change in the [D] $\left(\text{i.e. } \frac{\Delta[D]}{\Delta t}\right)$ may also be expressed as:
   1) $\frac{1}{2}\left(\frac{\Delta[A]}{\Delta t}\right)$ 2) $-\frac{1}{4}\left(\frac{\Delta[B]}{\Delta t}\right)$ 3) $-\frac{5}{4}\left(\frac{\Delta[B]}{\Delta t}\right)$
   4) More than one of the above.
   5) None of the above.

4. What is the average reaction rate (in M/s) during the time interval of 0 to 5 seconds?
   1) 0.200 2) -0.100 3) 0.200 4) 0.100 5) 500

Consider the following balanced equation when answering questions 5 - 6

$$3\ A + B \rightarrow 2\ C + D$$

5. If a graph of [A] (in M) vs. time (in min) has a slope of -0.237 at t = 2 min, then what is the instantaneous rate (in M/min) at 2 min?
   1) 0.118 2) 0.0395 3) 0.0790 4) -0.0790 5) -0.0395

6. Which of the following statements is true?
   1) The reaction is third order in A.
   2) The reaction is first order in B.
   3) The reaction is fourth order overall.
   4) More than one of the above statements is correct.
   5) Since no mention was made that this was a one step reaction, then the rate law can't be confirmed from the stoichiometric coefficients of the balanced chemical equation.

Consider the following information when answering questions 7 - 9

The reaction ---- A + 2 B → C ---- was found to be second order in A and third order overall.

7. What is the rate law?
   1) rate = k $[A]^2$ 2) rate = k $[A]^2$ [B] 3) rate = k [A] $[B]^2$
   4) rate = k $[A]^2$ [B] [C] 5) rate = k $[A]^2$ [B] / [C]

8. Which of the following could be units for the rate constant in this case?
   1) $M^{-2} \bullet s^{-1}$ 2) $\frac{1}{M^2 \bullet s^1}$ 3) $\frac{L^2}{mol^2 \bullet s^1}$
   4) Only two of above units are correct.
   5) All of above units are correct.

9. If the concentration of A is tripled and that of B is doubled, then the rate would increase by a factor of:
   1) 6 2) 18 3) 12 4) 5 5) 72

10. For the reaction --- A + B → C, the reaction goes three times as fast when the concentration of A is tripled and not affected when the concentration of B is doubled. Given this information, what is the overall order for the reaction.

1) 1 2) 2 3) 3 4) 4 5) 0

11. The reaction ---- 2 A + 2 B → C + D ---- has a rate law expression: Rate = k $[A]^2$ [B]. At some given starting concentration of A and B, the initial rate is 2.00 M/s. If the conditions are changed such that the [A] is cut in half and the [B] is tripled, what will its initial rate (in M/s) now be?

1) 2.67 2) 1.33 3) 0.750 4) 1.50 5) 3.00

12. Which of the following could be possible units for a **reaction rate**?

1) $\frac{M}{min}$ 2) $\frac{mol}{L \bullet min}$ 3) M • s

4) Only two of above units are correct.

5) All of above units are correct.

13. Considering the following information for the reaction of: A + 2 B → C,

- Tripling the concentration of A causes the rate to increase nine-fold.
- Doubling the concentration of B causes no change in reaction rate.

which of the following is true?

1) The reaction is first order overall.
2) The reaction occurs via a one-step mechanism.
3) If the [A] were quadrupled the reaction rate would increase by a factor of 12.
4) The rate law can't be deduced from the given information.
5) None of the above statements is correct.

14. The rate at which a chunk of $Mg_{(s)}$ reacts with $HCl_{(aq)}$ could possibly be increased if:

1) the [HCl] was increased.
2) the chunk of Mg was finely grounded.
3) the reaction temperature was increased.
4) Only two of the above statements are correct.
5) All of the above statements is correct.

15. The following gas phase reaction -- 2A + B → C -- was found to be first order in A, second order overall and to have a rate constant of 0.223 (whose time units are in min).

Which of the following statements is/are correct?

1) The reaction's rate law is: Rate = 0.223 [A] [B]
2) The rate constant has units of $M^{-2} \bullet min^{-2}$
3) A and B disappear at the same rate
4) The rate of appearance of C can also be expressed as: $\frac{2}{3} \frac{\Delta[A]}{\Delta t}$
5) Two of the above statements are correct.

16. Which of the following statements is correct about a reaction order?

1) The order with respect to a particular reactant must be determined experimentally.
2) The order is always equal to the stoichiometric coefficients.
3) The order increases with an increase in temperature.
4) If the order with respect to a particular reactant is zero, then the reaction rate is independent of that particular reactant's concentration.
5) More than one of the above statements is correct.

Consider the following balanced equation and data when answering questions 17 - 20

A + B → C

[A], M	[B], M	Initial Rate, M/s
0.30	0.35	2.05×10^{-3}
0.52	0.35	6.17×10^{-3}
0.10	0.50	3.26×10^{-4}

17. What is the order with respect to **A**?
    1) 1 2) 1.5 3) 2 4) 2.5 5) 3

18. What is the order with respect to **B**?
    1) 1 2) 1.5 3) 2 4) 2.5 5) 3

19. What is the rate law?
    1) $k [A]^2 [B]$ 2) $k [A] [B]^3$ 3) $k [A] [B]$ 4) $k [A] [B]^2$ 5) $k [A]^3 [B]$

20. What is the rate constant (in $M^{-2} \cdot s^{-1}$)?
    1) 2.05×10^{-3} 2) 6.51×10^{-2} 3) 1.95×10^{-2} 4) 1.05×10^{-1} 5) 1.54×10^{1}

Consider the following information when answering questions 21 - 27

The following gas phase reaction ---- D → 2 B + C ----- was conducted in a 1-L container with an initial concentration of D of 0.840 M. This reaction was found to be second order in D and to have a rate constant of 0.0729 $M^{-1} \cdot min^{-1}$.

21. What is the molarity of D after 19 min?
    1) 2.58 2) 0.0612 3) 0.0681 4) 0.0868 5) 0.388

22. What is the molarity of B after 19 min?
    1) 0.904 2) 0.452 3) 0.776 4) 0.0442 5) 0.388

23. What is the half-life (in min) for the reaction?
    1) 0.0612 2) 5.76 3) 9.51 4) 16.3 5) 0.105

24. What is the rate constant (in $M^{-1} \cdot min^{-1}$) after 1/3 of D has been consumed?
    1) 2.04×10^{-2} 2) 2.29×10^{-2} 3) 2.80×10^{-1} 4) 5.72×10^{-3} 5) 7.29×10^{-2}

25. What is the reaction rate (in M/min) after 1/3 of D has been consumed?
    1) 2.80×10^{-1} 2) 2.04×10^{-2} 3) 5.72×10^{-3} 4) 5.60×10^{-1} 5) 2.29×10^{-2}

26. What is the reaction rate (in M/min) when the concentration of D reaches 0.400 M?
    1) 1.17×10^{-2} 2) 1.41×10^{-2} 3) 2.99×10^{-3} 4) 1.16×10^{-1} 5) 1.46×10^{-2}

27. Which of the following plots would give a straight line?
    1) [D] vs. t 2) ln[D] vs. t 3) $\frac{1}{[D]}$ vs. t
    4) $[D]^2$ vs. t 5) $\frac{1}{[D]}$ vs. $\frac{1}{t}$

28. The reaction A → B is first order overall and its rate constant is 0.0693 s^{-}. What percentage of A will be left unreacted after the reaction has been allowed to proceed for 10 s?
    1) 50 2) 0.693 3) 37 4) 2.7 5) 2.0

29. The decomposition of compound X at 350°C occurs via a first order reaction with a half-life of 200 s. What percent of X remains unreacted after 150 s?

1) 59.5 2) 75.0 3) 37.0 4) 14.3 5) 54.3

Consider the following information when answering questions 30 - 32

The following gas phase reaction ---- 2 A → 3 B + C ----- was conducted in a 1-L container with an initial concentration of A of 0.400 M. This reaction was found to be zero order in A and to have a half-life of 2 hr.

30. What is the rate constant with the correct units (if any)?

1) 0.100 hr^{-1} 2) 0.100 M/hr 3) 10.0 $M^{-1} \cdot hr^{-1}$ 4) 10.0 hr^{-1} 5) 0.100

31. How many hours will it take for the reaction to reach a concentration of A which is 0.133 M?

1) 2.67 2) 5.33 3) 3.00 4) 0.333 5) 0.266

32. What will the molarity of **B** be after one half-life has passed?

1) 0.200 2) 0.0500 3) 0.100 4) 0.300 5) 0.133

Consider the following information when answering questions 33 - 34

The following gas phase reaction ---- 2 B → Products ----- was conducted in a 2.00-L vessel with the initial moles of B being equal to 0.620. This reaction was found to be first order in B and to have a rate constant of 0.200 min^{-}.

33. How many minutes will it take for 25.0% of B to react?

1) 5.00 2) 15.0 3) 13.10 4) 1.45 5) 6.93

34. What is the half-life (in s) for this reaction?

1) 46.5 2) 968 3) 208 4) 3.46 5) 6.00

Consider the following information when answering questions 35 - 37

The following gas phase reaction ---- 2 A + 3 B → 5 C + 4 D ----- was conducted in a 2-L container with 0.820 mol of A and 0.620 mol of B. This reaction was found to be zero order in A and first order in B and was found to have a rate constant of 0.0610 min^{-1}. [HINT: Reaction rates are dependent on molarity -- mol/L]

35. What is the initial reaction rate (in M/min)?

1) 0.0155 2) 0.0310 3) 0.0378 4) 0.0189 5) 0.0567

36. If the reaction proceeds until the molarity of A is 0.270 M, then what is the reaction rate (in M/min) at this point in time?

1) 6.10×10^{-3} 2) 2.47×10^{-2} 3) 1.22×10^{-1} 4) 2.68×10^{-2} 5) 6.67×10^{-3}

37. If the rate at which **A** is disappearing at some point in time is 1.20×10^{-2} M/min, then:

1) **B** is disappearing at a rate of 8.00×10^{-3} M/min.
2) **B** is disappearing at a rate of 1.80×10^{-2} M/min.
3) **C** is appearing at a rate of 2.40×10^{-4} M/min.
4) **D** is appearing at a rate of 3.00×10^{-3} M/min.
5) Two or more of the above statements are correct.

Consider the following information when answering questions 38 - 39.

The following gas phase reaction ---- M → 2 E + G ----- was conducted in a 1-L container with an initial concentration of M of 0.400 M. This reaction was found to be first order in M and to have a half-life of 947 min.

38. What is the rate constant with the correct units (if any)?

    1) 7.32×10^{-4} min^{-1} 2) 2.64×10^{-3} M^{-1} • min^{1} 3) 7.32×10^{-4} M/min
    4) 2.11×10^{-4} min^{-1} 5) 2.11×10^{-4} M/min

39. Approximately what fraction of the initial amount of M remains after 1500 min?

    1) 1/2 2) 1/3 3) 1/8 4) 1/16 5) 1/32

40. A plot of ln k vs. $^{1}/_{T}$ (K) for a first order reaction has a slope of -1.00×10^{3} and a y-intercept of 0.500 s^{-}. What is the energy of activation (in kJ/mol)?

    1) 500 2) 8.31 3) 5.03 4) 4.16×10^{-3} 5) 0.995

41. If a first order reaction has a frequency factor of 3.98×10^{13} s^{-} and an energy of activation of 160 kJ, then calculate the rate constant (in s^{-}) at 25°C?

    1) 3.98×10^{-1} 2) 3.47×10^{-15} 3) 8.18×10^{88} 4) 1.17×10^{93} 5) 3.23×10^{13}

42. If the following graph was obtained for the reaction of X → Products, then which of the following statements is true?

    1) The reaction is second order in X.
    2) The value of the rate constant is 0.025.
    3) the initial concentration of X = 0.50 M.
    4) Only two of the above statements are correct.
    5) All of the above statements are correct.

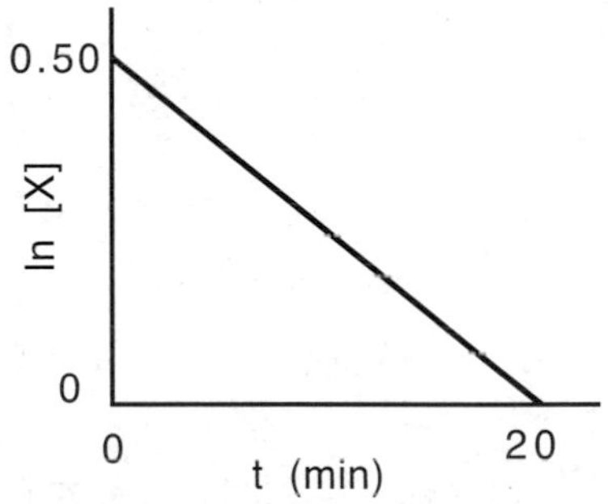

43. The one-step reaction of A → B has an activation energy of 350 kJ/mol. The reverse reaction, has an energy of activation of 260 kJ/mol. Given this information, which of the following statements is/are true?

    1) ΔH for the reaction is -90 kJ/mol.
    2) The reaction A → B is endothermic.
    3) The rate constant for the forward reaction is larger than that for the backward reaction.
    4) Two of the above statements are correct.
    5) None of the above statements are correct.

44. Which of the following best explains why an increase in temperature of 10°C, causes the reaction rate to double?

    1) The energy of activation was lowered to one-half of its original value.
    2) The total number of collisions doubled.
    3) The number of molecules with energy greater than the activation energy doubled.
    4) The average kinetic energy of molecules in the reaction mixture doubled.
    5) The activation energy doubled.

Consider the following information when answering questions 45 - 46

For a reaction, the rate constant at 20°C is 7.50×10^{-5} min^{-1} and that at 50°C is 6.00×10^{-4} min^{-1}.

45. What is the energy of activation (in kJ/mol)?
    1) 0.576 2) 54.5 3) 57.6 4) 0.125 5) 21.7

46. What is the rate constant (in min^{-1}) at 36°C?
    1) 7.91×10^{-5} 2) 1.35×10^{-4} 3) 3.15×10^{-4} 4) 2.39×10^{-4} 5) 3.15×10^{-5}

47. Which of the following would cause a change in the *rate constant* for the one-step reaction of A → B?
    1) Performing the reaction at a different temperature.
    2) The continuous passage of time causes it to change.
    3) An increase in the concentration of A.
    4) Two of the above statements are correct.
    5) None of the above statements are correct.

48. Which of the following statements is/are true about catalysts?
    1) Catalysts alter the reaction mechanism.
    2) Catalysts raise the energy of activation.
    3) Catalysts are not consumed during the overall reaction.
    4) Two of the above statements are correct.
    5) All of the above statements are correct.

49. Which of the following statements is/are true?
    1) The energy of activation for the forward reaction is always equal to ΔH.
    2) The more spontaneous a reaction is (i.e., the more negative the ΔG for the reaction), the faster the reaction will occur.
    3) An increase in reaction temperature causes a decrease in the energy of activation.
    4) A catalyst causes a non-spontaneous reaction to occur spontaneously.
    5) The transition state is a theorized short-lived, unstable high energy state that reactants must pass through before they are converted into products.

50. Assuming that the following proposed mechanism is consistent with sound chemical principles and kinetic data:

Step Number	Elementary Step	
1	$A_2 + B \longrightarrow BA + A$	slow
2	$BA + B \longrightarrow B_2A$	fast

Which of the following statements is/are **false**?
1) The reaction is first order in B.
2) The rate law is: Rate = k $[A_2]$ $[B]^2$
3) BA is a reaction intermediate.
4) The overall reaction is $A_2 + 2\,B \rightarrow B_2A + A$.
5) None of the above statements is false.

Consider the following information when answering questions 51 - 53

The following elementary steps, constitute a proposed mechanism for a reaction.

Step Number	Elementary Step	
1	$X_2 \rightleftharpoons 2X$	**fast**
2	$X + LMN \longrightarrow XL + MN$	**slow**
3	$MN + X \longrightarrow MNX$	**fast**

51. Which of the following statements is/are true?
    1) The last elementary step is rate-determining.
    2) The overall reaction is: $X_2 + X + LMN \rightarrow X + L + MN + MNX$
    3) LMN is a reaction intermediate.
    4) Two of the above statements are correct.
    5) None of the above statements are correct.

52. Which of the following statements is/are true?
    1) The first elementary step is bimolecular.
    2) The overall reaction is first order in LMN
    3) The overall reaction is 1/2 order in X_2.
    4) Two of the above statements are correct.
    5) All of the above statements are correct.

53. Which of the following rate expressions is/are correct?
    1) $rate_{overall} = k\,[X_2]\,[LMN]$ 2) $rate_2 = k_2\,[X]\,[LMN]$ 3) $k_{1f}\,[X_2] = k_{1r}[X]^2$
    4) Two of the above rate expressions are correct.
    5) None of the above rate expressions are correct.

MODULE 4 - ANSWERS

1. a) 0.375 M/s b) 0.125 M/s
2. a) M/t b) t^{-1} c) $M^{-1} \bullet t^{-1}$ d) $M^{-2} \bullet t^{-1}$ e) $M^{2} \bullet t^{-1}$ f) $M^{-1/2} \bullet t^{-1}$
3. a) Rate = k [B] = 0.0610 min⁻ [B] b) first c) increase by a factor of 2 d) 0.0241 M/min
4. a) Rate = k $[A]^2$ [B] b) 2 c) 1 d) 3 e) 76.5 $M^{-2} \bullet t^{-1}$
5. a) Rate = k $[A]^2$ b) 2 c) 0 d) 2 e) 8.28 $M^{-1} \bullet t^{-1}$
6. 11.6%
7. 1.25 atm
8. a) Rate = k $[A]^2$ [B] = 0.20 $M^{-2} \bullet t^{-1}[A]^2$ [B] b) 0.0144 M/s c) 0.0032 M/s
9. a) 0.863 hr b) 2.72 hr c) 8.91 hr d) 1.14 hr e) 4.20 hr f) 17.2 hr
   g) 0.431 hr h) 1.13 hr i) 2.97 hr
10. a) 2.00 M/hr b) 3.47 hr^{-1} c) 6.25 $M^{-1} \bullet hr^{-1}$
11. a) increases b) no change c) increases d) increases
12. 12 kJ
13. 18.2 kJ/mol
14. 0.976 M/hr
15. 323 K
16. a) 1.77 s⁻ b) 1.01 kJ/mol
17. a) increase b) increase c) increases; greater; increase d) increases; increase
18. At the top of the energy hill.
19. a) 100 kJ b) exothermic c) -25 kJ d) 125 kJ e) b
20. a) $CO + Cl_2 \rightarrow COCl_2$ b) 2 c) Cl and COCl
    d) k_{2f} [Cl] [CO] = k_{2r} [COCl] e) step 3 f) Rate = k' [Cl_2] [CO] where $k' = k_3k_{2f}k_{1f} / k_{2r}k_{1r}$
    g) While the energy diagram that is shown is that of an exothermic three step reaction, the energy of activation (E_a) for the 3rd step, which is supposed to be the slow or rate-determining step is not the largest. The first step of the reaction in the diagram that is shown is the one with the largest Ea; therefore, this diagram does not properly depict the energy changes occuring in this reaction.
21. Most elementary steps are either unimolecular or bimolecular. If this reaction where to occur via a one step-mechanism, then a four body collision would have to occur which is not very likely.

ANSWERS TO MULTIPLE CHOICE PRACTICE EXAM

1	2	3	4	5	6	7	8	9	10	11	12	13	14	15	16	17	18	19	20
1	3	3	4	3	5	2	5	2	1	4	4	5	5	1	5	3	1	1	2

21	22	23	24	25	26	27	28	29	30	31	32	33	34	35	36	37	38	39	40
5	1	4	5	5	1	3	1	1	2	1	4	4	3	4	1	2	1	2	2

41	42	43	44	45	46	47	48	49	50	51	52	53
2	2	2	3	2	4	1	4	5	2	5	4	4

MODULE 5. *Gas Phase and Heterogeneous Chemical Equilibria*

I. Chemical Equilibrium

Most chemical reactions do not go to completion (i.e., reactants do not get completely converted into products / reactant concentrations do not go down to zero). Instead, these reactions reach a state of *chemical equilibrium* in which:

$$\text{Rate}_{\text{forward reaction}} = \text{Rate}_{\text{reverse reaction}}$$

These reactions are also called *reversible reactions* and are represented by using a double arrow.

$$a\,\mathbf{A} + b\,\mathbf{B} \rightleftharpoons c\,\mathbf{C} + d\,\mathbf{D}$$

$$2\,\mathbf{A}_{(g)} + \mathbf{B}_{(g)} \rightleftharpoons \mathbf{C}_{(g)} + 2\,\mathbf{D}_{(g)}$$

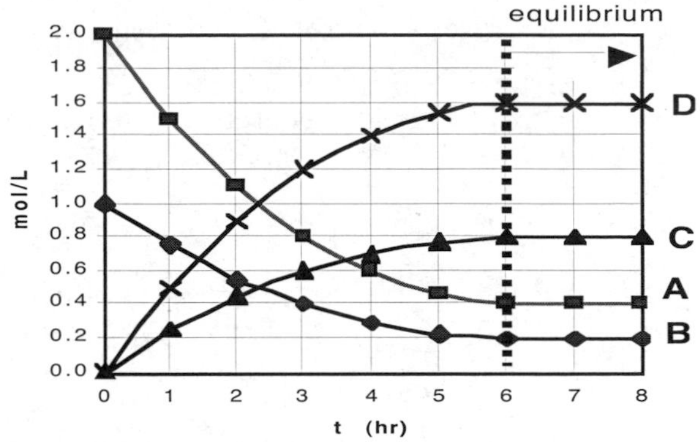

While at equilibrium, a *dynamic* process is still occurring - **A** and **B** are constantly reacting to produce **C** and **D**, while at the same time, **C** and **D** are constantly reacting to produce **A** and **B**. However, the net concentration of all species is not changing.

II. The Equilibrium Constant K_c and K_P in Gas Phase Reactions

In a gas phase reaction, you can keep track of how much of each gas is present at equilibrium by measuring gas molarities (M = mol/L) or gas partial pressures (or vapor pressures). In equilibrium calculations, the unit for pressure is atm. Recall from gas laws the relationship that exists between pressure and molarity (i.e., $P \propto M$ as shown below):

$$PV = nRT \;\rightarrow\; P = \frac{n}{V}RT \;\rightarrow\; P = MRT \quad \text{thus,} \quad P \propto M$$

For the following general gas phase reaction that is at equilibrium,

$$a\ A_{(g)} + b\ B_{(g)} \rightleftharpoons c\ C_{(g)} + d\ D_{(g)}$$

the equilibrium constants, K_c and K_P, are defined in the following *equilibrium expressions:*

Products

$$K_c = \frac{[C]^c\,[D]^d}{[A]^a\,[B]^b} \qquad K_P = \frac{(P_C)^c\,(P_D)^d}{(P_A)^a\,(P_B)^b}$$

Reactants

[ ] ➤ Concentration @ equilibrium (in molarity = M or mol/L)

P ➤ Partial Pressure @ equilibrium (in atm)

Whether one starts with large amounts of **A** and **B** or **C** and **D**, or any concentration mixture of **A**, **B**, **C**, and **D**, we find that when a system reaches equilibrium, the value of the equilibrium constant, K, is the same as long as the temperature remains constant. This is known as the *Law of Mass Action*.

Equilibrium constants in which M or atm are used can indeed have units. However, *equilibrium constants are unitless* because other units (i.e, activity and fugacity), which are unitless, are used to define an equilibrium constant. In very dilute solutions, molarity ≈ activity and atm ≈ fugacity. However, the concept of activity and fugacity are beyond the scope of this course. If one wanted to find the units for K_P -- write the equilibrium expression, the units will be $\text{atm}^{\Delta n}$ (where, $\Delta n = \Sigma$ (product exponents) - Σ (reactant exponents)]. Likewise, to find the units for Kc -- write the equilibrium expression, the units will be $M^{\Delta n}$.

For any reaction (as written), the value of K:

1. Varies only with temperature
2. Is a constant at a given temperature
3. Is independent of initial reactant concentration
4. Can't be used (by itself) to predict how long a reaction will take to reach equilibrium
5. Measures the extent of the reaction
    a) If K > 1 (Equilibrium is said to lie to the right or forward reaction is favored.)
    b) If K < 1 (Equilibrium is said to lie to the left or reverse reaction is favored.)

Example Problems:

1. Consider the following reaction: $N_2\,(g) + O_2\,(g) \rightleftharpoons 2\,NO\,(g)$ at 25°C.
    a) If at equilibrium at 25°C, $[N_2] = 0.68$ M, $[O_2] = 0.99$ M, and $[NO] = 5.5 \times 10^{-16}$ M, then calculate K_c?

    $$K_c = \frac{[NO]^2}{[N_2]\,[O_2]} = \frac{(5.5 \times 10^{-16})^2}{(0.68)\,(0.99)} = 4.5 \times 10^{-31}$$

    b) In what direction does the equilibrium lie (to the right or left)?

    Since $K_c < 1$ the equilibrium lies to the left (i.e., product formation is not favored).

    c) Write the equilibrium expression in terms of K_c for the reverse reaction.

    For the reverse reaction, $2\,NO\,(g) \rightleftharpoons N_2\,(g) + O_2\,(g)$, K_c is just the reciprocal [i.e., $1/K_c$ or K_c^{-1}) of the forward reaction.

    $$K_c = \frac{[N_2]\,[O_2]}{[NO]^2} = (4.5 \times 10^{-31})^{-1} = 2.2 \times 10^{30}$$

    d) Write the equilibrium expression in terms of K_c for: $6\,NO\,(g) \rightleftharpoons 3\,N_2\,(g) + 3\,O_2\,(g)$

    In comparison to the original reaction given, it has been reversed and all the coefficients have been multiplied by three, so K_c is the reciprocal of the given reaction cubed.

    $$K_c = \frac{[N_2]^3\,[O_2]^3}{[NO]^6} = (4.5 \times 10^{-31})^{-3} = 1.1 \times 10^{91}$$

    e) If the concentration of N_2 and O_2 that is present at equilibrium at 25°C, is 0.589 M and 0.697 M, respectively, then what is the equilibrium concentration of NO?

    By substituting into the equilibrium expression, we can find the concentration of NO at equilibrium.

    $$K_c = \frac{[NO]^2}{[N_2]\,[O_2]} = 4.5 \times 10^{-31} \rightarrow \frac{[NO]^2}{(0.589)\,(0.697)} = 4.5 \times 10^{-31}$$

    $$[NO]^2 = (0.589)\,(0.697)\,(4.5 \times 10^{-31})$$

    $$[NO] = \sqrt{(0.589)\,(0.697)\,(4.5 \times 10^{-31})} = 4.3 \times 10^{-16}\ \text{M}$$

    f) If $K_P = 4.5 \times 10^{-31}$ at 25°C, and the partial pressure at equilibrium of NO = 7.42×10^{-4} atm and that of $N_2 = 4.23 \times 10^5$ atm, then what is the equilibrium partial pressure (in atm) of O_2.

    $$K_P = \frac{(P_{NO})^2}{(P_{N_2})\,(P_{O_2})} \rightarrow 4.5 \times 10^{-31} = \frac{(7.42 \times 10^{-4})^2}{(4.23 \times 10^5)\,(P_{O_2})}$$

    $$P_{O_2} = \frac{(7.42 \times 10^{-4})^2}{(4.23 \times 10^5)\,(4.5 \times 10^{-31})} \rightarrow P_{O_2} = 2.9 \times 10^{18}\ \text{atm}$$

III. Interconversion Between K_P and K_c

The following relationship exists between **K_P and K_c**:

$$K_P = K_c(RT)^{\Delta n}$$

where Δn = (total mol gas)$_{products}$ - (total mol gas)$_{reactants}$

*The only R that can be used is, **0.0821** $\frac{L \cdot atm}{mol \cdot K}$, because P is defined in atm; T must be in Kelvin*

Example Problem:

1. When the following reaction was conducted at 500°C, $K_c = 0.286$.

$$N_2\,(g) + 3\,H_2\,(g) \rightleftharpoons 2\,NH_3\,(g)$$

Given this information, find K_P at this same temperature.

$$K_P = K_c(RT)^{\Delta n}$$

$$K_P = (0.286)\left[\left(0.0821\,\frac{L \cdot atm}{mol \cdot K}\right)(500 + 273\ K)\right]^{(2\ -\ 4)} = 7.10 \times 10^{-5}$$

IV. Heterogeneous Equilibria

Heterogeneous equilibria involve species in more than one phase. In writing an equilibrium expression for a heterogeneous equilibrium, you can omit any concentration terms for pure liquids and solids because their concentration stays constant throughout the reaction. So concentration terms for substances that are pure liquids and solids are not present in the equilibrium expression.

Example Problems:

1. Write both the K_c and K_P equilibrium expression for the following reaction.

$$N_2\,(g) + O_2\,(g) \rightleftharpoons 2\,NO\,(g)$$

$$K_c = \frac{[NO]^2}{[N_2]\,[O_2]} \qquad K_P = \frac{(P_{NO})^2}{(P_{N_2})\,(P_{O_2})}$$

2. Write the K_c equilibrium expression for the following reaction.

$$CO_2\,(g) + H_2O\,(l) \rightleftharpoons H_2CO_3\,(aq) \quad \rightarrow \quad K_c = \frac{[H_2CO_3]}{[CO_2]}$$

3. Consider the following equation: $BaCl_2 \cdot 2\,H_2O\,(s) \rightleftharpoons BaCl_2\,(s) + 2\,H_2O\,(g)$

When a certain amount of $BaCl_2 \cdot 2\,H_2O$ was placed in a 5.00 L vessel at 90°C, 0.237 g of water vapor was found to be present once equilibrium was established. Given this information,

a) Find K_c

$$K_c = [H_2O]^2 \quad \rightarrow \quad K_c = \left(\frac{0.237\ g\ H_2O\left(\frac{1\ mol\ H_2O}{18.0\ g\ H_2O}\right)}{5.00\ L}\right)^2 = 6.93 \times 10^{-6}$$

b) Find K_P

$$K_P = K_c(RT)^{\Delta n}$$

$$K_P = (6.93 \times 10^{-6})\left[\left(0.0821\,\frac{L \cdot atm}{mol \cdot K}\right)(90 + 273\ K)\right]^{(2\ -\ 0)} = 6.16 \times 10^{-3}$$

c) Find the partial pressure (or vapor pressure) of water (in atm) for this reaction at 90°C.

There are two ways of doing this problem.

1. Use of the Equilibrium Expression

$$K_P = (P_{H_2O})^2$$

$$6.16 \times 10^{-3} = (P_{H_2O})^2 \rightarrow \sqrt{6.16 \times 10^{-3}} = P_{H_2O} \rightarrow 7.85 \times 10^{-2} \text{ atm}$$

2. Use of the Ideal Gas Equation

PV = nRT (the gas in this particular case is water vapor)

$$P\,(5.00\ L) = \frac{0.237\ g}{18.0\ {}^{g}/_{mol}}\left(0.0821\,\frac{L \sum atm}{mol \sum K}\right)(90 + 273\ K)$$

$$P_{H_2O} = 7.85 \times 10^{-2} \text{ atm}$$

V. The Equilibrium Constant and Thermodynamics

You may recall from the thermodynamics module, that at equilibrium ΔG = 0. The following equation can be used to find the equilibrium constant, K, under standard conditions from thermodynamic data:

0 (@ equilibrium)

$\Delta G = \Delta G° + RT \ln K$ therefore, $\mathbf{\Delta G° = -RT \ln K}$

ΔG° represents the free energy change that would accompany complete conversion of all reactants initially present to products under standard conditions.

where R is the gas constant and T is the temperature in K(elvin). Standard state for gases is the most stable form of the element or compound at a pressure of 1 atm at a specified temperature. Standard state for an aqueous solution is at a solute concentration of 1 M at a pressure of 1 atm at a specified temperature. [NOTE: The "numerator" unit for R must match those of ΔG°.]

$$R \rightarrow 1.99 \times 10^{-3}\ \frac{\text{kcal}}{\text{mol·K}} = 1.99\ \frac{\text{cal}}{\text{mol·K}} = 8.31 \times 10^{-3}\ \frac{\text{kJ}}{\text{mol·K}} = 8.31\ \frac{\text{J}}{\text{mol·K}}$$

Thus, K can be obtained from ΔG°; conversely, ΔG° can be obtained from K. *For equilibria that involve only gases, the thermodynamic equilibrium constant (related to ΔG°) is* K_P. For those that involve species in solution, it is equal to K_c.

ΔG° can be obtained from Standard Gibbs Free Energy of Formation data in Appendix 1; however, this data only applies to reactions run at 25°C. If ΔG_f° is not available or if reaction is not run at 25°C, then remember that ΔG° can also be obtained from ΔH° and ΔS° by use of the following equation:

$$\Delta G° = \Delta H° - T\Delta S° \quad \text{(at any temperature)}$$

You may also recall, that ΔH° and ΔS° are basically temperature independent (as long as the substance is in the same phase); the same can not be said for ΔG°. Thus, the above equation can be used to evaluate ΔG° at various temperatures and in turn, K can then be obtained at different temperatures.

The *van't Hoff equation* can also be used to obtain K at different temperatures.

$$\ln \frac{K_2}{K_1} = \frac{\Delta H°}{R}\left(\frac{1}{T_1} - \frac{1}{T_2}\right)$$

where, ΔH° (is the enthalpy change for the reaction), R is the gas constant (*whose "numerator" unit must match those of ΔH°*), T is the temperature in Kelvin, and K_1 and K_2 (K_1 and K_2 must both be either K_P's - *for equilibria that involve gases* or K_c's - *for equilibria other than gas phase*) are the equilibrium constants at T_1 and T_2, respectively.

Example Problems:

1. Given that $\Delta G° = 16.16$ kcal and $\Delta H° = 27.1$ kcal for the following reaction:

$$COCl_{2\,(g)} \rightleftharpoons CO_{(g)} + Cl_{2\,(g)}$$

a) Find the equilibrium constant for this reaction at 25°C.

$\Delta G° = -RT \ln K$ *(Since this is a gas phase reaction $K = K_P$)*

$$16.16 \text{ kcal} = -\left(1.99 \times 10^{-3} \frac{\text{kcal}}{\text{mol·K}}\right)(25 + 273 \text{ K}) \ln K$$

$$\ln K = \frac{16.16}{-0.5930} \rightarrow K_{25°C} = e^{-27.25} = 1.46 \times 10^{-12}$$

b) Find the equilibrium constant for this reaction at 327°C (i.e., $K_{327°C}$).

By using the K_P obtained at 25°C (273 + 25 = 298 K) in the previous problem, the given $\Delta H°$, and the van't Hoff equation -- K_P @ 327°C (273 + 327 = 600 K) can be obtained:

$$\ln \frac{K_2}{K_1} = \frac{\Delta H°}{R}\left(\frac{1}{T_1} - \frac{1}{T_2}\right)$$

$$\ln \frac{K_2}{1.46 \times 10^{-12}} = \frac{27.1 \text{ kcal}}{1.99 \times 10^{-3} \frac{\text{kcal}}{\text{mol·K}}}\left(\frac{1}{298 \text{ K}} - \frac{1}{600 \text{ K}}\right)$$

$$\ln K_2 - \ln(1.46 \times 10^{-12}) = (1.362 \times 10^4)(1.689 \times 10^{-3})$$

$$\ln K_2 = 2.300 \times 10^1 - 27.25 \rightarrow K_{327°C} = e^{-4.25} = 1.43 \times 10^{-2}$$

NOTE: In this problem we see mathematically how for an endothermic reaction ($\Delta H° > 0$), as the temperature increases so does the equilibrium constant (i.e., the concentration of product(s) increases). Conversely, for an exothermic reaction ($\Delta H° < 0$), as the temperature increases the equilibrium constant decreases (i.e., the concentration of product(s) decreases).

2. At its normal boiling point of 100°C, ΔH_{vap} for water is 40.66 kJ. What is the vapor pressure (in atm) of water at 50°C?

The following is the "reaction" in question: $H_2O_{(l)} \rightleftharpoons H_2O_{(g)}$. Remember that the normal boiling point is the temperature at which the vapor pressure of the substance is 1 atm. Therefore, $P_{H_2O@100°C} = 1$ atm.

The equilibrium expression for this "reaction" is:

$$K_P = (P_{H_2O}) \rightarrow \text{at } 100°C \rightarrow K_P = 1$$

Now we can substitute into the van't Hoff equation to find K_P @ 50°C which is equal to $P_{H_2O@50°C}$

$$\ln \frac{K_2}{K_1} = \frac{\Delta H°}{R}\left(\frac{1}{T_1} - \frac{1}{T_2}\right)$$

$$\ln \frac{K_2}{1} = \frac{40.66 \text{ kJ}}{8.31 \times 10^{-3} \frac{\text{kJ}}{\text{mol·K}}}\left(\frac{1}{(273+100 \text{ K})} - \frac{1}{(273+50 \text{ K})}\right)$$

$$\ln K_2 - \ln(1) = (4.893 \times 10^3)(-4.150 \times 10^{-4})$$

$$\ln K_2 = (4.893 \times 10^3)(-4.150 \times 10^{-4}) + (0)$$

$$K_{50°C} = e^{-2.031} = 1.31 \times 10^{-1} \rightarrow P_{H_2O@50°C}$$

3. Given that $\Delta H° = 27.1$ kcal for the following reaction at 327°C, find $\Delta S°$ (in kcal).

$$COCl_{2\,(g)} \rightleftharpoons CO_{(g)} + Cl_{2\,(g)} \qquad K_{327°C} = 1.43 \times 10^{-2}$$

First we will use the following equation to find ΔG at 327°C.

$$\Delta G°_{327°C} = -RT \ln K$$

$$\Delta G°_{327°C} = -\left(1.99 \times 10^{-3}\,\frac{\text{kcal}}{\text{mol·K}}\right)(273 + 327\text{ K})\ \ln(1.43 \times 10^{-2}) = 5.07\text{ kcal}$$

Then we can use the following equation to find $\Delta S°$:

$$\Delta G° = \Delta H° - T\Delta S° \quad \rightarrow \quad 5.07\text{ kcal} = 27.1\text{ kcal} - (600\text{ K})\,\Delta S°$$

$$\Delta S° = \frac{5.07 - 27.1}{-600} = 0.0367\,\frac{\text{kcal}}{\text{K}}$$

VI. The Equilibrium Constant and Chemical Kinetics

As was previously mentioned, when a reaction reaches equilibrium, the rate of the forward reaction ($Rate_f$) is equal to the rate of the reverse reaction ($Rate_r$). If the rate law for both the forward and reverse reaction are known, then the reaction's equilibrium constant can be calculated as shown in the following example problem.

Example Problem:

1. Given that the rate law for both the forward and reverse reaction for the following one-step reversible reaction is:

$$A_{(g)} \underset{k_r}{\overset{k_f}{\rightleftharpoons}} B_{(g)} \qquad Rate_f = 1.6 \times 10^{-4}\ s^{-}\,[A] \qquad Rate_r = 2.3 \times 10^{-6}\ s^{-}\,[B]$$

Calculate the K_c.

Since at equilibrium, $Rate_f = Rate_r$, then $1.6 \times 10^{-4}\ s^{-}\,[A] = 2.3 \times 10^{-6}\ s^{-}\,[B]$. Solving for [B]/[A], then yields K_c as follows:

$$K_c = \frac{[B]}{[A]} = \frac{1.6 \times 10^{-4}}{2.3 \times 10^{-6}} = 70 \quad \Longleftarrow \quad K_c = \frac{k_f}{k_r}$$

VII. Factors that Affect Equilibria and the Le Chatelier Principle

A reaction at equilibrium can be thought of figuratively as a reaction in which the reactants are on one side of a see-saw and the products are on the other side and the see-saw moves freely back and forth. If a stress is applied, such as more product is added to a system at equilibrium, the see-saw will be tilting towards the products. To alleviate this situation, the reaction proceeds to make more reactants (i.e., the equilibrium is said to shift to the left) until equilibrium is re-established. This is the basic premise to the Le Chatelier Principle.

Once a system is at equilibrium it will remain there unless a stress is applied to the system. The following are stresses that can be applied to a system at equilibrium.

A. Addition / Removal of Reactants / Products

Consider the following reaction:

$$CO_{2\,(g)} + H_2O_{(l)} \rightleftharpoons H_2CO_{3\,(aq)}$$

If more CO_2 is added, the equilibrium shifts to the right to decrease the amount of CO_2.

If CO_2 is removed, the equilibrium shifts to the left in order to increase the CO_2.

If more H_2O is added or removed, the equilibrium does not shift because pure liquids and solids do not enter into the equilibrium expression.

If more H_2CO_3 is added, the equilibrium shifts to the left to decrease the amount of H_2CO_3.

If H_2CO_3 is removed, the equilibrium shifts to the right in order to produce more H_2CO_3.

B. **Changes in Pressure and Volume**

Changes in pressure have little effect on the concentrations of liquids and solids. However, changes in pressure can cause a significant effect on the concentration of gases. From the ideal gas equation, you can see why this is the case:

$$PV = nRT \quad \rightarrow \quad P = \frac{n}{V}\ RT \quad \rightarrow \quad P = MRT \quad \text{thus,} \quad P \propto M$$

An increase in the partial pressure of a gas is equivalent to an increase in its concentration (i.e., its molarity). Conversely, a decrease in its partial pressure is equivalent to a decrease in its concentration (i.e., its molarity).

A pressure change can also be obtained by changing the volume of the reaction container. From the ideal gas equation, it can be shown that: $P \propto \frac{1}{V}$

The side with the most moles of gas can be thought of as having pressure (P) as a "reactant" or "product". If the pressure is increased (by decreasing the volume of the reaction mixture) the reaction will shift to the direction that will produce the least moles of gas.

Example Problems:

1. For each of the following reactions, indicate in what direction, if any, will the reaction be shifted if there is an increase in pressure (obtained from a decrease in the volume of the container).

   a) $COCl_2\ (g) \rightleftharpoons CO\ (g) + Cl_2\ (g)$

   The products have more moles of gas, therefore, "P" can be thought of as a "product", ($COCl_2\ (g) \rightleftharpoons CO\ (g) + Cl_2\ (g)$ + "P"), to indicate this, a "P" is put on the side having the most moles of gas. An increase in "P" causes the equilibrium to shift to the left. [NOTE: A decrease in pressure would have caused the equilibrium to shift to the right.]

   b) $N_2\ (g) + O_2\ (g) \rightleftharpoons 2\ NO\ (g)$

   The number of moles of gases is the same on both sides, therefore, an increase in pressure has no effect.

C. **Changes in Temperature**

The direction in which the equilibrium will be shifted if a change in temperature occurs depends on whether the reaction is exothermic (ΔH is negative -- or heat is a "product") or whether the reaction is endothermic (ΔH is positive -- or heat is a "reactant").

Example Problems:

1. For each of the following reactions, indicate in what direction, if any, will the reaction be shifted if there is an increase in temperature.

   a) $COCl_2\ (g) \rightleftharpoons CO\ (g) + Cl_2\ (g) \qquad \Delta H° = 27.1\ \text{kcal}$

   The reaction is endothermic, therefore, consider that "heat", which we will label "T", is a reactant ($COCl_2\ (g)$ + "T" $\rightleftharpoons CO\ (g) + Cl_2\ (g)$). An increase in "T" causes the equilibrium to shift to right.

   b) $CO\ (g) + 3\ H_2\ (g) \rightleftharpoons CH_4\ (g) + H_2O\ (g) \qquad \Delta H° = -206.2\ \text{kJ}$

   The reaction is exothermic, therefore, consider that "heat" is a product ($CO\ (g) + 3\ H_2\ (g) \rightleftharpoons CH_4\ (g) + H_2O\ (g)$ + "T"). An increase in "T" causes the equilibrium to shift to left.

D. **Addition of a Catalyst**

The addition of a catalyst does not shift the equilibrium, it just merely speeds up the time it takes to get to equilibrium.

E. **Addition of an Inert Gas at Constant Volume**

A change in volume is not the only way to change the pressure in the reaction vessel. An inert gas (i.e., a noble gas) can be introduced into the system, thereby increasing the pressure. However, if this is done *at constant volume*, there will be *no* change in the position of the equilibrium. This is because there is no change in the concentration (i.e., pressure and/or volume) of any of the species involved in the reaction.

Example Problems:

1. Consider the following reaction: $C_{(s)} + H_2O_{(g)} \rightleftharpoons CO_{(g)} + H_{2(g)}$ $\Delta H° = 131$ kJ

   In which direction would the equilibrium be shifted by each of the following applied stresses?

   Before starting, let's re-write the equation to show the effect of T and P.

   $$\mathbf{C_{(s)} + H_2O_{(g)} + "T" \rightleftharpoons CO_{(g)} + H_{2(g)} + "P"}$$

   a) Addition of $C_{(s)}$

      The addition of pure liquids and solids would not affect the equilibrium.

   b) Addition of $He_{(g)}$ (while maintaining a constant volume)

      The addition of inert gases does not shift the equilibrium.

   c) Addition of $H_{2(g)}$

      The addition of H_2 would cause the equilibrium to shift to the left (to remove H_2).

   d) Increasing the volume of the reaction vessel.

      Since $P \propto 1/V$, an increase in V causes "P" to decrease. The largest number of gas moles is found on the right hand side (this side has the "greatest pressure"), so if "P" decreases, the equilibrium shifts to the right.

   e) A catalyst is added.

      A catalyst does not shift the equilibrium, it is just established quicker.

VIII. The Reaction Quotient

In the previous section we saw how the direction in which a reaction proceeds is affected by changes in concentration, pressure, volume, and temperature. The concept of the reaction quotient (or *mass action expression)* is very useful in determining if a system is at equilibrium; and if it is not, what kind of shift is necessary in order to establish equilibrium. The reaction quotient has the same form as the equilibrium constant, however, the concentrations (or partial pressures) that are plugged into the equation are not necessarily those at equilibrium. The *reaction quotient, Q*, for the following general reaction is:

$$a\,\mathbf{A}_{(g)} + b\,\mathbf{B}_{(g)} \rightleftharpoons c\,\mathbf{C}_{(g)} + d\,\mathbf{D}_{(g)} \qquad Q = \frac{[C]^c\,[D]^d}{[A]^a\,[B]^b}$$

← not necessarily equilibrium concentrations

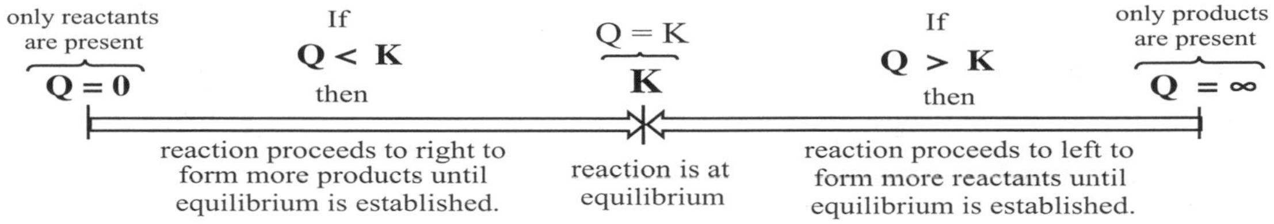
only reactants are present
Q = 0
If
Q < K
then
reaction proceeds to right to form more products until equilibrium is established.
Q = K
K
reaction is at equilibrium
If
Q > K
then
reaction proceeds to left to form more reactants until equilibrium is established.
only products are present
Q = ∞

Example Problems:

1. Consider the following reaction and information: $C_{(g)} \rightleftharpoons A_{(g)} + B_{(g)}$ $K_c = 2.0 \times 10^{-5}$

   $[C] = 0.20$ M, $[A] = 0.10$ M, and $[B] = 0.10$ M.

   a) Is this system at equilibrium?

      To find if this system is at equilibrium, find the reaction quotient, Q.

      $$Q = \frac{[A]\,[B]}{[C]} = \frac{(0.10)\,(0.10)}{(0.20)} = 0.05$$

      This system is not at equilibrium because $Q \neq K$.

   b) In what direction will the reaction be shifted in order to establish equilibrium?

      Since Q (0.05) > K (2.0×10^{-5}), the reaction will shift to the left (i.e., the reverse reaction to form more reactants will take place until equilibrium is established). Q being greater than K means that there is too much product (i.e., numerator in the reaction quotient ["Q expression"] is too large), thus in order to establish equilibrium, the products need to react to form more reactants (i.e., the equilibrium shifts to the left).

IX. Equiliburim Constant Calculations

You have been exposed to various ways in which the equilibrium constant for a reaction can be calculated: given the equilibrium concentration (or partial pressure) of all products and reactants (see problem 1a on page 5-2), given thermodynamic data (see problem 1a and 1b on page 5-5), and given kinetic data (see problem 1 on page 5-6).

We now wish to expose you to other methods by which the equilibrium constant for a reaction (at a particular temperature) can be calculated given initial reactant concentrations (or partial pressures) and either given: the equilibrium concentration of one of the species present in the reaction mixture (see Example A below), the % dissociation of a reactant (see Example B below), or the total pressure at equilibrium of a gas phase reaction (see Example C below).

Example A. Calculating K_c Given Initial Reactant Concentrations and the Equilibrium Concentration of One of the Species Present in the Reaction

When 1.00 mol of A and 1.00 mol of B were placed in 0.400-L container at 75°C, and allowed to come to equilibrium, 0.400 mol of D was found to be present. Given this information and the following balanced equation, find K_c.

	$A_{(g)}$ +	$B_{(g)}$ ⇌	$C_{(s)}$ +	$2\,D_{(g)}$
[ ]i:	$\frac{1.00\text{ mol}}{0.400\text{L}}$	$\frac{1.00\text{ mol}}{0.400\text{L}}$	0	0
[ ]change:	- x	- x	---	+ 2x
[ ]equil:	2.50 - x	2.50 - x	---	2x

$$\text{The "given" } [D]_{equil} = 1.00\text{ M}\left(\frac{0.400\text{ mol}}{0.400\text{ L}}\right) \rightarrow 2x = 1.00 \rightarrow x = 0.500\text{ M}$$

Equilibrium Concentrations

[A] 2.00 M [2.50 - x = 2.50 - 0.500]

[B] 2.00 M [2.50 - x = 2.50 - 0.500]

[C] ? (The concentration of liquids and solids is constant because they are practically incompressible (i.e., their volume is constant) and can be obtained from their density (i.e., g/mL can be converted into mol/L). Thus, if the density of C were known we could have calculated its concentration.)

[D] 1.00 M [2x = 2(0.500)]

Substituting into the equilibrium expression allows us then to obtain K_c.

$$K_c = \frac{[D]^2}{[A]\,[B]} \rightarrow K_c = \frac{[1.00]^2}{[2.00]\,[2.00]} = 0.250$$

Example B. Calculating K_c Given Initial Reactant Concentrations and % Dissociation Information

$NOCl_{(g)}$ dissociates to $NO_{(g)}$ and $Cl_{2\,(g)}$. When 1.0 mol of $NOCl_{(g)}$ was placed in a 1.0-L vessel at 500 K, 9.0% of it was found to have dissociated. Given this information, calculate K_c.

	$2\,NOCl_{(g)}$ ⇌	$2\,NO_{(g)}$ +	$Cl_{2\,(g)}$
[ ]i:	$\frac{1.0\text{ mol}}{1.0\text{ L}}$	0	0
[ ]change:	- 2x	+2x	+ x
[ ]equil:	1.0 - 2x	2x	x

If 9.0% of NOCl dissociates, 91.0% of it remains unreacted at equilibrium. Since $[NOCl]_i$ = 1.0 M, then 0.91 M (91.0% of 1.0 M) is present at equilibrium. Thus,

$$[NOCl]_{equil} = 1 - 2x = 0.91\ M \rightarrow x = \frac{0.91 - 1}{-2} = 0.045\ M$$

Equilibrium Concentrations

[NOCl]	0.91 M	[Obtained from % dissociation]
[NO]	0.090 M	$[2x = 2 \bullet 0.045]$
$[Cl_2]$	0.045 M	$[x = 0.045]$

$$K_c = \frac{[NO]^2\,[Cl_2]}{[NOCl]^2} = \frac{0.090^2 \bullet 0.045}{0.91^2} = 4.4 \times 10^{-4}$$

Example C. Calculating K_P Given Intial Reactant Concentrations and Total Pressure at Equilibrium

When 0.500 atm of NO_2 was allowed to come to equilibrium, the total pressure was 0.674 atm. Given this information and the following balanced equation, calculate K_P.

	$2\ NO_{2\,(g)}$ ⇌	$2\ NO_{(g)}$ +	$O_{2\,(g)}$
P_i:	0.500	0	0
P_{change}:	- 2x	+2x	+x
P_{equil}:	0.500 - 2x	2x	x

As you may remember from Dalton's Law, the total pressure is equal to the sum of the partial pressure of each gas.

$$P_T = P_{NO_2} + P_{NO} + P_{O_2}$$

$$0.674 = (0.500 - 2x) + (2x) + (x) \rightarrow 0.674 = 0.500 + x$$

$$x = 0.674 - 0.500 = 0.174$$

Equilibrium Partial Pressures

NO_2	0.152 atm	$[0.500 - 2x = 0.500 - 2(0.174)]$
NO	0.348 atm	$[2x = 2(0.174)]$
O_2	0.174 atm	$[x = 0.174]$

Substituting into the equilibrium expression allows us to then obtain K_P.

$$K_P = \frac{(P_{NO})^2\,(P_{O_2})}{(P_{NO_2})^2} \rightarrow K_P = \frac{[0.348]^2\,[0.174]}{[0.152]^2} = 0.912$$

X. Finding Equilibrium Concentrations

Once the equilibrium constant is known, given initial concentration data, equilibrium concentrations can then be calculated. In order to do this, many times a quadratic equation, will be involved. In preparation for a quadratic equation, $ax^2 + bx + c = 0$, lets review its solutions:

$$x = \frac{-b \pm \sqrt{b^2 - 4ac}}{2a}$$

As you may remember, this equation has two solutions. One of its solutions would lead to a physically impossible answer (i.e., obtaining a negative concentration or an equilibrium concentration for a reactant that was greater than its initial concentration).

We will show you several examples illustrating equilibrium calculations and along the way we will expose you to "tricks of the trade" in order to avoid using the very tedious quadratic formula.

After you have finished your calculations, always verify your answers by plugging in the equilibrium concentrations that you obtained into the equilibrium (or mass action) expression. Having done so, you should get the same or very close to the same equilibrium constant as that which was given.

Example 1: "Assuming that x is Small"

The amount that has reacted or formed (i.e., the change that has occurred in the initial concentration) as represented by x, can be assumed to be small in comparison to the initial concentration when one of the following two scenarios occurs. *In any case, you should always verify that x is indeed small.*

A. A shift in the equilibrium is occurring from left to right (→) and K is very small

When this kind of situation is occurring, this signifies that hardly any of the reactant(s) are reacting to form products. As a result, the initial reactant concentration is basically the same after equilibrium has been reached. Usually, K is considered very small when it is 0.01 times smaller than the initial concentration (i.e., if $K < [\ ]_i \times 10^{-2}$, then x can be considered small). The following example illustrates this point.

When 0.100 mol of H_2O are placed into a 1.00-L vessel, according to the following reaction, what is the concentration of H_2O, H_2, and O_2 at equilibrium?

	$2\ H_2O\ (g)$ ⇌	$2\ H_2\ (g)$ +	$O_2\ (g)$	$K_c = 7.3 \times 10^{-18}$
$[\ ]_i$:	$\frac{0.100\text{ mol}}{1.0\text{ L}}$	0	0	
$[\ ]_{change}$:	-2x	+ 2x	+x	
$[\ ]_{equil}$:	0.100 - 2x	2x	x	

Substituting into the equilibrium expression gives us,

$$K_c = \frac{[H_2]^2[O_2]}{[H_2O]^2} \rightarrow 7.3 \times 10^{-18} = \frac{(2x)^2(x)}{(0.100 - 2x)^2}$$

$$7.3 \times 10^{-18} = \frac{(2x)^2(x)}{(0.100 - 2x)^2}$$

Assume that x is small

Since K_c $(7.3 \times 10^{-18}) < [\ ]_i \times 10^{-2}$ (0.1×10^{-2}), x will be assumed to be small in comparison to the initial concentration of 0.100 and as such will be neglected.

$$7.3 \times 10^{-18} = \frac{4x^3}{(0.100)^2}$$

$$7.3 \times 10^{-20} = 4x^3$$

$$x = \sqrt[3]{\frac{7.3 \times 10^{-20}}{4}} = 2.6 \times 10^{-7}$$

Our assumption that x was small in comparison to the initial concentration was correct. ***A small x is considered one that is less than 10% of the initial concentration*** $[x\ (2.6 \times 10^{-7}) < 10\% \times [\ ]_i\ (0.1 \times 0.100 = 0.01)]$.

Equilibrium Concentrations

H_2O 0.100 M $[0.100 - 2x = 0.100 - 2(2.6 \times 10^{-7})]$

H_2 5.2×10^{-7} M $[2x = 2(2.6 \times 10^{-7})]$

O_2 2.6×10^{-7} M $[x = 2.6 \times 10^{-7}]$

B. A shift in the equilibrium is occurring from right to left (←) and K is very large

When this kind of situation is occurring, as the reaction is proceeding in the reverse direction, hardly any of the product(s) are reacting to form reactants. As a result, the initial product concentration is basically the same after equilibrium has been reached. Usually, K is considered very large when it is 100 times greater than the initial concentration (i.e., if $K > [\ ]_i \times 10^2$, then x can be considered small). The following example illustrates this point.

When 10.0 mol of $COCl_2$ are placed into a 5.00-L vessel, according to the following equation, what is the concentration of CO, Cl_2, and $COCl_2$ at equilibrium?

	$CO_{(g)}$	+	$Cl_{2\,(g)}$	$\rightleftharpoons$	$COCl_{2\,(g)}$	$K_c = 4.57 \times 10^9$
[ ]$_i$:	0		0		$\dfrac{10.0 \text{ mol}}{5.00 \text{ L}}$	
[ ]change:	+ x		+ x		- x	
[ ]equil:	x		x		2.00 - x	

Substituting into the equilibrium expression gives us,

$$K_c = \frac{[COCl_2]}{[CO]\,[Cl_2]} \quad \rightarrow \quad 4.57 \times 10^9 = \frac{(2.00 - x)}{(x)\,(x)}$$

Assume that x is small

$$4.57 \times 10^9 = \frac{(2.00 - x)}{x^2}$$

$$4.57 \times 10^9 \; x^2 = 2.00$$

$$x = \sqrt{\frac{2.00}{4.57 \times 10^9}} = 2.09 \times 10^{-5}$$

Since K_c (4.57×10^9) > [ ]$_i$ x 10^2 (2.00×10^2), x will be assumed to be small in comparison to the initial concentration of 2.00 and as such will be neglected.

Our assumption that x was small in comparison to the initial concentration was correct. *A small x is considered one that is less than 10% of the initial concentration.*

[x (2.09×10^{-5}) < 10% x [ ]$_i$ (0.1 x 2.00 = 0.2)]

Equilibrium Concentrations

CO 2.09×10^{-5} M [x = 2.09×10^{-5}]

Cl_2 2.09×10^{-5} M [x = 2.09×10^{-5}]

$COCl_2$ 2.00 M [2.00 - x = 2.00 - 2.09×10^{-5}]

Example 2. "Perfect Squares"

When 1.00 mol of Cl_2 is reacted with 1.00 mol of Br_2 in a 5.00 L flask at a particular temperature according to the following equation, what is the concentration of Cl_2, Br_2, and BrCl at equilibrium?

	$2 \text{ BrCl}_{(g)}$	$\rightleftharpoons$	$Cl_{2\,(g)}$	+	$Br_{2\,(g)}$	$K_c = 9.7$
[ ]$_i$:	0		$\dfrac{1.00 \text{ mol}}{5.00 \text{ L}}$		$\dfrac{1.00 \text{ mol}}{5.00 \text{ L}}$	
[ ]change:	+ 2x		-x		- x	
[ ]equil:	2x		0.200 - x		0.200 - x	

Substituting into the equilibrium expression gives us,

$$K_c = \frac{[Cl_2]\,[Br_2]}{[BrCl]^2} \quad \rightarrow \quad 9.7 = \frac{(0.200 - x)(0.200 - x)}{(2x)^2}$$

Since K_c (9.7) $\not>$ [ ]$_i$ x 10^2 (0.2 x 10^2 = 20), x will not be assumed to be small. [If you would have assumed that x was small, you would have obtained a value for x = 0.032 -- this is not small.]

[x (0.032) $\not<$ 10% x [ ]$_i$ (0.1 x 0.200 = 0.02)]

$$9.7 = \frac{(0.200 - x)^2}{(2x)^2}$$

This equation has a perfect square. To find x take the square root of both sides.

$$\sqrt{9.7} = \sqrt{\frac{(0.200 - x)^2}{(2x)^2}}$$

$$3.11 = \frac{(0.200 - x)}{(2x)} \quad \rightarrow \quad (2x)\,(3.11) = 0.200 - x \quad \rightarrow \quad 6.22\, x = 0.200 - x$$

$$x = \frac{0.200}{7.22} = 0.0277$$

Equilibrium Concentrations

BrCl	0.0554 M [2x = 2(0.0277)]
Cl_2	0.172 M [0.200 - x = 0.200 - 0.0277]
Br_2	0.172 M [0.200 - x = 0.200 - 0.0277]

Example 3: Oh-No!!! - Use of the Quadratic Formula Because All Else Failed

When 1.00 M of H_2 and 2.00 M of I_2 were reacted according to the following equation, what is the concentration of H_2, I_2, and HI at equilibrium?

$$H_{2\,(g)} + I_{2\,(g)} \rightleftharpoons 2\,HI_{(g)} \qquad K_c = 49.7$$

	$H_{2\,(g)}$	$I_{2\,(g)}$	$2\,HI_{(g)}$
$[\,]_i$:	1.00	2.00	0
$[\,]_{change}$:	- x	-x	+ 2x
$[\,]_{equil}$:	1.00 - x	2.00 - x	2x

Substituting into the equilibrium expression gives us,

$$K_c = \frac{[HI]^2}{[H_2]\,[I_2]} \rightarrow 49.7 = \frac{(2x)^2}{(1.00 - x)\,(2.00 - x)}$$

Since K_c (49.7) ≮ $[\,]_i$ x 10^{-2} (1.00 x x 10^{-2}), x will not be assumed to be small . We must then use the quadratic formula. [If you would have assumed that x was small, you would have obtained a value for x = 4.98 -- this is not small.]

[x (4.98) ≮ 10% x $[\,]_i$ (0.1 x 1.00= 0.1)]

$$49.7 = \frac{4x^2}{2.00 - 3.00\,x + x^2} \rightarrow 99.4 - 149.1\,x + 49.7\,x^2 = 4x^2$$

$$45.7\,x^2 - 149.1\,x + 99.4 = 0$$

$$x = \frac{-(-149.1) \pm \sqrt{(-149.1)^2 - 4(45.7)(99.4)}}{2(45.7)}$$

x = **0.934** or

2.33 (this root would lead to a negative equilibrium concentration for H_2 and I_2)

Equilibrium Concentrations

H_2	0.07 M [1.00 - x = 1.00 - 0.934]
I_2	1.07 M [2.00 - x = 2.00 - 0.934]
HI	1.87 M [2x = 2(0.934)]

EXERCISES

Equilibrium Constant (K_c and K_P)

1. Consider the hypothetical reaction, $2\,A_{(g)} + B_{(g)} \rightleftharpoons C_{(g)} + 2\,D_{(g)}$, whose change in concentration of reactants and products, at 25°C, as a function of time is shown graphically on page 1 of this module.
   a) Write the equilibrium constant expression in terms of K_c.
   b) What is the equilibrium constant, K_c, for this hypothetical reaction?

2. Given that at 1024°C, $K_c = 1.60 \times 10^5$ for the following reaction: $H_{2\,(g)} + Br_{2\,(g)} \rightleftharpoons 2\,HBr_{(g)}$
   a) Write the equilibrium constant expression in terms of K_c.
   b) What is the equilibrium molarity of HBr given that at equilibrium 0.2 mol of H_2 and 0.4 mol of Br_2 were present in a 5.00-L reaction vessel at 1024°C?
   c) At 1024°C write the K_c expression for: $\frac{1}{3}\,H_{2\,(g)} + \frac{1}{3}\,Br_{2\,(g)} \rightleftharpoons \frac{2}{3}\,HBr_{(g)}$
   d) Which reaction is more favorable, the forward or reverse?
   e) At 1024°C what is K_P?

3. Given that at 500°C, $K_c = 0.286$ for the following reaction: $N_{2\,(g)} + 3\,H_{2\,(g)} \rightleftharpoons 2\,NH_{3\,(g)}$
   a) If the equilibrium concentrations of $[N_2] = 2.36$ M and $[NH_3] = 4.75$ M, then calculate $[H_2]$ at equilibrium at 500°C.
   b) Which reaction is more favorable, the forward or reverse?
   c) At 500°C what is K_c for the reaction: $3\,N_{2\,(g)} + 9\,H_{2\,(g)} \rightleftharpoons 6\,NH_{3\,(g)}$
   d) At 500°C what is K_c for the reaction: $\frac{2}{3}\,NH_{3\,(g)} \rightleftharpoons \frac{1}{3}\,N_{2\,(g)} + H_{2\,(g)}$
   e) At 500°C what is K_P?

4. Given that at 30°C, $K_c = 0.130$ for the following reaction: $3\,A_{(g)} + 2\,B_{(s)} \rightleftharpoons 3\,B_{(l)}$
   a) Write the equilibrium constant expression in terms of K_c.
   b) Calculate the equilibrium concentration of A at 30°C.
   c) Calculate K_P at 30°C.
   d) Write the equilibrium constant expression in terms of K_P.
   e) Calculate the equilibrium partial pressure of A (in atm) at 30°C.

5. At 727°C, $K_c = 1.58 \times 10^2$ for the following reaction: $2\,NO_{2\,(g)} \rightleftharpoons 2\,NO_{(g)} + O_{2\,(g)}$. If the equilibrium partial pressures of NO and O_2 are 2.84 atm and 0.600 atm, respectively at 727°C, what is the equilibrium partial pressure of NO_2?

6. What is the value for both K_P & K_c (at 25°C) for the following physical change: $H_2O_{(l)} \rightleftharpoons H_2O_{(g)}$ given that at 25°C the partial pressure of water is 23.8 torr?

7. What is the vapor pressure (in atm) of H_2O in the reaction $CdCl_2{\cdot}H_2O_{(s)} \rightleftharpoons CdCl_{2\,(s)} + H_2O_{(g)}$ given that $K_P = 2.27 \times 10^{-3}$?

Equilibrium Constant (K_c and K_P) and Thermodynamics

8. Given that at 1024°C, $K_c = 1.60 \times 10^5$ for the following reaction: $H_{2\,(g)} + Br_{2\,(g)} \rightleftharpoons 2\,HBr_{(g)}$
   a) What is the Gibbs Free Energy Change (in kJ) at 1024°C for this reaction? [NOTE: Since this is a gas phase reaction K_P (which was obtained in 2e) must be used in the equation to find $\Delta G°$.]
   b) Given that $\Delta H° = -72.4$ kJ, what is K_c at 1222°C?

9. Given that $\Delta H° = -92.6$ kJ for the following reaction: $N_2\,(g) + 3\,H_2\,(g) \rightleftharpoons 2\,NH_3\,(g)$ and that at 500°C, $K_c = 0.286$

   a) What is the Gibbs Free Energy Change (in kJ) at 500°C? [NOTE: Since this is a gas phase reaction K_P (which was obtained in problem 3e) must be used in the equation to find $\Delta G°$.]

   b) What is K_P at 727°C?

   c) What is $\Delta G°$ (in kJ) at 727°C?

   d) What is K_c at 727°C?

10. Given that $K_c = 2.53 \times 10^{-32}$ at 50°C and that $K_c = 4.57 \times 10^{-31}$ at 25°C, what is $\Delta H°$ (in kJ) for the following reaction: $N_2\,(g) + O_2\,(g) \rightleftharpoons 2\,NO\,(g)$

11. The molar enthalpy of vaporization for the compound butane at its normal boiling point of -0.50°C is 21.93 kJ. What is the vapor pressure of butane (in atm) at 25°C?

Factors that Affect Equilibria and the Le Chatelier Principle

12. Consider the following reaction: $N_2\,(g) + 3\,H_2\,(g) \rightleftharpoons 2\,NH_3\,(g)$ $\Delta H° = -92.6$ kJ
    In which direction (if any) would the equilibrium be shifted by each of the following applied stresses?

    a) Addition of a catalyst.
    b) Addition of $Ne\,(g)$, while maintaining a constant volume.
    c) Removal of NH_3.
    d) Addition of H_2.
    e) Increasing the temperature.
    f) Increasing the volume of the reaction vessel.
    g) Decreasing the total pressure.
    h) Removal of N_2.

13. Consider the following reaction: $2\,HBr\,(g) \rightleftharpoons H_2\,(g) + Br_2\,(g)$ $\Delta H° = 124$ kJ
    In which direction (if any) would the equilibrium be shifted by each of the following applied stresses?

    a) Increasing the temperature.
    b) Addition of Br_2.
    c) Addition of $Ar\,(g)$, while maintaining a constant volume.
    d) Increasing the volume of the reaction vessel.

Finding Equilibrium Concentrations and Equilibrium Constants

14. At 1024°C, $K_c = 1.60 \times 10^5$ for the following reaction: $H_2\,(g) + Br_2\,(g) \rightleftharpoons 2\,HBr\,(g)$. If $[H_2] = 0.30$ M, $[Br_2] = 0.50$ M, and $[HBr] = 0.60$ M, is the reaction at equilibrium? If not, in what direction will the reaction proceed to achieve equilibrium?

15. At 300°C, $K_c = 2.3 \times 10^{-4}$ for the following reaction: $N_2\,(g) + 3\,H_2\,(g) \rightleftharpoons 2\,NH_3\,(g)$. If $[N_2] = 3.75$ M, $[H_2] = 0.799$ M, and $[NH_3] = 2.75$ M, is the reaction at equilibrium? If not, in what direction will the reaction proceed to achieve equilibrium?

16. At 1024°C, $K_P = 1.6 \times 10^5$ for the following reaction: $H_2\,(g) + Br_2\,(g) \rightleftharpoons 2\,HBr\,(g)$
    If the partial pressure for H_2, Br_2, and HBr is 0.100 atm, 0.100 atm, 0.900 atm, respectively, then:

    a) In what direction will the reaction proceed to achieve equilibrium?
    b) What is the equilibrium partial pressure (in atm) of H_2, Br_2, and HBr expressed in terms of x (i.e., x = change in partial pressure)?
    c) What is the equilibrium partial pressure (in atm) of H_2, Br_2, and HBr?

17. At 1000°C, $K_P = 0.58$ for the following reaction: $CO_{(g)} + H_2O_{(g)} \rightleftharpoons CO_{2\,(g)} + H_{2\,(g)}$. If 1.00 mol/L of each reactant and 2.00 mol/L of each product is placed in the reaction vessel:
    a) In what direction will the reaction proceed to achieve equilibrium?
    b) What is the equilibrium concentration (in M) of CO, H_2O, CO_2, and H_2 expressed in terms of x (i.e., x = the change in concentration)?
    c) What is the equilibrium concentration (in M) of CO, H_2O, CO_2, and H_2?

18. At 300°C, $K_c = 2.3 \times 10^{-4}$ for the following reaction: $N_{2\,(g)} + C_2H_{2\,(g)} \rightleftharpoons 2\ HCN_{(g)}$. If $[N_2]_i = 2.50$ M and $[C_2H_2]_i = 2.50$ M:
    a) What is the equilibrium concentration (in M) of N_2, C_2H_2, and HCN expressed in terms of x (i.e., x = the change in concentration)?
    b) What is the equilibrium concentration (in M) of N_2, C_2H_2, and HCN?

19. At 1000°C, $K_c = 0.58$ for the following reaction: $CO_{(g)} + H_2O_{(g)} \rightleftharpoons CO_{2\,(g)} + H_{2\,(g)}$. If 1.00 mol of CO are reacted with 1.00 mol of H_2O in a 50.0-L vessel:
    a) What is the equilibrium concentration (in M) of CO, H_2O, CO_2, and H_2 expressed in terms of x (i.e., x = the change in concentration)?
    b) What is the equilibrium concentration (in M) of CO, H_2O, CO_2, and H_2?

20. At 22°C, $K_c = 4.66 \times 10^{-3}$ for the following reaction: $N_2O_{4\,(g)} \rightleftharpoons 2\ NO_{2\,(g)}$. If 0.800 mol of N_2O_4 were placed in a 1.0-L vessel:
    a) What is the equilibrium concentration (in M) of N_2O_4 and NO_2 expressed in terms of x (i.e., x = the change in concentration)?
    b) What is the equilibrium concentration (in M) of N_2O_4 and NO_2?

21. At 100°C, $K_c = 4.57 \times 10^9$ for the following reaction: $CO_{(g)} + Cl_{2\,(g)} \rightleftharpoons COCl_{2\,(g)}$. If 1.00 mol of $COCl_2$ was placed in a 2.0-L vessel:
    a) What is the equilibrium concentration (in M) of CO, Cl_2, and $COCl_2$ expressed in terms of x (i.e., x = the change in concentration?
    b) What is the equilibrium concentration (in M) of CO, Cl_2, and $COCl_2$?

22. At a particular temperature, $K_c = 0.222$ for the following reaction: $A_{(g)} + B_{(s)} \rightleftharpoons 2\ C_{(g)}$. If 3.00 mol of A and B and 2.00 mol of C are mixed in a 2.00-L reaction vessel:
    a) Is the system at equilibrium. If not, in what direction will the reaction proceed to achieve equilibrium?
    b) What is the equilibrium concentration (in M) of A, B and C expressed in terms of x (i.e., x = the change in concentration).
    c) What is the equilibrium concentration (in M) of A , B and C?

23. At a particular temperature, $K_c = 5.76 \times 10^{-3}$ for the following reaction: $N_2O_{4\,(g)} \rightleftharpoons 2\ NO_{2\,(g)}$. If 0.050 mol of N_2O_4 was placed in a 2.0-L reaction vessel:
    a) What is the equilibrium concentration (in M) of N_2O_4 and NO_2 expressed in terms of x (i.e., x = the change in concentration?
    b) What is the equilibrium concentration (in M) of N_2O_4 and NO_2?

24. Calculate K_c for the following reaction: $2\ A_{(g)} + 2\ B_{(g)} \rightleftharpoons D_{(s)} + 5\ E_{(g)}$ given that when 0.158 mol of A and 0.238 mol of B were placed in a 6.00-L container and then allowed to come to equilibrium the concentration of A was found to be 0.0106 M.

25. Calculate K_c for the following reaction: $A_{(g)} + 2\ B_{(g)} \rightleftharpoons C_{(g)}$ given that when 1.00 mol of A and 1.80 mol of B were placed in a 5.00-L container and then allowed to come to equilibrium 1.00 mol of B was found to be present.

26. Calculate K_c for the following reaction: $2\ NOCl_{(g)} \rightleftharpoons 2\ NO_{(g)} + Cl_{2\,(g)}$ given that when 1.25 mol of NOCl were placed in a 2.50-L reaction vessel, and then the reaction was allowed to proceed to equilibrium, 1.10 mol of NOCl were found to be present.

MULTIPLE CHOICE PRACTICE EXAM FOR MODULE 5

Consider the following gas phase reaction and information when answering questions 1 - 4

$$3\ A_{(g)} + 2\ B_{(g)} \rightleftharpoons A_3B_{2\,(g)} \qquad K_c = 6.60\ (@\ 77°C)\ \text{and}\ \Delta H = -47.0\ kJ$$

1. What is the equilibrium concentration (**in M**) of B given that at equilibrium 0.450 mol of A and 0.970 mol of A_3B_2 were present in a 10.0-L reaction vessel at 77°C?

   1) 1.50 2) 12.7 3) 1.22 4) 150. 5) 6.68×10^{-3}

2. What is K_c at 77°C for the following reaction?

   $$4\ A_3B_{2\,(g)} \rightleftharpoons 12\ A_{(g)} + 8\ B_{(g)}$$

   1) 1.90×10^{3} 2) 2.64×10^{1} 3) 5.27×10^{-4} 4) 3.79×10^{-2} 5) 1.65

3. What is K_P at 77°C (for the original reaction given)?

   1) 1.52×10^{-6} 2) 4.13×10^{-3} 3) 2.90×10^{-17} 4) 7.71×10^{-10} 5) 9.68×10^{-6}

4. What is $\Delta G°$ (**in kJ**) at 77°C (for the original reaction given)?

   1) -2.4 2) -0.29 3) -1.3 4) 33.6 5) -5.5

5. Calculate K_P for the following reaction at 25.0°C: $2\ CO_{2\,(g)} \rightleftharpoons 2\ CO_{(g)} + O_{2\,(g)}$

Compound	ΔG_f^o (kJ/mol)
CO_2 (g)	-394.4
CO (g)	-137.3

   1) 1.4×10^{90} 2) 1.2×10^{45} 3) 6.9×10^{-91} 4) 8.6×10^{-46} 5) e^{-2474}

6. The molar enthalpy of vaporization for C_4H_{10} at its normal boiling point of -0.50°C is 21.93 kJ. What would K_p for the following physical change -- $C_4H_{10\,(l)} \rightleftharpoons C_4H_{10\,(g)}$ -- be at 25°C?

   1) 2.29 2) 1.0 3) 31.8 4) 21.93 5) 21.43

7. Consider the following reaction run at a particular temperature: $2\ A_{(g)} \rightleftharpoons A_{2\,(l)}$

   If the equilibrium partial pressure of A is 250 torr, then what is K_P for the reaction?

   1) 9.2 2) 4.0×10^{-3} 3) 6.3×10^{4} 4) 1.6×10^{-5} 5) 3.0

8. Given that ΔH for the following reaction at equilibrium is -92.6 kJ,

   $$A_{(g)} + B_{(s)} \rightleftharpoons 2\ L_{(g)} + D_{(l)}$$

   which of the following conditions will shift the equilibrium to produce more B?

   a) increase the temperature b) increase [A] c) decrease the pressure
   d) decrease [D] e) add some L f) add some $He_{(g)}$ at constant volume

   1) only b, c, d, & g 2) only b, e & f 3) only c and e
   4) only a & e 5) none of the choices

9. Consider the following reaction: $A_{(g)} + B_{(s)} \rightleftharpoons 2\ D_{(g)}$

   When 3.00 mol of A and 2.00 mol of B are placed in a 2.50-L reaction vessel and allowed to come to equilibrium, 2.65 mol of D was found to be present. Given this information, what is K_c?

   1) 2.34 2) 1.58 3) 1.67 4) 8.03 5) 6.95

10. Consider the following reaction: $A_{(g)} \rightleftharpoons 2\,B_{(g)}$

For which of the following reaction conditions will the reaction proceed from left → right.

	[A], M	[B], M	K_c	T, °C
1)	1	2	6×10^{-2}	25
2)	0.4	0.6	0.9	35
3)	0.9	0.6	1.0	40

4) Two of the above reaction conditions cause the reaction to proceed from left → right.
5) None of the above reaction conditions cause the reaction to proceed from left → right.

Consider the following gas phase reaction and information when answering questions 11 - 12

$$COCl_{2\,(g)} \rightleftharpoons CO_{(g)} + Cl_{2\,(g)} \qquad K_P\ @\ 25°C = 6.70 \times 10^{-3}$$

When a sample of $COCl_2$ is placed in a closed 15.0-L vessel at 25°C it exerts a pressure of 4.65 atm as it starts to decompose.

11. What will the partial pressure (**in atm**) of CO at 25°C be at equilibrium?
1) 0.566 2) 0.177 3) 0.206 4) 1.16 5) 2.14

12. What will the total pressure (**in atm**) at 25°C be at equilibrium?
1) 4.83 2) 1.68 3) 3.80 4) 5.03 5) 4.65

13. For the following reaction: $A_{(g)} + B_{(g)} \rightleftharpoons D_{(g)} + E_{(g)}$

K_c = 144 at 200°C. If 0.400 mol of both A and B are placed in a 2.00-L vessel at 200°C, then what will the concentration (**in M**) of D be at equilibrium?

1) 1.13 2) 0.185 3) 0.200 4) 1.64 5) 0.015

14. Given that 2.00 mol per L of the boldfaced and underlined specie (in the choices below) were placed in a container and allowed to come to equilibrium, for which of the following gas phase reactions would x (i.e., the amount that the concentration changes by) be expected to be small (i.e., acceptable to neglect it)?

1) 2 **<u>A</u>** $\rightleftharpoons$ P $K = 6.5 \times 10^{2}$
2) 2 M $\rightleftharpoons$ **<u>G</u>** $K = 9.6 \times 10^{-4}$
3) **<u>P</u>** $\rightleftharpoons$ A + J   K = 0.099
4) Two of the above.
5) None of the above.

15. For the following reaction: $2\,A_{(g)} \rightleftharpoons 2\,D_{(g)} + E_{(g)}$ $K_c = 5.7 \times 10^{-6}$ at 37°C

If 0.400 mol of A were placed in a 4.00-L vessel at 37°C, then what will the molarity of D be at equilibrium?

1) 0.100 2) 4.8×10^{-3} 3) 2.4×10^{-3} 4) 5.7×10^{-7} 5) 2.0×10^{-2}

16. For the following reaction: $2\,A_{(g)} \rightleftharpoons D_{(g)} + E_{(g)}$ K_c = 0.51 at 37°C

If 0.400 mol of A, D and E were placed in a 4.00-L vessel at 37°C, then what will the [A] (in M) be at equilibrium?

1) 0.0118 2) 0.111 3) 0.124 4) 0.436 5) 0.366

17. Which of the following statements is (are) correct?
    1) The equilibrium constant is dependent on initial reactant concentrations.
    2) An equilibrium constant greater than one means that reactant formation is favored.
    3) If the equilibrium constant (K) is less than the reaction quotient (Q), then the reverse reaction predominates until equilibrium is established.
    4) Two of the above statements are correct.
    5) None of the above statements are correct.

18. Which of the following equilibrium constants would favor the forward reaction (i.e., the formation of products) the most?

    1) 0.0791 2) 0.000941 3) 421 4) 1.00 5) 4.49

19. Which of the following statement(s) is/are **false** for the following fictitious <u>one-step</u> (in both directions) reversible reaction

$$A_{(g)} \underset{k_r}{\overset{k_f}{\rightleftharpoons}} B_{(g)} + 2\,C_{(g)}$$

given the graph to your right that shows how the concentration of each specie (at 25°C) is changing with time?

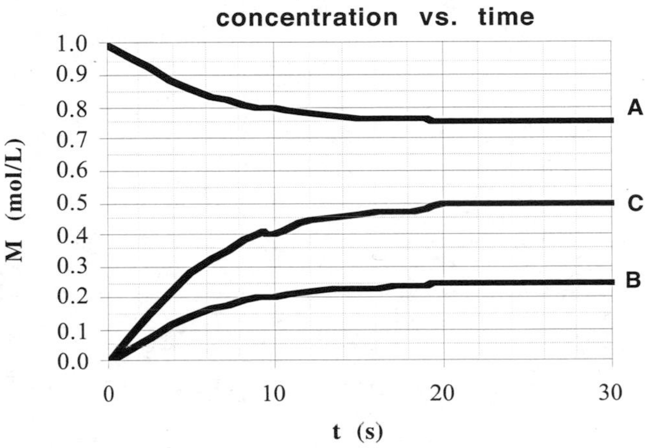

1) The reverse reaction is more favored than the forward reaction.
2) The equilibrium constant (K_c) for the forward reaction is equal to 0.17.
3) K_c for the reverse reaction is equal to 12.
4) k_f/k_r is equal to 0.083.
5) More than one of the above statements is false.

MODULE 5 - ANSWERS

1. a) $K_c = \frac{[C]\,[D]^2}{[A]^2\,[B]}$ b) $K_c = \frac{[0.8]\,[1.6]^2}{[0.4]^2\,[0.2]} = 64$ Equilibrium concentrations were obtained from graph.

2. a) $\frac{[HBr]^2}{[H_2]\,[Br_2]} = 1.60 \times 10^5$ b) 22.6 M c) $\frac{[HBr]^{2/3}}{[H_2]^{1/3}\,[Br_2]^{1/3}} = 5.43 \times 10^1$ d) forward e) 1.60×10^5

3. a) 3.22 M b) reverse c) 2.34×10^{-2} d) 1.52 e) 7.10×10^{-5}

4. a) $\frac{1}{[A]^3} = 0.130$ b) 1.97 M c) 8.44×10^{-6} d) $\frac{1}{(P_A)^3} = 8.44 \times 10^{-6}$ e) 49.1 atm

5. 1.93×10^{-2}

6. $K_P = 3.13 \times 10^{-2}$ and $K_c = 1.28 \times 10^{-3}$

7. 2.27×10^{-3}

8. a) -129 kJ b) 6.57×10^4

9. a) 61 kJ b) 2.69×10^{-6} c) 107 kJ d) 1.81×10^{-2}

10. -92.6 kJ

11. 2.29 atm

12. a) no change b) no change c) right d) right e) left
 f) left g) left h) left

13. a) right b) left c) no change d) no change ($\Delta n = 0$)

14. Since Q_c (2.4) $\neq$ K_c (1.60×10^5) the reaction is not at equilibrium. Since $Q_c < K_c$ the reaction will proceed to the right (i.e., forward reaction, to produce more product, will predominate until equilibrium is established).

15. Since Q_c (3.95) $\neq$ K_c (2.3×10^{-4}) the reaction is not at equilibrium. Since $Q_c > K_c$ the reaction will proceed to the left (i.e., reverse reaction, to produce more reactants, will predominate until equilibrium is established).

16. a) Since Q_P (81) < K_P (1.6×10^5) the reaction will proceed to the right (i.e., forward reaction, to produce more products, will predominate until equilibrium is established).
 b) P (H_2) = 0.100 - x, P (Br_2) = 0.100 - x, P (HBr) = 0.900 + 2x
 c) P (H_2) = 0.0027 atm, P (Br_2) = 0.0027 atm, P (HBr) = 1.095 atm (x by "perfect squares" $\rightarrow$ 0.0973M)

17. a) Kp was given for this reaction; however, concentrations (in M) are given; thus, Kp needs to be converted into Kc. Fortunately, Kp = Kc. Since Q_C (4) > K_C (0.58) the reaction will proceed to the left (i.e., reverse reaction, to produce more reactants, will predominate until equilibrium is established).
 b) [CO] = 1.00 + x, [H_2O] = 1.00 + x, [CO_2] = 2.00 - x, [H_2] = 2.00 - x
 c) [CO] = 1.70 M, [H_2O] = 1.70 M [CO_2] = 1.30 M, [H_2] = 1.30 M (x by "perfect squares" $\rightarrow$ 0.70 M)

18. a) [N_2] = 2.5 - x, [C_2H_2] = 2.5 - x, [HCN] = 2x
 b) [N_2] = 2.48 M, [C_2H_2] = 2.48 M, [HCN] = 0.0376 (x by "perfect squares" $\rightarrow$ 0.0188 M)

19. a) [CO] = 0.0200 - x, [H_2O] = 0.0200 - x, [CO_2] = x, [H_2] = x
 b) [CO] = 0.0114 M, [H_2O] = 0.0114 M, [CO_2] = 0.0086 M, [H_2] = 0.0086 M (x by "perfect squares" $\rightarrow$ 0.0086 M)

20. a) [N_2O_4] = 0.800 - x, [NO_2] = 2x
 b) [N_2O_4] = 0.770 M, [NO_2] = 0.0610 M (x by assuming it is "small" $\rightarrow$ 0.0305 M)

21. a) [CO] = x, [Cl_2] = x, [$COCl_2$] = 0.50 - x
 b) [CO] = 1.05×10^{-5} M, [Cl_2] = 1.05×10^{-5} M, [$COCl_2$] = 0.50 (x by assuming it is "small" $\rightarrow$ 1.05×10^{-5} M)

22. a) Since Q (0.667) $\neq$ K_c (0.222) the reaction is not at equilibrium. Since $Q_c > K_c$ the reaction will proceed to the left (i.e., reverse reaction, to form more reactants, will predominate until equilibrium is established).

    b) $[A]_{equil} = 1.50 + x$, $[C]_{equil} = 1.00 - 2x$, $[B]_{equil} = ?$ (B is a solid. While the volume of gases is the same as that of the container that they are in, the same can't be said for liquids and solids. Since we don't know the volume that B occupies nor do we know its density, we are not able to say what its concentration at equilibrium is.]

    c) $[A]_{equil} = 1.69$, $[C]_{equil} = 0.61$, $[B]_{equil} = ?$ (x by using quadratic $\rightarrow$ 0.193)

23. a) $[N_2O_4] = 0.025 - x$, $[NO_2] = 2x$

    b) $[N_2O_4] = 0.020$ M, $[NO_2] = 0.0106$ M (x by using quadratic $\rightarrow$ 0.0053 M)

24. 1.45

25. 16.7

26. 5.6×10^{-4}

ANSWERS TO MULTIPLE CHOICE PRACTICE EXAM

1	2	3	4	5	6	7	8	9	10	11	12	13	14	15	16	17	18	19
2	3	5	4	3	1	1	4	3	3	2	1	2	5	2	3	3	3	2

MODULE 6. *Acid-Base Equilibria*

I. Acid-Base Strength

Strong acids and bases are strong electrolytes that totally ionize in water. There are comparatively very few strong acids and bases. If an acid or base is not strong (see table below), then it is classified as weak and thus will not totally ionize in water. It is the equilibria of weak acids and bases that is our main focus in this module.

HCl, HBr, HI $HClO_4$, $HClO_3$ HNO_3, H_2SO_4 (only first H^+)	Strong acids and strong electrolytes that totally ionize in water.

IA hydroxides IIA hydroxides except $Be(OH)_2$ and $Mg(OH)_2$	Strong bases and strong electrolytes that totally ionize in water.

II. Acid-Base Theories

You should recall from first semester general chemistry the following three acid-base theories. In this module we are going to work with the Arrhenius and Brønsted-Lowry concept of acids and bases.

Theory	Acid	Base
Arrhenius	Substance that produces H^+ (or H_3O^+) when placed in water	Substance that produces OH^- when placed in water
Brønsted-Lowry	H^+ (proton) donor	H^+ (proton) acceptor
Lewis	e^- pair acceptor	e^- pair donor

The following are examples of acid-base reactions according to Arrhenius' theory.

$$\underset{\text{acid}}{HCl} \xrightarrow{H_2O} \underset{\text{produces } H^+}{H^{\oplus}} + Cl^{\ominus}$$

$$\underset{\text{base}}{NaOH} \xrightarrow{H_2O} Na^{\oplus} + \underset{\text{produces } OH^-}{OH^{\ominus}}$$

Our focus in this chapter is to deal with substances that are considered as Bronsted-Lowry acids and bases in an aqueous environment. In an aqueous solution, water can act as either a Brønsted-Lowry acid or base.

Water will act as a Brønsted-Lowry base with substances that by convention have an H written in front of their formula. The following examples show how water acts as a base. Notice in each case how either a single arrow (used for strong acids that ionize completely) or double arrow (used for weak acids that partially ionize) is used.

$$\underset{\text{acid}}{HCl} + \underset{\text{base}}{H_2O} \longrightarrow \underset{\text{conjugate acid}}{H_3O^{\oplus}} + \underset{\text{conjugate base}}{Cl^{\ominus}}$$

$$\underset{\text{acid}}{HNO_2} + \underset{\text{base}}{H_2O} \rightleftharpoons \underset{\text{conjugate acid}}{H_3O^{\oplus}} + \underset{\text{conjugate base}}{NO_2^{\ominus}}$$

Water acts as a Brønsted-Lowry acid in the presence of ammonia (NH_3) and its derivatives. Derivatives of ammonia (aka, nitrogenous bases) are organic compounds known as amines. Amines are substances in which one, two or all three H's in ammonia have been replaced with a hydrocarbon (C_xH_y).

$$\underset{\text{base ammonia}}{\ddot{N}H_3} + \underset{\text{acid}}{H_2O} \rightleftharpoons \underset{\text{conjugate acid}}{NH_4^{\oplus}} + \underset{\text{conjugate base}}{OH^{\ominus}}$$

$$\underset{\text{base, a derivative of ammonia called an amine}}{CH_3\ddot{N}H_2} + \underset{\text{acid}}{H_2O} \rightleftharpoons \underset{\text{conjugate acid}}{CH_3NH_3^{\oplus}} + \underset{\text{conjugate base}}{OH^{\ominus}}$$

The following is an example of an acid-base reaction according to Lewis's theory.

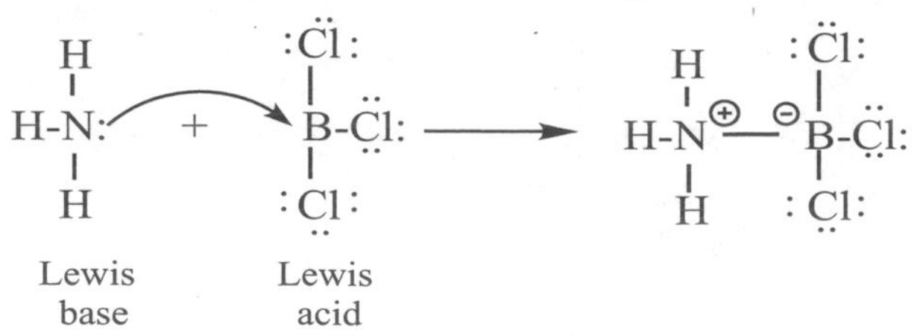

III. **Auto Ionization and Ion-Product of Water**

Water can react with itself (i.e., undergo self ionization or autoionization) to produce H_3O^+ (i.e., H^+) and OH^-.

$$H_2O_{(l)} + H_2O_{(l)} \rightleftharpoons H_3O^+_{(aq)} + OH^-_{(aq)}$$

Often, this reaction is simplified as follows, where, $\mathbf{H_3O^+ = H^+}$:

$$H_2O_{(l)} \rightleftharpoons H^+_{(aq)} + OH^-_{(aq)}$$

Remembering that water is a "weak" electrolyte, it would then stand to reason that it would hardly undergo ionization. Since water is a pure liquid, its initial concentration of ~56 M (i.e., 1.0 g/mL = 56 mol/L) is not considered in the equilibrium expression. The equilibrium expression for water is called the **ion-product for water ($\mathbf{K_w}$)** and is written as follows:

$$K_w = [H^+][OH^-]$$

	$H_2O_{(l)}$	$\rightleftharpoons$	$H^+_{(aq)}$	+	$OH^-_{(aq)}$
$[\ ]_i$:	56		0		0
$[\ ]_{change}$:	-x		+x		+x
$[\ ]_{equil}$:	56 - x		x		x

At 25°C, $K_w = 1.0 \times 10^{-14}$ (at other temperatures, $K_w \neq 1.0 \times 10^{-14}$). Assuming a temperature of 25°C, substitution into the ion-product gives:

$$1.0 \times 10^{-14} = (x)(x)$$

$$x = 1.0 \times 10^{-7} = [H^+] = [OH^-]$$

The following table gives the K_w for water at various temperatures.

	10°C	20°C	30°C	50°C	100°C
K_w	2.93×10^{-15}	6.81×10^{-15}	1.47×10^{-14}	5.48×10^{-14}	5.13×10^{-13}

Unless otherwise stated, assume that the temperature is 25°C; therefore, when water autoionizes, $[H^+]$ and $[OH^-]$ equals 1.0×10^{-7} M. *Since, the ion-product is an equilibrium expression, its value is the same in pure water or in an acid or base aqueous solution (as long as the temperature remains constant).* Thus, by looking at $[H^+]$ and $[OH^-]$ we can determine if a susbstance is acidic, basic, or neutral.

	acid	base	neutral
$[H^+]$	$> 1 \times 10^{-7}$ M	$< 1 \times 10^{-7}$ M	$= 1 \times 10^{-7}$ M
$[OH^-]$	$< 1 \times 10^{-7}$ M	$> 1 \times 10^{-7}$ M	$= 1 \times 10^{-7}$ M

IV. pH and pOH

Normally, $[H^+]$ and $[OH^-]$ are very small numbers; in order to remedy this, we use the pH scale to measure the acidity or basicity/alkalinity of a substance. Normally, the pH scale is written from 0 - 14. The following gives the pH values for some common substances at 25°C.

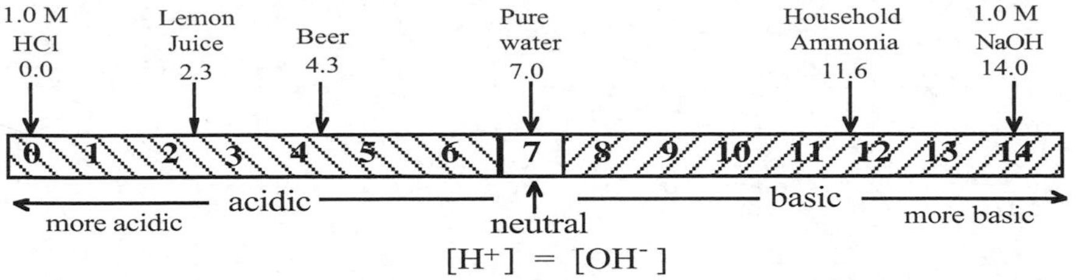

It is important to note that the pH scale is logarithmic (see definition below) and as such, an increase in pH by 2 units means that the acidity is decreasing by 2 orders of magnitude (i.e., there is a 10^2 or a 100-fold decrease in acidity).

pH and pOH are defined as follows:

$$pH = -\log [H^+] \quad \leftarrow \quad \text{negative log of hydrogen ion concentration}$$

$$pOH = -\log [OH^-] \quad \leftarrow \quad \text{negative log of hydroxide ion concentration}$$

$$pH + pOH = 14.00 \quad (@\ 25°C)$$

The following table gives a comparison of pH, pOH, $[H^+]$ and $[OH^-]$ values.

$-\log [H^+]$ ↓ pH	$-\log [OH^-]$ ↓ pOH	10^{-pH} ↓ $[H^+]$	10^{-pOH} ↓ $[OH^-]$	
0	14	10^0	10^{-14}	acidic
1	13	10^{-1}	10^{-13}	
2	12	10^{-2}	10^{-12}	
3	11	10^{-3}	10^{-11}	
4	10	10^{-4}	10^{-10}	
5	9	10^{-5}	10^{-9}	
6	8	10^{-6}	10^{-8}	
7	7	10^{-7}	10^{-7}	neutral
8	6	10^{-8}	10^{-6}	basic
9	5	10^{-9}	10^{-5}	
10	4	10^{-10}	10^{-4}	
11	3	10^{-11}	10^{-3}	
12	2	10^{-12}	10^{-2}	
13	1	10^{-13}	10^{-1}	
14	0	10^{-14}	10^0	

└ pH + pOH = 14 ┘

<u>Example Problems</u>:

1. If $[H^+]$ of an aqueous solution is 3.7×10^{-4} M, then:

   a) Is the substance acidic, basic, or neutral?

   The substance is acidic because $[H^+] > 1 \times 10^{-7}$ M.

b) Calculate $[OH^-]$.

Remember that we are going to assume that the temperature is 25°C. Using the ion-product of water we can get $[OH^-]$.

$$K_w = [H^+]\,[OH^-]$$

$$1.0 \times 10^{-14} = (3.7 \times 10^{-4})\,[OH^-]$$

$$[OH^-] = \frac{1.0 \times 10^{-14}}{3.7 \times 10^{-4}} = 2.7 \times 10^{-11}\text{ M}$$

c) What is the pH of the solution?

$$pH = -\log [H^+] = -\log (3.7 \times 10^{-4}) = 3.43$$

d) What is the pOH of the solution?

$$pOH = -\log [OH^-] = -\log (2.7 \times 10^{-11}) = 10.57$$

OR

$$pH + pOH = 14.00$$
$$3.43 + pOH = 14.00$$
$$pOH = 14.00 - 3.43 = 10.57$$

V. pH, pOH, $[H^+]$ and $[OH^-]$ Calculation of Strong Acids and Bases

Strong acids and bases are strong electrolytes that totally ionize in water. We can use the ion-product of water to find $[H^+]$ & $[OH^-]$ present in an acid or base. Once we have the $[H^+]$ or $[OH^-]$, we can then find the pH and pOH.

A. Strong Acids

As long as the concentration of a strong acid is greater than ~ 2×10^{-7} M, the H^+ produced by the autoionization of water can be ignored. ***Provided that the concentration of the acid is sufficiently large, for a strong <u>monoprotic</u> acid (HX), [HX] = [H+].*** In very dilute solutions, the contribution of H^+ from the autoionization of water can <u>not</u> be ignored and must be included in the calculations. We will not do these kinds of calculations, however, suffice it to say, in very dilute acid solutions (i.e., those whose concentration is less than ~2×10^{-7} M) the pH is ~6.9.

<u>Example Problems</u>:

1. Calculate the pH of a 0.010 M HCl solution.

Since HCl is a strong acid and since 1 mol of HCl produces 1 mol H^+, $[H^+] = [HCl]$

	$HCl_{(aq)}$	→	$H^+_{(aq)}$	+	$Cl^-_{(aq)}$
$[\,]_i$:	0.0100		0		0
$[\,]_{change}$:	-0.0100		+0.0100		+0.0100
$[\,]_{end}$:	0		0.0100		0.0100

$$pH = -\log [H^+] = -\log (0.0100) = 2.00$$

2. What is the molarity of an HBr solution whose pH is 2.15?

Since HBr is a strong acid and since 1 mol of HBr produces 1 mol H^+, $[H^+] = [HBr]$

$$pH = -\log [H^+] \rightarrow [H^+] = 10^{-pH}$$

$$[H^+] = 10^{-2.15} = 7.08 \times 10^{-3}\text{ M} \rightarrow [HBr]$$

3. What is $[OH^-]$ in an HI solution whose pH is -1.00?

   Since HI is a strong acid and since 1 mol of HI produces 1 mol H^+, $[H^+] = [HI]$

   $pH = -\log [H^+] \quad \rightarrow \quad [H^+] = 10^{-pH} = 10^{-(-1.00)} = 10.0\ M$

   Using the ion product of water we can then find $[OH^-]$.

   $K_w = [H^+]\ [OH^-]$

   $1.0 \times 10^{-14} = (10.0)\ [OH^-] \quad \rightarrow \quad [OH^-] = \dfrac{1.0 \times 10^{-14}}{10.0} = 1.0 \times 10^{-15}\ M$

4. What is the pH of a 1.60×10^{-10} M HNO_3 solution?

   In this particular case, we can't say: $[H^+] = 1.60 \times 10^{-10}$ and thus have pH = 9.80 [pH = - log (1.60×10^{-10})]. The pH of an acidic solution must be less than 7. What happened in this particular case is that the solution was very dilute. As mentioned previously, in a *very dilute* solution of a strong acid (i.e., a solution in which $[H^+]$ is less than ~ 2×10^{-7} M), the pH ~ 6.9.

B. **Strong Bases**

As long as the concentration of a strong base is greater than ~ 2×10^{-7} M, the OH^- produced by the autoionization of water can be ignored. ***Provided that the concentration of the base is sufficiently large, for a strong base containing one "OH" (MOH), [MOH] = [OH⁻].*** In very dilute solutions, the contribution of OH^- from the autoionization of water can not be ignored and must be included in the calculations. We will not do these kinds of calculations, however, suffice it to say, in very dilute base solutions (i.e., those whose concentration is less than ~2×10^{-7} M) the pH is ~7.1.

Example Problems:

1. Calculate the pH of a 10.0 M KOH solution.

   Since KOH is a strong base with one "OH", $[OH^-] = [KOH]$ The easiest thing to do is to first find the pOH and then convert it to pH.

   $pOH = -\log [OH^-] = -\log (10.0) = -1.00$

   $pH + pOH = 14.00 \rightarrow pH + (-1.00) = 14.00 \rightarrow pH = 14.00 + 1.00 = 15.00$

2. What is the molarity of an NaOH solution whose pH is 7.95?

   Since NaOH is a strong base with one "OH", $[OH^-] = [NaOH]$. From the pH we can find the pOH, then from the pOH we can find $[OH^-]$ which is equal to [NaOH].

   $pH + pOH = 14.00$

   $7.95 + pOH = 14.00 \rightarrow pOH = 14.00 - 7.95 = 6.05$

   $pOH = -\log [OH^-] \rightarrow [OH^-] = 10^{-pOH}$

   $[OH^-] = 10^{-6.05} = 8.91 \times 10^{-7}\ M \rightarrow [NaOH]$

3. Answer the following questions about a 2.50×10^{-3} M $Ba(OH)_2$ solution?

   a) What is the $[OH^-]$?

   Since $Ba(OH)_2$ is a strong base, it will totally ionize in water. The difference in this case is, that for every 1 mol of $Ba(OH)_2$ that ionizes, 2 mol of OH^- will be produced. Thus, $[OH^-] = 2\ [Ba(OH)_2]$.

   $[OH^-] = 2\ (2.50 \times 10^{-3})\ M = 5.00 \times 10^{-3}\ M$

b) What is the pOH of the solution?

$pOH = - \log [OH^-] \rightarrow pOH = - \log (5.00 \times 10^{-3}) = 2.30$

c) What is the pH of the solution?

$pH + pOH = 14.00 \rightarrow pH + 2.30 = 14.00 \rightarrow pH = 14.00 - 2.30 = 11.70$

d) What is the $[H^+]$?

$pH = - \log [H^+]$

$11.70 = - \log [H^+]$

$[H^+] = 10^{-11.70} = 2.00 \times 10^{-12}$ M

OR

$K_w = [H^+][OH^-]$

$1.0 \times 10^{-14} = [H^+](5.00 \times 10^{-3})$

$$[H^+] = \frac{1.0 \times 10^{-14}}{5.00 \times 10^{-3}} = 2.00 \times 10^{-12} \text{ M}$$

VI. pH, pOH, $[H^+]$ & $[OH^-]$ Calculation of Weak Monoprotic Acids and Monobasic Bases

Weak acids and bases are weak electrolytes that do not totally ionize in water. There are very few strong acids and bases. A weak acid is one that is not one of the strong acids listed in the first page of this module. Likewise, a weak base is one that is not one of the strong bases given above.

A. Weak Monoprotic Acids

Consider the following generalized example of a weak acid equilibrium,

$$HA_{(aq)} \rightleftharpoons H^+_{(aq)} + A^-_{(aq)} \qquad K_a = \frac{[H^+][A^-]}{[HA]}$$

K_a is called the **acid ionization constant**. Instead of K_a, we can use pK_a, which is defined as:

$$pK_a = -\log K_a$$

NOTE: Organic acids (i.e., acids that are derived from a hydrocarbon) have the following general formula: RCOO**H** [where, the R is the hydrocarbon portion (C_xH_y) and the acidic proton is written at the end]. For example, acetic acid can be written as: **H**$C_2H_3O_2$ or as CH_3COO**H**.

The following table gives examples of the K_a and pK_a of several weak acids.

Acid (HA)	K_a	pK_a
HIO_3	1.7×10^{-1}	0.77
HNO_2	4.5×10^{-4}	3.35
C_6H_5COOH	6.6×10^{-5}	4.18
HClO	3.5×10^{-8}	7.46

Acid (HA)	K_a	pK_a
CH_3COOH	1.8×10^{-5}	4.74
HBrO	2.1×10^{-9}	8.68
HCN	4.9×10^{-10}	9.31
HIO	2.3×10^{-11}	10.64

The larger the K_a of an acid (HA), the stronger an acid it is (i.e., the numerator is larger → more H^+ → more ionization). The % ionization is a measure of the extent of acid ionization in water and is given as follows:

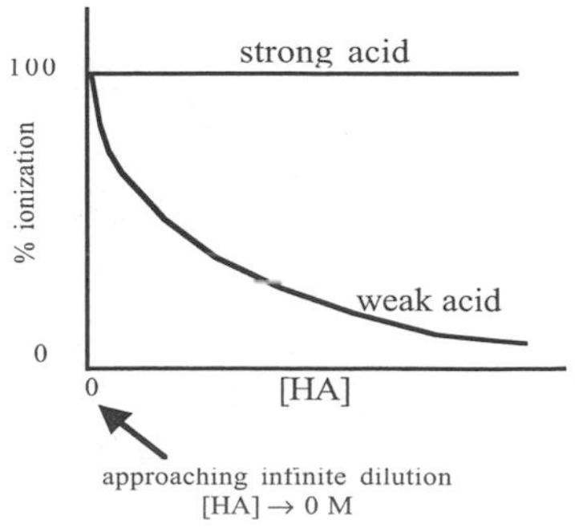

$$\% \text{ ionization} = \frac{[HA]_c}{[HA]_i} \times 100$$

NOTE: for monoprotic acids, $[HA]_c = [H^+]_e$

i = initial, c = change, e = equil.

It is of interest to note that as the concentration of the weak acid is decreased (i.e., as the [HA] becomes more dilute), the % ionization increases. In fact, at infiinite dilution, the % ionization approaches 100% .

Example Problems:

1. With the aid of the K_a (or pK_a) of the acids in the previous page answer the following questions.
   a) Which is the strongest acid?
      HIO_3 - the strongest acid is the one that has the smallest pK_a or largest K_a.
   b) Which is the weakest acid?
      HIO - the weakest acid is the one that has the largest pK_a or smallest K_a.
   c) Which has a higher pH, a 0.1 M HCN solution or a 0.1 M HIO solution?
      The 0.1 M HIO solution - Since the initial concentration of both weak acids is the same, the acid that is the weakest (largest pK_a or smallest K_a) has the highest pH. If the initial concentrations were not the same, then you would have to perform calculations like those in problem 2a shown below. A caveat to this would be if the weakest acid on the list had the smallest concentration - then for sure, it would have the highest pH. No matter how dilute a solution you have of an acid, its pH will always be less than 7.
   d) Which will have the greater % ionization, a 0.1 M CH_3COOH solution or a 1 M CH_3COOH solution?
      As stated above, as the concentration of the acid is decreased (i.e., as the acid becomes more dilute), the % ionization increases; therefore, a 0.1 M CH_3COOH solution has the greater percent ionization.

2. For a 0.350 M HF solution ($K_a = 7.2 \times 10^{-4}$), calculate:
   a) The pH.
      Since HF is a weak acid, it will not totally ionize in water. Since this is an acid: pH < 7, pOH > 7, $[H^+] > 1 \times 10^{-7}$ M, $[OH^-] < 1 \times 10^{-7}$ M, $[H^+] > [OH^-]$,

$$HF_{(aq)} \rightleftharpoons H^+_{(aq)} + F^-_{(aq)}$$

	$HF_{(aq)}$	$H^+_{(aq)}$	$F^-_{(aq)}$
$[\,]_i$:	0.350	0	0
$[\,]_{change}$:	-x	+x	+x
$[\,]_{equil}$:	0.350 - x	x	x

$$K_a = \frac{[H^+][F^-]}{[HF]}$$

$$7.2 \times 10^{-4} = \frac{(x)(x)}{(0.350 - x)}$$

Assume that x is small

Since K_a $(7.2 \times 10^{-4}) < [\,]_i \times 10^{-2}$ $(0.350 \times 10^{-2} = 3.50 \times 10^{-3})$, x will be assumed to be small in comparison to the initial concentration of 0.350 and as such will be neglected.

$$2.5 \times 10^{-4} = x^2$$

$$x = \sqrt{2.5 \times 10^{-4}} = 1.6 \times 10^{-2}$$

Our assumption that x was small in comparison to the initial concentration was correct. ***A small x is considered one that is less than 10% of the initial concentration.***

$[x\ (1.6 \times 10^{-2}) < 10\% \times [\,]_i\ (0.1 \times 0.35 = 0.035)]$

$$x = [H^+] = 1.6 \times 10^{-2}$$

$$pH = -\log[H^+] = -\log(1.6 \times 10^{-2}) = 1.80$$

   b) The % ionization.

$$\%\ \text{ionization} = \frac{[H^+]_e}{[HF]_i} \times 100 \rightarrow \frac{1.6 \times 10^{-2}\ M}{0.35\ M} \times 100 = 4.6\ \%$$

3. What is the molarity of an $HC_2H_3O_2$ ($K_a = 1.8 \times 10^{-5}$) solution whose pH is 3.00?
   From the pH, we can get $[H^+]_e$.

$$pH = -\log[H^+] \rightarrow 3.00 = -\log[H^+] \rightarrow [H^+] = 10^{-3.00} = 1.00 \times 10^{-3}\ M$$

	$HC_2H_3O_2\ (aq)$	⇌	$H^+\ (aq)$	+	$C_2H_3O_2^-\ (aq)$
[ ]i:	a_i		0		0
[ ]change:	-1.00×10^{-3}		$+1.00 \times 10^{-3}$		$+1.00 \times 10^{-3}$
[ ]equil:	$a_i - 1.00 \times 10^{-3}$		1.00×10^{-3}		1.00×10^{-3}

$a_i = [HC_2H_3O_2]_i$

The change in concentration was obtained from the given pH.

$$K_a = \frac{[H^+][C_2H_3O_2^-]}{[HC_2H_3O_2]} \rightarrow 1.8 \times 10^{-5} = \frac{(1.00 \times 10^{-3})(1.00 \times 10^{-3})}{(a_i - 1.00 \times 10^{-3})}$$

$$(1.8 \times 10^{-5}\ a_i) - (1.80 \times 10^{-8}) = 1.00 \times 10^{-6}$$

$$a_i = \frac{(1.00 \times 10^{-6} + 1.80 \times 10^{-8})}{1.8 \times 10^{-5}} = 5.66 \times 10^{-2}\ \text{M} \rightarrow [HC_2H_3O_2]_i$$

4. The pH of a 0.100 M solution of a weak monoprotic acid HA is 1.85.

   a) Calculate K_a.

   From the pH, we can get $[H^+]_e$.

   $pH = -\log [H^+]$

   $1.85 = -\log [H^+] \rightarrow [H^+] = 10^{-1.85} = 1.41 \times 10^{-2}$

	$HA\ (aq)$	⇌	$H^+\ (aq)$	+	$A^-\ (aq)$
[ ]i:	0.100		0		0
[ ]change:	-1.41×10^{-2}		$+1.41 \times 10^{-2}$		$+1.41 \times 10^{-2}$
[ ]equil:	$0.100 - 1.41 \times 10^{-2}$		1.41×10^{-2}		1.41×10^{-2}

$$K_a = \frac{[H^+][A^-]}{[HA]} \rightarrow K_a = \frac{(1.41 \times 10^{-2})(1.41 \times 10^{-2})}{(0.100 - 1.41 \times 10^{-2})} = 2.31 \times 10^{-3}$$

   b) Calculate its pK_a.

   $pK_a = -\log K_a = -\log(2.31 \times 10^{-3}) = 2.64$

5. The % ionization of a 0.0100 M solution of a weak monoprotic acid HA is found to be 4.2%. What is the K_a of the acid?

$$\%\ \text{ionization} = \frac{[H^+]_e}{[HA]_i} \times 100$$

$$4.2\ \% = \frac{[H^+]_e}{0.0100\ \text{M}} \times 100 \rightarrow [H^+]_{equil} = 4.2 \times 10^{-4}\ \text{M}$$

	$HA\ (aq)$	⇌	$H^+\ (aq)$	+	$A^-\ (aq)$
[ ]i:	0.0100		0		0
[ ]change:	-4.2×10^{-4}		$+4.2 \times 10^{-4}$		$+4.2 \times 10^{-4}$
[ ]equil:	$0.0100 - 4.2 \times 10^{-2}$		4.2×10^{-4}		4.2×10^{-4}

$$K_a = \frac{[H^+][A^-]}{[HA]} \rightarrow K_a = \frac{(4.2 \times 10^{-4})(4.2 \times 10^{-4})}{(0.0100 - 4.2 \times 10^{-4})} = 1.8 \times 10^{-5}$$

6. What is $[H^+]$ in a 0.0200 M $HClO_2$ ($K_a = 1.1 \times 10^{-2}$) solution?

$$HClO_2 \, (aq) \rightleftharpoons H^+ \, (aq) + ClO_2^- \, (aq)$$

	$HClO_2$	H^+	ClO_2^-
[ ]i:	0.0200	0	0
[ ]change:	-x	+x	+x
[ ]equil:	0.0200 - x	x	x

$$K_a = \frac{[H^+][ClO_2^-]}{[HClO_2]}$$

$$1.1 \times 10^{-2} = \frac{[x][x]}{[0.0200 - x]}$$

Since K_a (1.2 x 10^{-2}) $\nless$ [ ]$_i$ x 10^{-2} (0.020 x 10^{-2}), x can not be assumed to be small in comparison to the initial concentration of 0.020 and as such can not be neglected.

$$2.2 \times 10^{-4} - 1.1 \times 10^{-2} x = x^2$$

$$x^2 + 1.1 \times 10^{-2} x - 2.2 \times 10^{-4} = 0$$

$$x = \frac{-(1.1 \times 10^{-2}) \pm \sqrt{(1.1 \times 10^{-2})^2 - 4(1)(-2.2 \times 10^{-4})}}{2(1)}$$

x = **0.0103** or -0.0213 (not possible -- a negative concentration would be obtained).

$$x = [H^+] = 0.0103 \text{ M}$$

B. Weak Monobasic Bases

The common weak bases that are encountered are NH_3 and its derivatives, which are called amines. *Amines* are substances in which one, two or all three H's in ammonia have been replaced by a hydrocarbon (C_xH_y).

	H-N-H / H	H-N-CH$_3$ / H	CH$_3$-N-CH$_3$ / H	CH$_3$-N-CH$_3$ / CH$_3$
condensed formula	NH_3	CH_3NH_2	$(CH_3)_2NH$	$(CH_3)_3N$

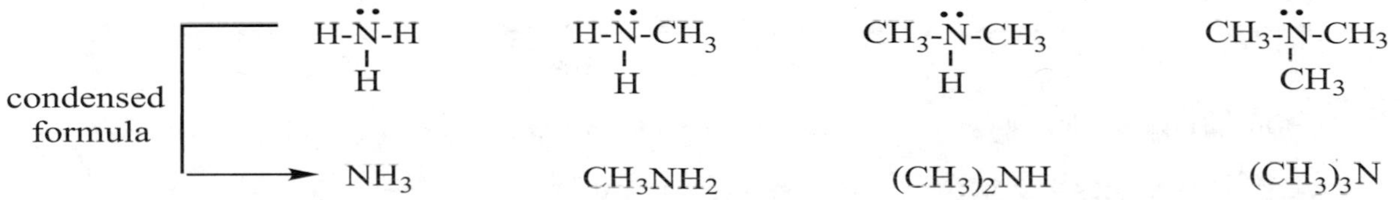

Ammonia and amines are Arrhenius bases because they produce OH$^-$ when placed in water.

Consider the following weak generic nitrogenous base ionization equilibrium reaction,

$$K_b = \frac{\left[-N^+ \right][OH^-]}{[-N-]}$$

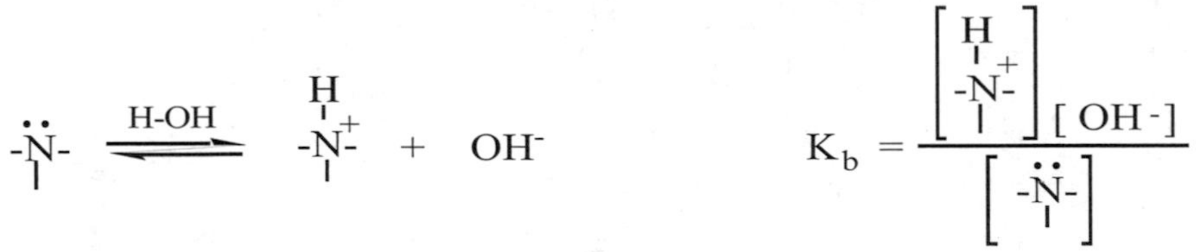

K_b is called the **base ionization constant**. Instead of K_b, we can use pK_b, which is defined as:

$$pK_b = -\log K_b$$

The following table gives examples of the K_b and pK_b of several weak bases.

Base (B:)	K_b	pK_b	Base (B:)	K_b	pK_b
$(CH_3)_2NH$	7.4 x 10^{-4}	3.13	NH_3	1.8 x 10^{-5}	4.74
CH_3NH_2	5.0 x 10^{-4}	3.30	C_5H_5N	1.5 x 10^{-9}	8.82
$(CH_3)_3N$	7.4 x 10^{-5}	4.13	$C_6H_5NH_2$	4.2 x 10^{-10}	9.38

The larger the K_b of a base, the stronger a base (B:) it is (i.e., the numerator is larger → more OH^- → more ionization). The % ionization is a measure of the extent of base ionization in water and is given as follows:

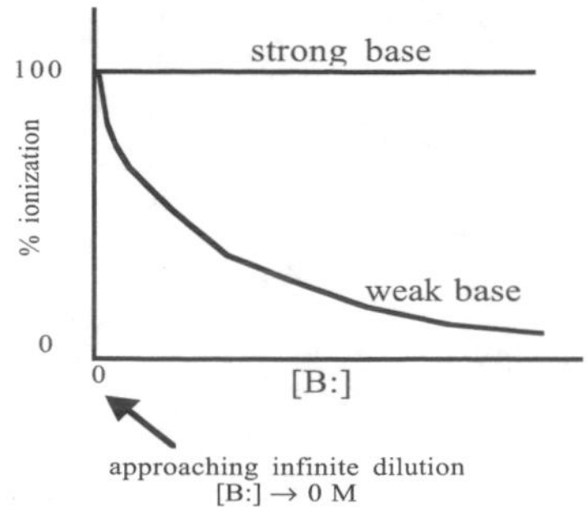

$$\% \text{ ionization} = \frac{[B:]_c}{[B:]_i} \times 100$$

NOTE: for monobasic bases, $[B:]_c = [OH^-]_e$

i = initial, c = change, e = equil.

As with weak acids, as the [B:] decreases (i.e., as the [B:] becomes more dilute), the % ionization increases. In fact, at infinite dilution, the % ionization of a weak base approaches 100%.

Example Problems:

1. With the aid of the K_b / pK_b of the bases in the previous page answer the following questions.
   a) Which is the strongest base?
      $(CH_3)_2NH$ - the strongest base is the one that has the smallest pK_b or largest K_b.
   b) Which is the weakest base?
      $C_6H_5NH_2$ - the weakest base is the one that has the largest pK_b or smallest K_b.
   c) Which has a lower pH, a 0.1 M C_5H_5N solution or a 0.1 M $C_6H_5NH_2$ solution?
      The 0.1 M $C_6H_5NH_2$ solution - Since the initial concentration of both weak bases is the same, the base that is the weakest (largest pK_b or smallest K_b) would have the lowest pH. If the initial concentrations were not the same, then you would have to perform calculations like those in problem 2a shown below. A caveat to this would be if the weakest base on the list had the smallest concentration - then for sure, it would have the lowest pH. No matter how dilute a solution you have of a base, its pH will always be greater than 7.
   d) Which will have the lower % ionization, a 0.1 M C_5H_5N solution or a 1 M C_5H_5N solution?
      As stated above, as the concentration of the base is decreased, the % ionization increases; therefore, a 1 M C_5H_5N solution has the lower percent ionization.

2. For a 0.0100 M $C_6H_5NH_2$ ($K_b = 4.2 \times 10^{-10}$) solution, calculate:
   a) The concentration of H^+ present at equilibrium.
      Since $C_6H_5NH_2$ is a weak nitrogenous base, it will not totally ionize in water. Since this is a base: $[H^+] < 1 \times 10^{-7}$ M, $[OH^-] > 1 \times 10^{-7}$ M, $[H^+] < [OH^-]$, pH > 7, p OH < 7.

$$C_6H_5NH_2\,(aq) \underset{}{\overset{H\text{-}OH}{\rightleftharpoons}} C_6H_5NH_3^+\,(aq) + OH^-\,(aq)$$

	$C_6H_5NH_2$ (aq)	$C_6H_5NH_3^+$ (aq)	OH^- (aq)
$[\ ]_i$:	0.0100	0	0
$[\ ]_{change}$:	-x	+x	+x
$[\ ]_{equil}$:	0.0100 - x	x	x

$$K_b = \frac{[C_6H_5NH_3^+][OH^-]}{[C_6H_5NH_2]}$$

$$4.2 \times 10^{-10} = \frac{(x)\ (x)}{(0.0100 - x)}$$

Assume that x is small

Since K_b (4.2×10^{-10}) < $[\ ]_i \times 10^{-2}$ (0.010×10^{-2}), x will be assumed to be small in comparison to the initial concentration of 0.0100 and as such will be neglected.

$$4.2 \times 10^{-12} = x^2$$

$$x = \sqrt{4.2 \times 10^{-12}} = 2.0 \times 10^{-6}$$

$$x = [OH^-] = 2.0 \times 10^{-6}\ M$$

Our assumption that x was small in comparison to the initial concentration was correct. ***A small x is considered one that is less than 10% of the initial concentration.***

[x (2.0×10^{-6}) < 10% x $[\ ]_i$ (0.1 x 0.0100 = 0.00100)]

$$K_w = [H^+][OH^-] \quad \rightarrow \quad 1.0 \times 10^{-14} = [H^+]\ (2.0 \times 10^{-6})$$

$$[H^+] = \frac{1.0 \times 10^{-14}}{2.0 \times 10^{-6}} = 5.0 \times 10^{-9}\ M \qquad \{\ pH = -\log(5.0 \times 10^{-9}) = 8.30\ \}$$

b) The % ionization.

$$\%\ \text{ionization} = \frac{[OH^-]_e}{[C_6H_5NH_2]_i} \times 100 \rightarrow \frac{2.0 \times 10^{-6}\ M}{0.0100\ M} \times 100 = 0.020\%$$

3. What is the initial concentration of a $(CH_3)_3N$ ($K_b = 7.4 \times 10^{-5}$) solution that is 12.6% ionized?

$$\%\ \text{ionization} = \frac{[OH^-]_e}{[(CH_3)_3N]_i} \times 100 \xrightarrow{\text{let } [(CH_3)_3N]_i = b_i} 12.6 = \frac{[OH^-]_e}{b_i} \times 100$$

Solving for $[OH^-]_e$ gives:

$$[OH^-]_e = 0.126\ b_i$$

The equilibrium expression for the weak base, $(CH_3)_3N$ is:

	$(CH_3)_3N_{(aq)}$ $\xrightleftharpoons{\text{H-OH}}$	$(CH_3)_3NH^+_{(aq)}$ +	$OH^-_{(aq)}$
$[\ ]_i$:	b_i	0	0
$[\ ]_{change}$:	-x	+x	+x
$[\ ]_{equil}$:	b_i - x	x	x

where, $x = [OH^-]_e = [(CH_3)_3NH^+]_e = 0.126\ b_i$ ← as obtained from % ionization

$$K_b = \frac{[(CH_3)_3NH^+][OH^-]}{[(CH_3)_3N]} \rightarrow 7.4 \times 10^{-5} = \frac{(0.126\ b_i)(0.126\ b_i)}{b_i - 0.126\ b_i}$$

Factoring out b_i gives:

$$7.4 \times 10^{-5} = \frac{b_i}{b_i}\ \frac{(0.126)^2\ b_i}{(1 - 0.126)}$$

$$b_i = \frac{7.4 \times 10^{-5}\ (1 - 0.126)}{(0.126)^2} = 4.07 \times 10^{-3}\ M \rightarrow [(CH_3)_3N]_i$$

VII. pH, pOH, $[H^+]$ & $[OH^-]$ Calculation of Weak Polyprotic Acids

A polyprotic acid is one that has more than one acidic H (e.g., H_2SO_3 (diprotic) and H_3PO_4 (triprotic)). The ionization of polyprotic acids occur stepwise, i.e., one proton at a time is lost. An ionization constant expression can be written for each step. Consider the following fictitious diprotic acid, H_2A.

$$H_2A_{(aq)} \rightleftharpoons H^+_{(aq)} + HA^-_{(aq)} \qquad K_{a_1} = \frac{[H^+][HA^-]}{[H_2A]}$$

$$HA^-_{(aq)} \rightleftharpoons H^+_{(aq)} + A^{2-}_{(aq)} \qquad K_{a_2} = \frac{[H^+][A^{2-}]}{[HA^-]}$$

There is a large decrease in successive ionization constants (i.e., $K_{a2} < K_{a1}$). This means that each ionization occurs to a lesser extent than the previous step. A perfect example of this is H_2SO_4 -- the first H^+ comes off completely (remember that H_2SO_4 is considered a strong acid); however, the second H^+ does not come off completely.

Example Problems:

1. Ascorbic acid (Vitamin C) is a diprotic acid ($H_2C_6H_6O_6$).

   Calculate the molarity of all species present in a 0.10 M ascorbic acid solution ($K_{a_1} = 7.9 \times 10^{-5}$ and $K_{a_2} = 1.6 \times 10^{-12}$).

	$H_2C_6H_6O_6$ (aq)	$\rightleftharpoons$	H^+ (aq)	+	$HC_6H_6O_6^-$ (aq)
$[\ ]_i$:	0.10		0		0
$[\ ]_{change}$:	-x		+x		+x
$[\ ]_{equil}$:	0.10 - x		x		x

$$K_{a_1} = \frac{[H^+][HC_6H_6O_6^-]}{[H_2C_6H_6O_6]}$$

$$7.9 \times 10^{-5} = \frac{(x)\ (x)}{(0.10 - \cancel{x})}$$

Assume that x is small

Since K_a (7.9×10^{-5}) < $[\ ]_i \times 10^{-2}$ (0.10×10^{-2}), x will be assumed to be small in comparison to the initial concentration of 0.10 and as such will be neglected.

$$7.9 \times 10^{-6} = x^2$$

$$x = \sqrt{7.9 \times 10^{-6}} = 2.8 \times 10^{-3}$$

Our assumption that x was small in comparison to the initial concentration was correct. ***A small x is considered one that is less than 10% of the initial concentration.***

[x (2.8×10^{-3}) < 10% x $[\ ]_i$ ($0.1 \times 0.10 = 0.010$)]

x = 2.8×10^{-3} = $[H^+]$ and $[HC_6H_6O_6^-]$. These values can be substituted into the second equilibrium expression.

	$HC_6H_6O_6^-$ (aq)	$\rightleftharpoons$	H^+ (aq)	+	$C_6H_6O_6^{2-}$ (aq)
$[\ ]_i$:	2.8×10^{-3}		2.8×10^{-3}		0
$[\ ]_{change}$:	-y		+y		+y
$[\ ]_{equil}$:	2.8×10^{-3} - y		2.8×10^{-3} + y		y

$$K_{a_2} = \frac{[H^+][C_6H_6O_6^{2-}]}{[HC_6H_6O_6^-]}$$

$$1.6 \times 10^{-12} = \frac{(2.8 \times 10^{-3} + \cancel{y})\ (y)}{(2.8 \times 10^{-3} - \cancel{y})}$$

Assume that y is small

Since K_a (1.6×10^{-12}) < $[\ ]_i \times 10^{-2}$ ($2.8 \times 10^{-3} \times 10^{-2}$), y will be assumed to be small in comparison to the initial concentration of 2.8×10^{-3} and as such will be neglected.

$$y = 1.6 \times 10^{-12} = [C_6H_6O_6^{2-}]$$

Our assumption that y was small in comparison to the initial concentration was correct. ***A small y is considered one that is less than 10% of the initial concentration.***

[y (1.6×10^{-12}) < 10% x $[\ ]_i$ ($0.1 \times 2.8 \times 10^{-3} = 2.8 \times 10^{-4}$)]

At equilibrium

$[H_2C_6H_6O_6]$ = 0.097 (0.10 - x = 0.10 - 2.8×10^{-3})

$[HC_6H_6O_6^-]$ = 2.8×10^{-3} (2.8×10^{-3} - y = 2.8×10^{-3} - 1.6×10^{-12})

$[H^+]$ = 2.8×10^{-3} (2.8×10^{-3} + y = 2.8×10^{-3} + 1.6×10^{-12})

$[OH^-]$ = 3.6×10^{-12} ($K_w / [H^+] = 1.0 \times 10^{-14} / 2.8 \times 10^{-3}$)

$[C_6H_6O_6^{2-}]$ = 1.6×10^{-12} (y = 1.6×10^{-12}) → Notice how $[C_6H_6O_6^{2-}] = K_{a_2}$.

[**NOTE:** For diprotic acids (H_2A), $[A^{2-}]$ is usually equal K_{a_2}.]

EXERCISES

Acid-Base Theories

1. Considering Brønsted-Lowry acid-base theory, complete the following reactions. Label each substance as either: acid (a), base (b), conjugate acid (ca), conjugate base (cb).

   a) H_2O + $(CH_3)_2NH$ $\rightleftharpoons$ b) H_2O + CH_3CH_2COOH $\rightleftharpoons$

   c) C_5H_5N + H_2O $\rightleftharpoons$ d) C_7H_5COOH + H_2O $\rightleftharpoons$

2. Explain how Fe^{3+} can be considered an acid according to the Lewis acid-base concept, but not in the Brønsted-Lowry acid-base concept.

3. Why are ammonia and its derivatives considered Arrhenius bases?

4. At 50°C, $K_w = 5.48 \times 10^{-14}$. At 50°C, at what pH would a substance be considered:
   a) acidic b) basic or alkaline c) neutral

pH, pOH, $[H^+]$ and $[OH^-]$ Calculation of Strong Acids and Bases

5. Complete the following table.

pH	pOH	$[H^+]$, M	$[OH^-]$, M	acidic, basic, or neutral
	13.00			
		2.7×10^{-12}		
			1.0×10^{-7}	
	4.75			
-1.00				

6. Complete the following table.

Substance	Concentration	pH	pOH	$[H^+]$, M	$[OH^-]$, M
HNO_3	0.15 M				
HI		4.35			
NaOH	10.0 M				
LiOH			0.00		
$Ba(OH)_2$	1.4×10^{-2} M				
$Sr(OH)_2$					9.5×10^{-1}
KOH	4.6 g / 270 mL soln				

pH, pOH, $[H^+]$ and $[OH^-]$ Calculation of Weak Monoprotic Acids and Monobasic Bases

7. Complete the following table in reference to HNO_2 ($K_a = 4.5 \times 10^{-4}$)

Concentration, M	pH	pOH	$[H^+]$, M	$[OH^-]$, M	% ionization
1.0×10^{-1}					
2.2×10^{-1}					
	1.63				
					14.6

8. Which of the following acids has the highest % ionization:
   a) 1.7 M HNO_2 or 0.17 M HNO_2
   b) 1.0 M HNO_2 or 1.0 M HNO_3
   c) 1.0 M HNO_2 ($K_a = 4.5 \times 10^{-4}$) or 1.0 M HCN ($K_a = 4.9 \times 10^{-10}$)

9. What is the pK_a of HNO_2 ($K_a = 4.5 \times 10^{-4}$)?

10. A 1.75 M solution of a weak monoprotic acid has a pH of 3.75. What is this acid's ionization constant?

11. What is the molarity of $HClO_2$ ($K_a = 1.1 \times 10^{-2}$) solution whose pH is 2.60?

12. A 0.37 M solution of a weak monobasic base has a pH of 10.30. What is this base's ionization constant?

13. Complete the following table in reference to $(CH_3)_3N$ ($K_b = 7.4 \times 10^{-5}$)

Concentration, M	pH	pOH	$[H^+]$, M	$[OH^-]$, M	% ionization
1.0×10^{-2}					
4.80×10^{-2}					
	11.10				
					2.5

14. Which of the following bases has the highest % ionization:
   a) 1.7 M NH_3 or 0.17 M NH_3
   b) 1.0 M NH_3 or 1.0 M $Ca(OH)_2$
   c) 1.0 M NH_3 ($K_b = 1.8 \times 10^{-5}$) or 1.0 M $C_6H_5NH_2$ ($K_b = 4.2 \times 10^{-10}$)

15. What is the pK_b of NH_3 ($K_b = 1.8 \times 10^{-5}$)?

16. What is the pK_b of a base given that a 0.00500 M solution of it is 0.053% ionized?

pH, pOH, $[H^+]$ and $[OH^-]$ Calculation of Weak Polyprotic Acids

17. For a 2.50 M H_2SO_3 ($K_{a_1} = 1.3 \times 10^{-2}$ and $K_{a_2} = 6.3 \times 10^{-8}$) solution:
   a) Calculate the $[OH^-]$ (in M).
   b) Calculate the % H_2SO_3 that ionizes in the first step.
   c) Calculate the % HSO_3^- that ionizes in the second step.

18. What is the molarity of all the species present in a 0.20 M H_2TeO_3 ($K_{a_1} = 2 \times 10^{-3}$ and $K_{a_2} = 1 \times 10^{-8}$) solution?

19. For a 0.25 M H_2SO_3 ($K_{a_1} = 1.3 \times 10^{-2}$ and $K_{a_2} = 6.3 \times 10^{-8}$) solution:
   a) Calculate its pH.
   b) Calculate the molarity of SO_3^{2-}.

20. For a 0.10 M H_2SO_4 ($K_{a_2} = 1.2 \times 10^{-2}$) solution:
   a) Calculate $[H_2SO_4]$, $[HSO_4^{1-}]$, $[SO_4^{2-}]$, $[H^+]$, and $[OH^-]$ (in M).
   b) What is the extent of the ionization of the second step?

MULTIPLE CHOICE PRACTICE EXAM FOR MODULE 6

1. In a sample of pure water, which of the following is always true at all temperatures and pressures?
   1) $[H^+] = 1.0 \times 10^{-7}$ M 2) pH = 7.00 3) $[H^+] = [OH^-]$
   4) $[OH^-] = 1.0 \times 10^{-7}$ M
   5) More than one of the above is correct.

2. A solution having a pH of 0 would:
   1) not be acidic 2) have an $[H^+] = 1.0$ M 3) have an $[OH^-] = 14$ M
   4) Two of the above choices are correct.
   5) None of the above choices are correct.

3. What is the molarity of an HCl solution whose pH is 2.80?
   1) 1.6×10^{-3} 2) 6.3×10^{-3} 3) 4.2×10^{-3} 4) 6.3×10^{-2} 5) 4.2×10^{-2}

4. What is the pH of a 500. mL solution containing 0.0124 g of $Ca(OH)_2$ (MM = 74.1)?
   1) 3.17 2) 9.68 3) 11.04 4) 10.82 5) 2.96

Consider the following information when answering questions 5 - 7.

Given that the pH of a 0.50 M solution of an acid HX was 4.00, then:

5. What is the $[H^+]$ (in molarity) of the solution?
   1) 10^{-4} 2) -4.00 3) 3.50 4) 2.00 5) 0.50

6. What is the pOH of the solution?
   1) 0.5 2) 13.50 3) 12.00 4) 2.00 5) 10.00

7. What is the pK_a of HX?
   1) 4.00 2) 7.70 3) 3.70 4) 2.0×10^{-8} 5) 2.00

8. Calculate the pH of 0.350 M HF ($K_a = 7.2 \times 10^{-4}$).
   1) 1.80 2) 0.46 3) 0.016 4) 2.25 5) 3.50

9. Calculate the % ionization of a 0.100 M HNO_2 ($K_a = 4.5 \times 10^{-4}$) solution.
   1) 1.9 2) 6.7×10^{-2} 3) 4.5 4) 2.3 5) 6.7

10. Calculate the pH of 0.10 M NH_3 ($K_b = 1.8 \times 10^{-5}$).
    1) 12.00 2) 9.36 3) 11.13 4) 10.89 5) 8.47

11. Calculate the % ionization of a 0.30 M $C_6H_5NH_2$ ($K_b = 4.2 \times 10^{-10}$) solution.
    1) 0.89 2) 6.7×10^{-4} 3) 0.37 4) 0.0037 5) 0.0030

12. What is the initial molarity of a CH_3COOH ($K_a = 1.8 \times 10^{-5}$) solution that is 2.0% ionized?
    1) 0.044 2) 0.011 3) 0.022 4) 0.055 5) 0.0020

Consider the following information when answering questions 13 - 14.

HNO_2 ($K_a = 4.5 \times 10^{-4}$) and HCN ($K_a = 4.9 \times 10^{-10}$)

13. Which of the following has the smallest % ionization?
    1) 0.5 M HCN 2) 0.5 M HNO_2 3) 0.5 M HNO_3 4) 1.0 M HCN 5) 0.4 M HNO_3

14. Which of the following has the highest pH?
    1) 0.5 M HCN 2) 0.5 M HNO_2 3) 0.5 M HNO_3 4) 1.0 M HCN 5) 0.4 M HNO_3

Consider the following information when answering questions 15 - 16.

CH_3NH_2 (pK_b = 3.30) and C_5H_5N (pK_b = 8.82)

15. Which of the following has the smallest % ionization?
    1) 0.5 M C_5H_5N 2) 0.5 M CH_3NH_2 3) 1.0 M RbOH 4) 1.0 M C_5H_5N 5) 0.4 M RbOH

16. Which of the following has the highest pH?
    1) 0.5 M C_5H_5N 2) 0.5 M CH_3NH_2 3) 1.0 M RbOH 4) 1.0 M C_5H_5N 5) 0.4 M RbOH

Consider the following information when answering questions 17 - 18.

The hypothetical acid, H_2X, has a $K_{a1} = 1.0 \times 10^{-7}$ and $K_{a2} = 5.0 \times 10^{-11}$. If $[H_2X]$ = 1.60 M:

17. Calculate $[HX^-]$ (in M):
    1) 1.0×10^{-7} 2) 6.3×10^{-5} 3) 4.0×10^{-4} 4) 3.0×10^{-4} 5) 2.2×10^{-6}

18. Calculate $[X^{2-}]$ (in M):
    1) 3.8×10^{-18} 2) 5.0×10^{-11} 3) 1.0×10^{-7} 4) 4.6×10^{-13} 5) 5.8×10^{-14}

19. Which of the following 0.10 M aqueous solutions will have the lowest pH?
    1) HA (pK_a = 3.79) 2) HX (pK_a = 4.79) 3) HZ (pK_a = 5.78)
    4) $:NX_3$ (pK_b = 1.89) 5) $:NR_3$ (pK_b = 6.89)

20. Which of the following 0.10 M aqueous solutions will have the lowest pH?
    1) HCl 2) HBr 3) HI
    4) It is impossible to say since their K_a is not given in the problem.
    5) All have the same pH.

21. Which of the following has the smallest pK_a?
    1) HA ($K_a = 1.79 \times 10^{-8}$) 2) HX ($K_a = 3.72 \times 10^{-8}$) 3) HZ ($K_a = 5.66 \times 10^{-4}$)
    4) HL (pK_a = 3.23) 5) HJ ($K_a = 5.75 \times 10^{-4}$)

22. Which of the following statements is **true**?
    1) A 0.10 M aqueous HX solution (pK_a = 3.79) has a lower pH than a 0.10 M aqueous HA (pK_a = 2.79) solution.
    2) A 0.10 M aqueous $:NX_3$ solution ($K_b = 5.75 \times 10^{-4}$) has a higher pH than a 0.10 M aqueous $:NZ_3$ ($pK_b = 3.72 \times 10^{-8}$) solution.
    3) A 0.10 M aqueous HCN solution has the same pH as a 0.10 M aqueous HCl solution.
    4) Two of the above statements are true.
    5) None of the above statements is true.

23. Which of the following statements is **true**?
    1) The pH of a 0.10 M HF solution is 1.00.
    2) The pOH of a 0.10 M aqueous NH_3 solution is 1.00.
    3) The pH of a 0.10 M HCl solution is 1.00.
    4) All of the above statements are true.
    5) None of the above statements is true.

24. Which of the following statements is **true**?
    1) A 0.10 M NH_3 solution is more alkaline than a 0.20 M NH_3 solution.
    2) The pH of a 0.10 M HF solution is greater than 1.00
    3) The pH of a 0.10 M HCl solution is less than the pH of a 0.20 M HCl solution.
    4) The pH of a 0.10 M NH_3 solution is greater than 13.00.
    5) More than one of the above statements are true.

25. Which of the following statements is **true**?
    1) A solution having a pH = 2.00 is five times more acidic than a solution having a pH = 10.00.
    2) A solution having a pH = 1.00 has two times $[H^+]$ as a solution having a pH = 2.00.
    3) The pOH of a 1.00×10^{-9} M LiOH solution is 9.00.
    4) A solution having pH = 6.00 is one-thousand times less basic than a solution having a pH = 9.00.
    5) More than one of the above statements are true.

26. Which of the following statements is **true** about diprotic acids (i.e., H_2A) and their ionization in water?
    1) Usually, $[A^{2-}] = K_{a_2}$
    2) $K_{a_2} > K_{a_1}$
    3) Most ionization occurs in the second step.
    4) $K_{a_1} = \frac{[H^+][A^{2-}]}{[HA^-]}$
    5) More than one of the above statements is true.

MODULE 6 - ANSWERS

1. a) $H_2O + (CH_3)_2NH \rightleftharpoons OH^- + (CH_3)_2NH_2^+$
   a, b, cb, ca

   b) $H_2O + CH_3CH_2COOH \rightleftharpoons H_3O^+ + CH_3CH_2COO^-$
   b, a, ca, cb

   c) $C_5H_5N + H_2O \rightleftharpoons C_5H_5NH^+ + OH^-$
   b, a, ca, cb

   d) $C_6H_5COOH + H_2O \rightleftharpoons C_6H_5COO^- + H_3O^+$
   a, b, cb, ca

   a = acid
   b = base
   ca = conjugate acid
   cb = conjugate base

2. Fe^{3+} can be considered a Lewis acid (defined as an electron pair acceptor) because since it has a positive charge, it is able to accept a pair of electrons provided by a Lewis base (defined as an electron pair donor). Since it does not have a proton (H^+), it can't be a Brønsted-Lowry acid (defined as proton donor).

3. Ammonia and its derivatives (aka - amines) are Arrhenius bases because when they are placed in water, they produce OH^-.

4. a) pH < 6.63 b) pH > 6.63 c) pH = 6.63

5.

pH	pOH	$[H^+]$, M	$[OH^-]$, M	acidic, basic, or neutral
1.00	13.00	1.0×10^{-1}	1.0×10^{-13}	acidic
11.57	2.43	2.7×10^{-12}	3.7×10^{-3}	basic
7.00	7.00	1.0×10^{-7}	$1 .0 \times 10^{-7}$	neutral
9.25	4.75	5.6×10^{-10}	1.8×10^{-5}	basic
-1.00	15.00	1.0×10^{1}	1.0×10^{-15}	acidic

6.

Substance	Concentration	pH	pOH	$[H^+]$, M	$[OH^-]$, M
HNO_3	0.15 M	0.82	13.18	0.15	6.7×10^{-14}
HI	4.5×10^{-5} M	4.35	9.65	4.5×10^{-5}	2.2×10^{-10}
NaOH	10.0 M	15.00	-1.00	1.0×10^{-15}	10.0
LiOH	1.0 M	14.00	0.00	1.0×10^{-14}	1.0
$Ba(OH)_2$	1.4×10^{-2} M	12.45	1.55	3.6×10^{-13}	2.8×10^{-2}
$Sr(OH)_2$	4.75×10^{-1} M	13.98	0.02	1.1×10^{-14}	9.5×10^{-1}
KOH	4.6 g / 270 mL soln	13.48	0.52	3.3×10^{-14}	3.0×10^{-1}

7.

Concentration, M	pH	pOH	$[H^+]$, M	$[OH^-]$, M	% ionization
1.0×10^{-1}	2.17	11.83	6.7×10^{-3}	1.5×10^{-12}	6.7
2.2×10^{-1}	2.00	12.00	9.9×10^{-3}	1.0×10^{-12}	4.5
1.2	1.63	12.37	2.3×10^{-2}	4.3×10^{-13}	1.9
1.8×10^{-2}	2.58	11.42	2.6×10^{-3}	3.8×10^{-12}	14.6

8. a) 0.17 M HNO_2 (the more dilute an acid is, the greater its % ionization)
   b) 1.0 M HNO_3 (strong acids are 100% ionized)
   c) 1.0 M HNO_2 (the larger the K_a, the greater the % ionization)

9. 3.35

10. 1.8×10^{-8}

11. 0.0031 M

12. 1.1×10^{-7}

13.

Concentration, M	pH	pOH	$[H^+]$, M	$[OH^-]$, M	% ionization
1.0×10^{-2}	10.93	3.07	1.2×10^{-11}	8.6×10^{-4}	8.6
4.80×10^{-2}	11.28	2.72	5.3×10^{-12}	1.9×10^{-3}	3.9
2.27×10^{-2}	11.10	2.90	7.9×10^{-12}	1.3×10^{-3}	5.5
1.2×10^{-1}	11.46	2.54	3.5×10^{-12}	2.9×10^{-3}	2.5

14. a) 0.17 M NH_3 (the more dilute a base is, the greater its % ionization)
    b) 1.0 M $Ca(OH)_2$ (strong bases are 100% ionized)
    c) 1.0 M NH_3 (the larger the K_b, the greater the % ionization)
15. 4.74
16. 8.85
17. a) $[OH^-] = 5.6 \times 10^{-14}$ M b) 7.2 % c) 3.5×10^{-5} %
18. $[H^+] = [HTeO_3{}^{1-}] = 1.9 \times 10^{-2}$ M, $[H_2TeO_3] = 0.181$ M, $[TeO_3{}^{2-}] = 1 \times 10^{-8}$ M, $[OH^-] = 5.3 \times 10^{-13}$ M
19. a) 1.29 ---- must use quadratic for first step (x = 0.0509) b) 6.3×10^{-8}
20. a) $[H_2SO_4] = 0$ M (first ionization occurs 100%) ---- must use quadratic for second step (x = 0.0099) --
    $[HSO_4{}^{1-}] = 0.09$ M (0.10 - 0.0099), $[SO_4{}^{2-}] = 0.010$ M, $[H^+] = 0.11$ M (0.1 + 0.0099), and $[OH^-] = 9.1 \times 10^{-14}$ M
    b) 10%

ANSWERS TO MULTIPLE CHOICE PRACTICE EXAM

1	2	3	4	5	6	7	8	9	10	11	12	13	14	15	16	17	18	19	20	21	22	23	24	25	26
3	2	1	4	1	5	2	1	5	3	4	1	4	1	4	3	3	2	1	5	4	2	3	2	4	1

MODULE 7. *Buffers*

I. Buffers

A buffer is a solution that is able to resist a change in pH upon the addition of small amounts of acids and bases. Buffers are very important in chemical and biological systems, for example, the pH of the blood is maintained at 7.4 because of buffers that are present in the blood. As you will soon learn, the most common type of buffers contain weak acid-weak base conjugate pairs.

There are two common types of buffer solutions:

a) A weak acid and a soluble ionic salt derived from the weak acid (e.g., HF & NaF).

b) A weak base and a soluble ionic salt derived from the weak base (e.g., $NH_3 = NH_4OH$ & NH_4Cl).

A conjugate acid-base pair derived from a weak acid and weak base are the constituents of a buffer.

conjugate acid-base pair		spectator ion	conjugate acid-base pair		spectator ion
HF	and F^-	(or Na F)	NH_3	and NH_4^+	(or NH_4 Cl)
(weak acid)	(weak base)	salt derived from weak acid	(weak base)	(weak acid)	salt derived from weak base

The operation of a buffer works on the common ion effect, a special case of the LeChatelier's Principle. The term ***common ion effect*** is used when a solution is composed of two substances in which each contains the same ion. For example, a solution that contains the weak acid HF and NaF experiences a common ion effect (i.e., both HF and NaF contain the common ion F^-). The ionization of the weak acid, HF, is suppressed by the addition of its common ion salt, NaF, in accordance to the LeChatelier Principle.

$$HF_{(aq)} \underset{}{\overset{H_2O}{\rightleftharpoons}} H^+_{(aq)} + F^-_{(aq)}$$

F^- (from NaF) causes the equilibrium to shift to the left, thus suppressing the ionization of HF.

Thus, a solution that contains a weak acid plus its common ion salt is always less acidic than a solution that contains the same concentration of the weak acid alone.

As previously seen in the acid-base equilibria module, when NH_3 is placed in water, NH_4^+ and OH^- are formed. A solution that contains the weak base $NH_{3\ (aq)}$ and NH_4Cl experiences a common ion effect (i.e., both $NH_{3\ (aq)}$ and NH_4Cl contain the common ion NH_4^+). The ionization of the weak base, NH_3, is suppressed by the addition of its common ion salt, NH_4Cl, in accordance to the LeChatelier Principle.

$$NH_{3\ (aq)} \overset{H-OH}{\rightleftharpoons} NH_4^+{}_{(aq)} + OH^-_{(aq)}$$

NH_4^+ (from NH_4Cl) causes the equilibrium to shift to the left, thus suppressing the ionization of NH_3.

Thus, a solution that contains a weak base plus its common ion salt is always less basic than a solution that contains the same concentration of the weak base alone.

A. Weak Acid and Common Ion Salt Buffer

To make a buffer, we need a weak acid and its common ion salt. The common ion salt of a weak acid is obtained by replacing one of the acid's H's with a IA metal.

Consider the following weak acid (HA) equilibrium in the context that in a buffer solution, there are both a weak acid (HA) and its salt ($IA^+ A^-$). The salt's anion (A^-) is the conjugate base of the weak acid (HA). Let, [HA] = a , and that of its common ion salt, $[IA^+ A^-] = [A^-] = s$.

	$HA_{(aq)}$	$\rightleftharpoons$	$H^+_{(aq)}$	+	$A^-_{(aq)}$
$[\ ]_i$:	a		0		s
$[\ ]_{change}$:	-x		+x		+x
$[\ ]_{equil}$:	a - x		x		s + x

$$K_a = \frac{[H^+]\ [A^-]}{[HA]}$$

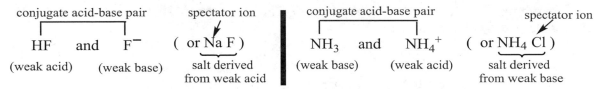

Substitution of the above concentrations into the equilibrium expression, gives,

$$K_a = \frac{(x)(s + x)}{(a - x)}$$

In buffer problems, for all practical purposes x will be smaller than both s and a. This being the case, x can be neglected. **[NOTE: $[A^-]$ = [salt] only in cases where there is 1:1 mole ratio between A^- and s. See Multiple Choice Problem 3, where this is not the case.]**

$$K_a = \frac{(x)(s)}{(a)} \quad \text{where, } x = [H^+]$$

$$K_a = \frac{[H^+](s)}{(a)}$$

rearranging this equation, gives us a very useful equation that we can use to find the $[H^+]$ of a buffer solution.

Weak Acid Buffer Formula

$$[H^+] = \frac{a}{s} K_a$$

where $a = [HA]$ or mol HA
$s = [A^-]$ or mol A^-

The logarithmic form of the Weak Acid Buffer Formula given above, which is referred to as the ***Henderson-Hasselbalch Equation,***

$$pH = \log\left(\frac{s}{a}\right) + pK_a$$

can also be used to perform buffer calculations.

Example Problems:

1. Would a solution composed of the following act as a buffer?
   a) HCl and NaCl
      This is not a buffer because this is a strong acid and its common ion salt. A buffer is made up of a weak acid and its common ion salt.
   b) H_3PO_4 and NaH_2PO_4
      This is a buffer because this is a weak acid and its common ion salt.

2. What is the pH of an equimolar solution of HF ($K_a = 6.5 \times 10^{-4}$) and KF?

   Equimolar means that [HF] = [KF]; therefore, a = s and $[H^+] = K_a$ or $pH = pK_a$

   $$[H^+] = \frac{a}{s} K_a = 6.5 \times 10^{-4}$$

   $$pH = -\log[H^+] = -\log(6.5 \times 10^{-4}) = 3.19$$

3. If a buffer is composed of 1.0 M of $HC_2H_3O_2$ ($K_a = 1.8 \times 10^{-5}$) and 1.2 M of $NaC_2H_3O_2$, then:
   a) What is the pH of this buffer solution?

   $$[H^+] = \frac{a}{s} K_a = \frac{1.0}{1.2}(1.8 \times 10^{-5}) = 1.5 \times 10^{-5}$$

   $$pH = -\log[H^+] = -\log(1.5 \times 10^{-5}) = 4.82$$

   b) What is the pH after the addition of 0.10 mol of HCl to 1.0-L of the buffer solution? Assume that there is no volume change due to the addition of the HCl.

   When HCl is added, it completely reacts with the salt (which is a Brønsted base -- a proton acceptor).

	$NaC_2H_3O_2$	+	HCl	→	$HC_2H_3O_2$	+	NaCl
$[\ ]_i$:	1.2 M		$\frac{0.10 \text{ mol}}{1.0 \text{ L}}$		1.0 M		
$[\ ]_{change}$:	-0.10		-0.10		+0.10		
$[\ ]_{end}$:	1.1		0		1.1		

[**NOTE**: As will be discussed in the next module, a salt derived from a strong acid and a strong base (e.g., NaCl, KBr, $LiNO_3$, etc.) is neutral (i.e., pH = 7, $[H^+] = [OH^-]$).

$$[H^+] = \frac{a}{s} K_a = \frac{1.1}{1.1}(1.8 \times 10^{-5}) = 1.8 \times 10^{-5}$$

$pH = -\log [H^+] = -\log (1.8 \times 10^{-5}) = 4.74$

Notice how the addition of HCl hardly changed the pH [4.82 → 4.74].

c) What is the pH after the addition of 0.10 mol of NaOH to 1.0-L of the buffer solution? Assume that there is no volume change due to the addition of the NaOH.

When NaOH is added, it completely reacts with $HC_2H_3O_2$.

	$HC_2H_3O_2$	+	NaOH	→	$NaC_2H_3O_2$	+	H_2O
[ ]i:	1.0		0.10		1.2		
[ ]change:	-0.10		-0.10		+0.10		
[ ]end:	0.9		0		1.3		

$$[H^+] = \frac{a}{s} K_a = \frac{0.9}{1.3}(1.8 \times 10^{-5}) = 1.2 \times 10^{-5}$$

$pH = -\log [H^+] = -\log (1.2 \times 10^{-5}) = 4.92$

Notice how the addition of NaOH hardly changed the pH [4.82 → 4.92].

B. **Weak Base and Common Ion Salt Buffer**

Another way of making a buffer, is to have a weak base and its common ion salt. The most common weak bases used to prepare buffers are either ammonia or amines (as discussed in the acid-base module). The following is a generalized example of how to make a common ion salt, *most commonly a hydrochloride salt,* of a weak nitrogenous base.

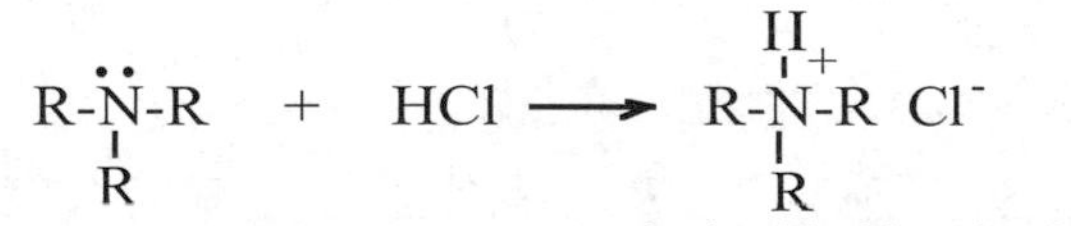

nitrogenous base (ammonia or an amine) — hydrochloride salt of nitrogenous base

where R = H or a hydrocarbon (C_xH_y)

[NOTE: Cl^- is a spectator ion]

Consider the following weak base (B:) equilibrium in the context that in a buffer solution, there are both a weak base and its salt ($BH^+ Cl^-$) present. The salt's cation (BH^+) is the conjugate acid of the weak base (B:). Let, [B:] = b, and that of its common ion salt, $[BH^+Cl^-] = [BH^+] = s$.

	B: (aq)	$\xrightleftharpoons{H\text{-}OH}$	BH^+ (aq)	+	OH^- (aq)
[ ]i:	b		s		0
[ ]change:	-x		+x		+x
[ ]equil:	b - x		s + x		x

$$K_b = \frac{[BH^+][OH^-]}{[B:]}$$

$$K_b = \frac{(x)(s + x)}{(b - x)}$$

In buffer problems, for all practical purposes x will be smaller than both s and b. This being the case, it can be neglected. **[NOTE: $[BH^+]$ = [salt] only in cases where there is 1:1 mole ratio between BH^+ and s.]**

$$K_b = \frac{(x)(s)}{(a)} \quad \text{where, } x = [OH^-]$$

$$K_b = \frac{[OH^-](s)}{(b)}$$

rearranging this equation, gives us a very useful equation that we can use to find the $[OH^-]$ of a buffer solution.

Weak Base Buffer Formula

$$[OH^-] = \frac{b}{s} K_b$$

where $b = [B:]$ or mol B:
$s = [BH^+]$ or mol BH^+

The logarithmic form of the Weak Base Buffer Formula given above, gives another form of the ***Henderson-Hasselbalch Equation,***

$$pOH = \log\left(\frac{s}{b}\right) + pK_b$$

can also be used to perform buffer calculations.

Example Problems:

1. Which of the following are buffers?
   a) NaOH and HCl

      This is not a buffer because this is a strong base and a strong acid. A buffer is made up of a weak base and its common ion salt or a weak acid and its common ion salt.

   b) $(CH_3CH_2)_2NH$ and $(CH_3CH_2)_2NH_2^+ Br^-$

      This is a buffer because this is weak base and its common ion salt.

2. Explain why when the following two solutions - 1.0 L of 2.0 M CH_3NH_2 and 1.0 L of 1.0 M HCl - are mixed, a buffered solution results.

   When CH_3NH_2 (a weak base) is mixed with HCl (an acid) a neutralization reaction occurs. CH_3NH_2 is the excess reagent and the HCl is the limiting reagent. The resulting solution will act as a buffer because a weak base (CH_3NH_2) and a salt ($CH_3NH_3^+ Cl^-$) derived from the weak base are present in the solution.

   weak base + salt derived from weak base ⟹ buffer

   $$CH_3NH_2 + HCl \longrightarrow CH_3NH_3^+ Cl^-$$

   excess reagent (CH_3NH_2); limiting reagent (HCl)

3. What is the pH of an equimolar solution of CH_3NH_2 ($K_b = 5.0 \times 10^{-4}$) and $CH_3NH_3^+ Cl^-$?

   Equimolar means that $[CH_3NH_2] = [CH_3NH_3^+ Cl^-]$; therefore, $b = s$ and $[OH^-] = K_b$ or $pOH = pK_b$

   $$[OH^-] = \frac{b}{s} K_b = 5.0 \times 10^{-4}$$

   $$pOH = -\log [OH^-] = -\log (5.0 \times 10^{-4}) = 3.30$$

   $$pH + pOH = 14.00 \rightarrow pH + 3.30 = 14.00 \rightarrow pH = 10.70$$

4. A buffer solution is made by mixing 150. mL of 0.175 M of CH_3NH_2 ($K_b = 5.0 \times 10^{-4}$) with 250. mL of 0.125 M of $CH_3NH_3^+ Cl^-$. Given this information,

   a) What is pH of this buffer solution?

      When a solution of CH_3NH_2 (a weak base) and $CH_3NH_3^+ Cl^-$ (its common ion salt) are mixed, a buffered solution forms. When two solutions are mixed, the concentration of each component in the solution is now more dilute. Thus, the *dilution formula*:

      $$\mathbf{V_1 \cdot C_1 = V_2 \cdot C_2}$$

      needs to be used to obtain the concentration of each component making up the buffer.

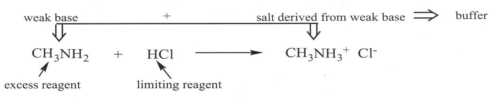

Total solution volume (assuming that the volumes are additive) = 400 . mL (150. + 250.)

$[CH_3NH_2]$ = 0.0656 M → (150. mL • 0.175 M) = (400. mL • C_2)

$[CH_3NH_3^+ Cl^-]$ = 0.0781 M → (250. mL • 0.125 M) = (400. mL • C_2)

If the moles of each substance were desired, since:

$$\textbf{mol} = \textbf{M}\left(\frac{\textbf{mol}}{\textbf{L}}\right) \textbf{x L}$$

the number of moles of each component in the buffer is:

mol CH_3NH_2 = 0.0262 → (0.175 mol/L • 0.150 L)

mol $CH_3NH_3^+ Cl^-$ = 0.0312 → (0.125 mol/L • 0.250 L)

Now, we can substitute into the weak base buffer formula. Remember that we can either use moles or molarity. The same answer would be obtained either way. Using the molarity of each component in the buffer we have:

$$[OH^-] = \frac{b}{s} K_b = \frac{0.0656}{0.0781}(5.0 \times 10^{-4}) = 4.2 \times 10^{-4}$$

$$pOH = -\log[OH^-] = -\log(4.2 \times 10^{-4}) = 3.38$$

$$pH + pOH = 14.00 \rightarrow pH + 3.38 = 14.00 \rightarrow pH = 14.00 - 3.38 = 10.62$$

b) What is the pH after the addition of 20.0 mL of 0.190 M of HCl to the above buffer solution?

When HCl (an acid) is added, it reacts with the base component (CH_3NH_2) of the buffer. The addition of an HCl solution to the buffer solution causes further dilution of the concentration of each component of the buffer, as well as, to the HCl solution itself. However, the initial moles of each component does not change prior to them undergoing an acid-base reaction. Thus, *in problems involving the mixing of solutions, it is more convenient to work with moles*.

In the previous problem we obtained the number of moles of each buffer component. Now all we need to do is obtain the moles of HCl that were added: (0.190 M • 0.0200 L) = 0.00380 mol

	CH_3NH_2	+ HCl	→ $CH_3NH_3^+ Cl^-$
mol_i:	0.0262	0.0038	0.0312
mol_{change}:	-0.00380	-0.00380	+0.00380
mol_{end}:	0.0224	0	0.0350

$$[OH^-] = \frac{b}{s} K_b = \frac{0.0224}{0.0350}(5.0 \times 10^{-4}) = 3.2 \times 10^{-4}$$

$$pOH = -\log[OH^-] = -\log(3.2 \times 10^{-4}) = 3.49$$

$$pH + pOH = 14.00 \rightarrow pH + 3.49 = 14.00 \qquad pH = 14.00 - 3.49 = 10.51$$

Notice how the addition of HCl hardly changed the pH [10.62 → 10.51].

c) What is the pH after the addition of 25.0 mL of 0.110 M of NaOH to the above buffer solution?

When NaOH (a base) is added, it reacts with the acid component ($CH_3NH_3^+ Cl^-$, which is a Brønsted acid -- a proton donor) of the buffer . As previously stated, in problems involving the mixing of solutions, it is more convenient to work with moles.

In problem 4a, we obtained the number of moles of each buffer component. Now all we need to do is obtain the moles of NaOH that were added: (0.110 M • 0.0250 L) = 0.0028

	$CH_3NH_3^+ Cl^-$	+	NaOH	→	CH_3NH_2	+	NaCl + H_2O
mol_i:	0.0312		0.0028		0.0262		
mol_{change}:	-0.0028		-0.0028		+0.0028		
mol_{end}:	0.0284		0		0.0290		

$$[OH^-] = \frac{b}{s} K_b = \frac{0.0290}{0.0284}(5.0 \times 10^{-4}) = 5.1 \times 10^{-4}$$

$$pOH = -\log[OH^-] = -\log(5.1 \times 10^{-4}) = 3.29$$

$$pH + pOH = 14.00 \rightarrow pH + 3.29 = 14.00 \rightarrow pH = 14.00 - 3.29 = 10.71$$

Notice how the addition of NaOH hardly changed the pH [10.62 → 10.71].

5. How many grams of CH_3NH_2 ($K_b = 5.0 \times 10^{-4}$, MM = 31.0) must be added to 400. mL of a 0.200 M $CH_3NH_3^+ Cl^-$ solution so that the pH of the buffer is 8.00. Assume no change in volume.

In order to use the weak base buffer formula, we need to: 1) convert pH into $[OH^-]$, 2) find mol of s ($CH_3NH_3^+ Cl^-$), 3) solve for b (CH_3NH_2) - which will be in mole, and 4) convert mol CH_3NH_2 into grams.

$$pH + pOH = 14.00$$

$$8.00 + pOH = 14.00$$

$$pOH = 14.00 - 8.00 = 6.00 \rightarrow [OH^-] = 10^{-pOH} = 10^{-6}$$

$$[OH^-] = \frac{b}{s} K_b$$

$$10^{-6} = \frac{b}{(0.200 \text{ M} \times 0.400 \text{ L})}(5.0 \times 10^{-4})$$

$$b = \frac{(10^{-6} \times 0.200 \times 0.400)}{5.0 \times 10^{-4}} = 1.60 \times 10^{-4} \text{ mol } CH_3NH_2$$

$$? \text{ g } CH_3NH_2 = 1.60 \times 10^{-4} \text{ mol } CH_3NH_2 \left(\frac{31.0 \text{ g } CH_3NH_2}{1 \text{ mol } CH_3NH_2}\right) = 4.96 \times 10^{-3} \text{ g}$$

EXERCISES

The following ionization constants will be necessary in answering several of the following questions.

Acid	K_a
HIO_3	1.7×10^{-1}
HNO_2	4.5×10^{-4}
CH_3COOH ($HC_2H_3O_2$)	1.8×10^{-5}

base	K_b
CH_3NH_2	5.0×10^{-4}
NH_3	1.8×10^{-5}
$(CH_3)_3N$	7.4×10^{-5}

Buffers

1. A solution composed of which of the following would be expected to act as a buffer?
   a) HOCl and NaOCl b) CsBr and HBr c) CH_3NH_2 and CH_3NH_3Cl
   d) $NaHSO_3$ and H_2SO_3 e) CH_3COOH and CH_3COOK f) NaOH and NaCl
2. What is the concentration (in mol/L) of $NaNO_2$, given that a buffer having 0.200 M HNO_2 and an unknown amount of $NaNO_2$ has a pH of 3.80?
3. What is the pH of a solution that contains 0.330 M HNO_2 and 0.210 M $NaNO_2$?
4. What mass, in grams, of $NaC_2H_3O_2$ (sodium acetate, MM = 82.0) must be added to 500. mL of 0.200 M CH_3COOH (acetic acid) to prepare a pH = 5.00 solution? Assume that the volume of the solution does not change when the sodium acetate is added.
5. Before calculating the pH for each of the following solutions, arrange them in order of increasing pH. Explain your order. [NOTE: The volume of each solution is the same.]
   a) 0.500 M CH_3COOH + 0.500 M CH_3COONa
   b) 0.500 M CH_3COOH + 0.200 M CH_3COONa
   c) 0.200 M CH_3COOH + 0.500 M CH_3COONa
6. A solution contains 500 mL of 0.200 M HNO_2 and 0.563 M $NaNO_2$:
   a) What is the pH of this buffer?
   b) What is pH of the buffer solution after 50.0 mL of 0.500 M HCl have been added to it?
   c) What is the pH of the buffer solution after 50.0 mL of 0.500 M NaOH have been added to it?
7. What is the pH of a buffer prepared by mixing 0.25 mol of $(CH_3)_3N$ and 0.40 mol of $(CH_3)_3NH^+Cl^-$ in 500 mL of solution?
8. A buffer having 0.180 M NH_3 and an unknown amount of $NH_4^+Cl^-$ has a pH of 9.49. Given this information, what is the molarity of $NH_4^+Cl^-$?
9. A buffer solution is 2.10 M in NH_3 and 2.40 M NH_4Cl.
   a) What is the pH of this buffer?
   b) If 260. mL of the buffer are mixed with 20.0 mL of 2.90 M HCl, then what is the pH of the solution?
10. A buffer solution is 2.80 M in CH_3NH_2 and 2.10 M $CH_3NH_3^+Cl^-$. If 130 mL of the buffer are mixed with 31.0 mL of 4.00 M NaOH, what is the final pH of the solution?
11. Calculate the initial pH and the pH after 0.0100 mol of $HCl_{(g)}$ have been added to 250. mL of the following solutions.
    a) 0.0500 M NH_3 / 0.150 M NH_4Cl b) 0.500 M NH_3 /1.50 M NH_4Cl

    After perfoming the above calculations, answer the following questions.
    c) Is the initial pH the same for both solutions? EXPLAIN.
    d) Is the buffering capacity for each of the solutions different? EXPLAIN.

MULTIPLE CHOICE PRACTICE EXAM FOR MODULE 7

1. The addition of NaF to an aqueous solution of HF will:
   1) decrease the pH of the solution.
   2) increase the pH of the solution.
   3) not affect the pH of the solution.
   4) increase the % ionization of HF.
   5) Two of the above choices are correct.

2. An equimolar solution composed of which of the following would act as a buffer.
   1) $HClO_4$ and $LiClO_4$ 2) $C_6H_5NH_2$ and $C_6H_5NH_3^+Cl^-$ 3) HBrO and NaOH
   4) Two of the above choices are correct.
   5) All of the above choices are correct.

3. What is the pH of a solution that is 0.100 M HCN ($K_a = 4.0 \times 10^{-10}$) and 0.0500 M $Ba(CN)_2$?
   1) 9.10 2) 9.40 3) 4.60 4) 11.70 5) 4.90

4. What is the $[OH^-]$ (in M) of a solution that is 0.20 M NH_3 ($K_b = 1.8 \times 10^{-5}$) and 0.30 M $NH_4^+Cl^-$?
   1) 2.4×10^{-7} 2) 6.4×10^{-4} 3) 4.5×10^{-6} 4) 1.2×10^{-5} 5) 2.7×10^{-5}

5. Calculate the ratio of $[HC_2H_3O_2]/[NaC_2H_3O_2]$ that would yield a solution with a pH of 5.00. K_a ($HC_2H_3O_2$) = 1.8×10^{-5}
   1) 0.56 2) 0.63 3) 0.36 4) 0.44 5) 0.28

Consider the following information when answering questions 6 - 8.

Given that a buffer solution is 4.2 M $(CH_3)_3N$ ($K_b = 7.4 \times 10^{-5}$) and 2.7 M $(CH_3)_3NH^+Cl^-$, then:

6. What is the $[H^+]$ (in M) in the buffer?
   1) 8.69×10^3 2) 3.94 3) 7.4×10^{-5} 4) 1.15×10^{-4} 5) 8.70×10^{-11}

7. If 120. mL of the buffer solution are mixed with 22.0 mL of 3.40 M NaOH, then what will be the resulting pH?
   1) 9.87 2) 9.97 3) 10.24 4) 10.06 5) 10.57

8. If 120. mL of the buffer solution are mixed with 25.0 mL of 3.00 M HI, then what will be the resulting pH?
   1) 10.24 2) 9.50 3) 4.13 4) 9.90 5) 0.286

Consider the following information when answering questions 9 - 11.

Given that a solution contains 3.60 M C_6H_5COOH ($K_a = 6.6 \times 10^{-5}$) and 2.40 M C_6H_5COOK, then:

9. What is the $[OH^-]$ (in mol/L)?
   1) 4.4×10^{-5} 2) 2.3×10^{-10} 3) 1.5×10^{-2} 4) 1.0×10^{-10} 5) 9.9×10^{-5}

10. If 200. mL of the initial solution are mixed with 13.0 mL of 3.60 M HBr, then what will the resulting pH be?
    1) 4.43 2) 4.00 3) 3.93 4) 3.82 5) 5.14

11. What is the pH after 0.200 mol of KOH are added to 500. mL of the intial solution? Assume that there is no change in volume.
    1) 4.06 2) 3.89 3) 5.14 4) 4.24 5) 4.12

12. How many grams of HNO_2 (K_a = 4.5 x 10^{-4}, MM = 47.0) must be added to 2.00 L of 0.500 M $LiNO_2$ in order to prepare a pH 3.79 buffer? Assume that there is no change in volume.
1) 17. 2) 8.5 3) 47. 4) 0.36 5) 0.18

13. If equal volumes of the following solutions are mixed, which would act as a buffer?
1) 1 M HF + 1 M NaOH
2) 2 M HF + 1 M NaOH
3) 1 M HF + 2 M NaOH
4) More than one of the above.
5) None of the above.

14. If 0.30 mol of $CH_3COOH_{(l)}$ (pK_a = 4.7) are mixed with 0.030 mol of $NaC_2H_3O_{2\,(s)}$, the solution's pH will be ______. If this solution, was then diluted with water so that the total volume was double of what its initial volume was, the resulting pH of the solution will be ______.
1) 3.7 ; 3 .7. 2) 3.7 ; 4.7 3) 4.7 ; 3.7 4) 5.7 ; 5.7
5) There is not enough information given in the problem to answer this question.

15. If equal volumes of the following solutions are mixed, which statement is **false**?

Solution A. 1.0 M HF + 1.0 M NaF
Solution B. 1.0 M HF + 0.80 M KF
Solution C. 0.10 M HF + 0.10 M LiF
Solution D. 0.10 M HF + 0.080 M LiF

1) The pH of Solution A is greater than that of Solution B.
2) The pH of Solution A is the same as that of Solution C.
3) The buffering capacity of Solution A is greater than that of Solution C.
4) The [H^+] in Solution B is greater than that in Solution D.
5) None of the above.

16. Consider the following equilibrium: [ENRICHMENT]

$$CO_3^{2-}{}_{(aq)} + H_2O_{(l)} \rightleftharpoons HCO_3^-{}_{(aq)} + OH^-{}_{(aq)}$$

Which of the following would cause a shift in the equilibrium in the indicated direction?
1) Addition of a small amount of $HCl_{(aq)}$: shift right
2) Addition of a small amount of $NaHCO_{3\,(s)}$: no shift
3) pH increase: shift right
4) More than one of the above.
5) None of the above.

MODULE 7 - ANSWERS

1. The most common type of buffers are composed of a weak acid-weak base conjugate pair. Stated another way, the most common type of buffer is composed of a weak acid and a salt derived from the weak acid [this applies to: a, d, and e] or a weak base and a salt derived from the weak base [this applies to: c]
2. 0.568 M
3. 3.15
4. 14.8 g
5. b < a < c The solution that has the greatest molar ratio of acid:salt will be the most acidic and will have the lowest pH. From the weak acid buffer formula:

$$[H^+] = \frac{a}{s} K_a$$

   we see that the greater the ratio of acid (a) to salt (s), the greater the $[H^+]$, which leads to the solution being more acidic and thus having a lower pH.

   a) 4.74 b) 4.35 c) 5.14
6. a) 3.80 b) 3.66 c) 3.96
7. 9.67
8. 0.10 M
9. a) 9.20 b) 9.11
10. 11.21
11. a) pH initial = 8.77, pH after addition of HCl = 7.97
    b) pH initial = 8.77, pH after addition of HCl = 8.73
    c) Yes. The pH is the same for both solutions because the molar ratio of base:salt is the same for both solutions.
    d) Yes. Even though the initial pH is the same for both solutions, their buffering capacity is different because solution b has a greater concentration of base (i.e., NH_3) in the buffer. The greater the concentration of the components in a buffer, the more the buffer is able to withstand changes in pH when either an acid or a base is added.

ANSWERS TO MULTIPLE CHOICE PRACTICE EXAM

1	2	3	4	5	6	7	8	9	10	11	12	13	14	15	16
2	2	2	4	1	5	3	4	4	3	5	1	2	1	4	1

MODULE 8. *Hydrolysis*

I. Hydrolysis

In this module we will be discussing the acidity, bascity, or neutrality of soluble salts. When a soluble salt is placed in water, it will completely ionize in water. The ions produced can then react with water to form an acidic, basic, or neutral solution. What this means is that compounds other than acids (HA) can be acidic (i.e., produce H^+ or H_3O^+ in water). Likewise, compounds other than bases (MOH or nitrogenous bases) can be basic (i.e., produce OH^- in water).

In this module we will discuss what salts hydrolyze (i.e., react with water) to form acidic, basic, or neutral solutions.

The following is an illustration of steps that lead to the hydrolysis of ions.

1) Complete Ionization of Soluble Salt to Produce Respective Ions

$$\underbrace{M}X \xrightarrow{H_2O} M^+ + X^- \quad \text{or} \quad \underbrace{BH}X \xrightarrow{H_2O} BH^+ + X^-$$

monatomic cation (M); cation derived from ammonia or one of its derivatives (BH)

2) Possible Reaction of Ions with Water (Hydrolysis)

The ions produced will undergo hydrolysis if the product of hydrolysis is a weak electrolyte. Remember that weak electrolytes do not completely ionize in water (i.e., they stay partially intact). In the hydrolysis of an ion, the weak electrolyte formed is either a weak acid or a weak base. Remember that there are very few strong acids and bases -- those that are not strong are therefore weak. Again, you must remember which are the strong acids and bases.

A solution of a soluble salt will be acidic, basic or neutral, depending on which of the following individual scenarios predominate.

Ion hydrolysis occurs if a weak electrolyte is formed.

$$BH^+ \underset{}{\overset{H\text{-}OH}{\rightleftharpoons}} B + H_3O^+$$

BH^+: cation from salt; B: weak base and weak electrolyte

(solution is acidic because H_3O^+ is produced)

$$X^- \overset{H\text{-}OH}{\rightleftharpoons} HX + OH^-$$

X^-: anion from salt; HX: weak acid and weak electrolyte

(solution is basic because OH^- is produced)

No ion hydrolysis occurs if a strong electrolyte is formed.

$$M^+ \overset{H\text{-}OH}{\rightleftharpoons} MOH + H^+$$

M^+: cation from salt; MOH: strong base and strong electrolyte

$$MOH \longrightarrow M^+ + OH^-$$

(OH^- and H^+ together: H_2O)

Since the products are the same as the reactants (M^+ and H_2O), no hydrolysis occurs and the solution is neutral.

$$X^- \overset{H\text{-}OH}{\rightleftharpoons} HX + OH^-$$

X^-: anion from salt; HX: strong acid and strong electrolyte

$$HX \longrightarrow X^- + H^+$$

(OH^- and H^+ together: H_2O)

Since the products are the same as the reactants (X^- and H_2O), no hydrolysis occurs and the solution is neutral.

In the sections below we will discuss how to recognize which salts hydrolyze to form acidic, basic or neutral solutions.

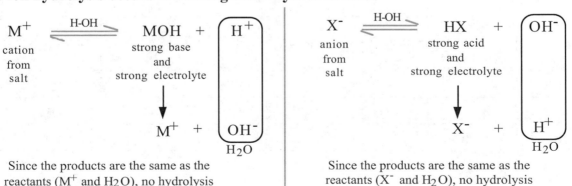

II. Hydrolysis Equilbrium Constants

Consider the following weak acid equilibrium:

$$HA \rightleftharpoons H^+ + A^- \qquad K_a = \frac{[H^+]\,[A^-]}{[HA]}$$

The hydrolysis constant for the conjugate base (A^-) of the weak acid (HA) is really nothing more than a base hydrolysis constant, K_b.

$$A^- \xrightarrow{\text{H-OH}} \underset{\text{weak acid}}{HA} + OH^- \qquad K_b = \frac{[HA]\,[OH^-]}{[A^-]}$$

Consider the following weak base equilibrium:

$$-\ddot{N}- \xrightarrow{\text{H-OH}} -\overset{H}{\underset{|}{\overset{+}{N}}}- + OH^- \qquad K_b = \frac{\left[-\overset{H}{\underset{|}{\overset{+}{N}}}-\right][OH^-]}{\left[-\ddot{N}-\right]}$$

The hydrolysis constant for the conjugate acid $\left(-\overset{H}{\underset{|}{\overset{+}{N}}}-\right)$ of the weak base $\left(-\ddot{N}-\right)$ is really nothing more than an acid hydrolysis constant, K_a.

$$-\overset{H}{\underset{|}{\overset{+}{N}}}- \xrightarrow{\text{H-OH}} \underset{\text{weak base}}{\left[-\ddot{N}-\right]} + H_3O^+ \qquad K_a = \frac{\left[-\ddot{N}-\right][H_3O^+]}{\left[-\overset{H}{\underset{|}{\overset{+}{N}}}-\right]}$$

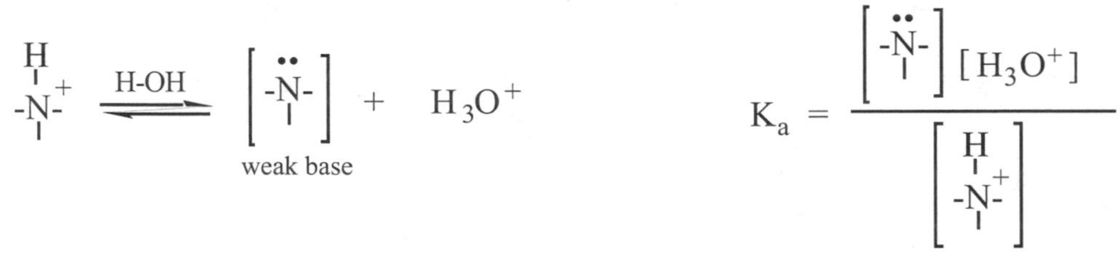

K_a and K_b (for any conjugate acid-base pair) is related to K_w (ion-product for water) in the following manner.

$$K_w = K_a\,K_b \qquad (K_w = 1.0 \times 10^{-14}\ @\ 25°C)$$

NOTE: Assume that all hydrolysis reactions are conducted at 25°C, unless otherwise noted.

The following table gives examples of conjugate acid-base pairs along with their respective K_a and K_b. Note that conjugate acid-base pairs differ from each other by an H^+. An acid (e.g., HF) has one more H than its conjugate base (e.g., F^-). Likewise, a base (e.g., NH_3) has one less H than its conjugate acid (e.g., NH_4^+).

Acid	K_a acid ionization constant	Conjugate base	K_b base hydrolysis constant	Base	K_b base ionization constant	Conjugate Acid	K_a acid hydrolysis constant
HF	7.2×10^{-4}	F^-	1.4×10^{-11}	NH_3	1.8×10^{-5}	NH_4^+	5.6×10^{-10}
$HC_2H_3O_2$	1.8×10^{-5}	$C_2H_3O_2^-$	5.6×10^{-10}	CH_3NH_2	5.0×10^{-5}	$CH_3NH_3^+$	2.0×10^{-10}
HCN	4.0×10^{-10}	CN^-	2.5×10^{-5}	$C_6H_5NH_2$	4.2×10^{-10}	$C_6H_5NH_3^+$	2.4×10^{-5}

III. Salts that are Neutral (pH = 7)

A soluble salt will be neutral if its:

a) **cation** is derived from a <u>strong base</u> [metals from -- IA and IIA (except: Be^{2+} and Mg^{2+})]

b) **anion** is derived from a <u>strong acid</u> [Cl^-, Br^-, I^-, ClO_4^-, ClO_3^-, NO_3^-]

Salts that are neutral have pH = 7, pOH = 7, $[H^+] = 10^{-7}$ M, $[OH^-] = 10^{-7}$ M.

<u>Example Problems</u>

1. Which of the following salts is expected to yield a neutral solution?

    a) KNO_3

    This salt will yield a neutral solution because K^+ is derived from a strong base (KOH) and NO_3^- is derived from a strong acid (HNO_3).

    b) CuCl

    This salt will <u>not</u> yield a neutral solution because Cu^+ is <u>not</u> derived from a strong base (CuOH).

    c) $CsClO_3$

    This salt will yield a neutral solution because Cs^+ is derived from a strong base (CsOH) and ClO_3^- is derived from a strong acid ($HClO_3$).

IV. Salts that are Acidic (pH < 7)

A soluble salt will be acidic if its:

a) **cation** is derived from a <u>weak base</u> [The most common weak bases are ammonia and its derivatives, amines. Cations from these weak bases have the general formula given on page 2.]

b) **anion** is derived from a <u>strong acid</u> [Cl^-, Br^-, I^-, ClO_4^-, ClO_3^-, NO_3^-]

Step 1. Ionization of Salt

$$
\underbrace{-\overset{\overset{\textstyle H}{|}}{\underset{|}{N}}{}^+}_{\substack{\text{cation derived from a} \\ \text{weak nitrogenous base}}} \underbrace{X^-}_{\substack{\text{anion derived from} \\ \text{strong acid}}} \xrightarrow{\ H_2O\ } -\overset{\overset{\textstyle H}{|}}{\underset{|}{N}}{}^+ \ + \ \underset{\substack{\text{ion does} \\ \text{not} \\ \text{hydrolyze}}}{X^-}
$$

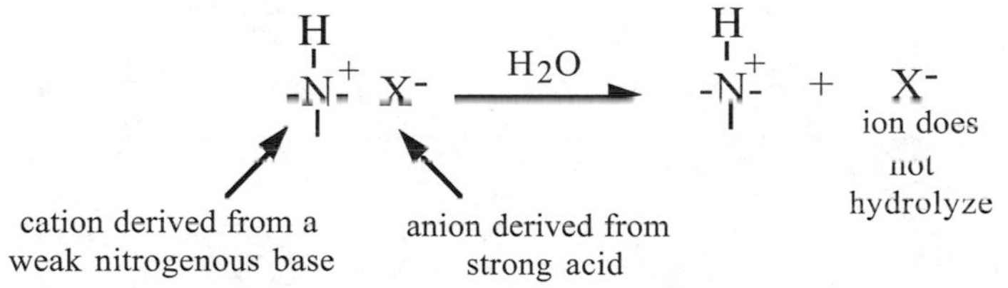

Step 2. Hydrolysis of Cation to Yield an Acidic Solution

$$
-\overset{\overset{\textstyle H}{|}}{\underset{|}{N}}{}^+ \ \overset{H_2O}{\rightleftharpoons} \ \underset{\text{weak base}}{\left[-\overset{\cdot\cdot}{\underset{|}{N}}-\right]} \ + \ H_3O^+ \qquad\qquad K_a = \dfrac{\left[-\overset{\cdot\cdot}{\underset{|}{N}}-\right][H_3O^+]}{\left[-\overset{\overset{\textstyle H}{|}}{\underset{|}{N}}{}^+-\right]}
$$

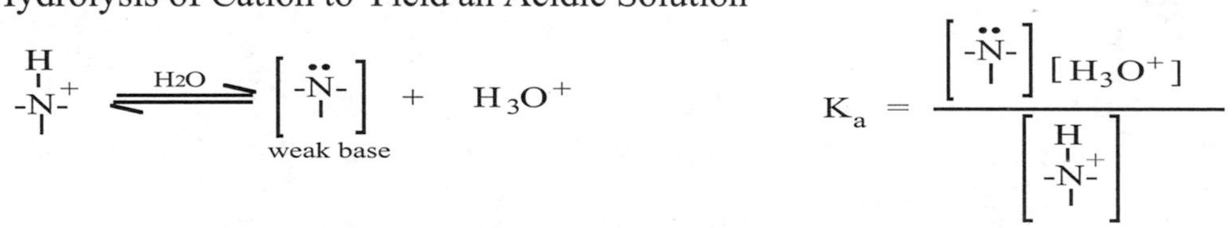

To find the H^+, OH^-, pH, and pOH of a salt that yields an acidic solution, we must evaluate the equilibrium expression for the hydrolysis of the cation as shown above.

The % hydrolysis for a salt that are acidic is given as:

$$
\%\ \text{hydrolysis} = \frac{\left[-\overset{\overset{\textstyle H}{|}}{\underset{|}{N}}-\right]^+_c}{\left[-\overset{\overset{\textstyle H}{|}}{\underset{|}{N}}-\right]^+_i} \times 100
$$

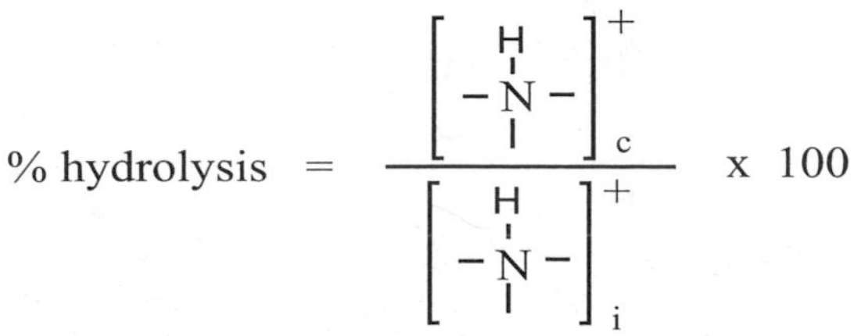

NOTE:

$[-NH^+]_c = [H_3O^+]_e = [H^+]_e$

i = initial, c = change, e = equil.

Example Problems

1. Which of the following salts is expected to yield an acidic solution?
   a) NaCl

      This salt will not yield an acidic solution because Na^+ is not derived from a weak base (NaOH). As a matter of fact, this solution will be neutral because Na^+ is derived from a strong base (NaOH) and Cl^- is derived from a strong acid (HCl).

   b) $CH_3NH_3^+Br^-$

      This salt will yield an acidic solution because $CH_3NH_3^+$ is derived from a weak amine base (CH_3NH_2) and Br^- is derived from a strong acid (HBr).

   c) $C_5H_5NH^+ NO_3^-$

      This salt will yield an acidic solution because $C_5H_5NH^+$ is derived from a weak amine base (C_5H_5N) and NO_3^- is derived from a strong acid (HNO_3).

2. For a 0.100 M $NH_4^+Cl^-$ solution, calculate: $K_b (NH_3) = 1.8 \times 10^{-5}$.
   a) The solution's pH.

      Cl^- will not hydrolyze, but NH_4^+ will. For every one mole of $NH_4^+Cl^-$ that ionizes, one mole of NH_4^+ will be produced.

	NH_4^+	$\overset{H_2O}{\rightleftharpoons}$	NH_3	+	H_3O^+
[ ]$_i$:	0.100		0		0
[ ]$_{change}$:	-x		+x		+x
[ ]$_{equil}$:	0.100 - x		x		x

The equilibrium expression, is:

$$K_a = \frac{[NH_3]\,[H_3O^+]}{[NH_4^+]} \quad \text{where,} \quad K_a = \frac{K_w}{K_b} = \frac{1.0 \times 10^{-14}}{1.8 \times 10^{-5}} = 5.6 \times 10^{-10}$$

$$5.6 \times 10^{-10} = \frac{(x)\ (x)}{(0.100 - x)}$$

Assume that x is small

Since K_a (5.6×10^{-10}) < [ ]$_i \times 10^{-2}$ (0.100×10^{-2}), x will be assumed to be small in comparison to the initial concentration of 0.100 and as such will be neglected.

$$5.6 \times 10^{-11} = x^2$$

$$x = \sqrt{5.6 \times 10^{-11}} = 7.5 \times 10^{-6}$$

Our assumption that x was small in comparison to the initial concentration was correct. ***A small x is considered one that is less than 10% of the initial concentration.***

[x (7.5×10^{-6}) < 10% x [ ]$_i$ ($0.1 \times 0.100 = 0.0100$)]

$$x = [H_3O^+] = [H^+] = 7.5 \times 10^{-6}\ M$$

$$pH = -\log [H^+] = -\log (7.5 \times 10^{-6}) = 5.13$$

   b) The % hydrolysis.

$$\%\ \text{hydrolysis} = \frac{[H_3O^+]_e}{[NH_4^+]_i} \times 100 = \frac{7.5 \times 10^{-6}}{0.100} \times 100 = 0.0075\ \%$$

3. If the pH of a solution made by dissolving 0.125 mole of $CH_3NH_3^+I^-$ into enough distilled water to produce 500. mL of solution was found to be 5.15, then calculate the K_b of CH_3NH_2.

I^- will not hydrolyze, but $CH_3NH_3^+$ will. For every one mole of $CH_3NH_3^+I^-$ that ionizes, one mole of $CH_3NH_3^+$ will be produced.

	$CH_3NH_3^+$	$\overset{H_2O}{\rightleftharpoons}$	CH_3NH_2	+	H_3O^+
$[\ ]_i$:	$\frac{0.125 \text{ mol}}{0.500 \text{ L}}$		0		0
$[\ ]_{change}$:	-x		+x		+x
$[\ ]_{equil}$:	0.250 - x		x		x

$x = [H_3O^+] = [H^+]$ can be obtained from the pH.

$[H^+] = 10^{-pH} = 10^{-5.15} = 7.1 \times 10^{-6} = x$

The equilibrium expression, is:

$$K_a = \frac{[CH_3NH_2]\,[H_3O^+]}{[CH_3NH_3^+]}$$

$$K_a = \frac{(7.1 \times 10^{-6})\,(7.1 \times 10^{-6})}{(0.250 - 7.1 \times 10^{-6})} = 2.0 \times 10^{-10}$$

$$K_b \text{ (for } CH_3NH_2) = \frac{K_w}{K_a} = \frac{1.0 \times 10^{-14}}{2.0 \times 10^{-10}} = 5.0 \times 10^{-5}$$

V. **Salts that are Basic (pH > 7)**

A soluble salt will be basic if its:

a) **cation** is derived from a strong base [metal ion from -- IA and IIA (except: Be^{2+} and Mg^{2+})]

b) **anion** is derived from a weak acid [anion othcr than Cl^-, Br^-, I^-, ClO_4^-, ClO_3^-, NO_3^-]

Step 1. Ionization of Salt

$$\underset{\text{salt}}{MX} \xrightarrow{H_2O} \underset{\text{ion does not hydrolyze}}{M^+} + X^-$$

Step 2. Hydrolysis of Anion to Yield a Basic Solution

$$X^- \overset{H\text{-}OH}{\rightleftharpoons} \underset{\text{weak acid}}{HX} + OH^- \qquad K_b = \frac{[HX]\,[OH^-]}{[X^-]}$$

To find the H^+, OH^-, pH, and pOH of a salt that yields a basic solution, we must evaluate the equilibrium expression for the hydrolysis of the anion as shown above.

The % hydrolysis for a salt that is basic is given as:

$$\% \text{ hydrolsis} = \frac{[X^-]_c}{[X^-]_i} \times 100$$

NOTE: $\mathbf{[X^-]_c = [OH^-]_e}$

i = initial, c = change, e = equil.

Example Problems

1. Which of the following salts is expected to yield a basic solution?

   a) LiI

   This salt will not yield a basic solution because I^- is not derived from a weak acid (HI). As a matter of fact, this solution will be neutral because Li^+ is derived from a strong base (LiOH) and I^- is derived from a strong acid (HI).

   b) $NaNO_2$

   This salt will yield a basic solution because Na^+ is derived from a strong base (NaOH) and NO_2^- is derived from a weak acid (HNO_2) and will hydrolyze to yield OH^-.

2. For 500. mL of a 0.100 M NaClO solution, calculate: K_a (HClO) = 3.5 x 10^{-8}.

   a) The solution's pH.

   Na^+ will not hydrolyze, but ClO^- will. For every one mole of NaClO that ionizes, one mole of ClO^- will be produced.

	ClO^-	$\xrightleftharpoons{\text{H-OH}}$	HClO	+	OH^-
$[\ ]_i$:	0.100		0		0
$[\ ]_{change}$:	-x		+x		+x
$[\ ]_{equil}$:	0.100 - x		x		x

The equilibrium expression, is:

$$K_b = \frac{[HClO][OH^-]}{[ClO^-]} \quad \text{where,} \quad K_b = \frac{K_w}{K_a} = \frac{1.0 \times 10^{-14}}{3.5 \times 10^{-8}} = 2.9 \times 10^{-7}$$

$$2.9 \times 10^{-7} = \frac{(x)\ (x)}{(0.100 - x)}$$

Assume that x is small

Since K_b (2.9 x 10^{-7}) < $[\ ]_i$ x 10^{-2} (0.100 x 10^{-2}), x will be assumed to be small in comparison to the initial concentration of 0.100 and as such will be neglected.

$$2.9 \times 10^{-8} = x^2$$

$$x = \sqrt{2.9 \times 10^{-8}} = 1.7 \times 10^{-4}$$

$$x = [OH^-] = 1.7 \times 10^{-4}$$

Our assumption that x was small in comparison to the initial concentration was correct. ***A small x is considered one that is less than 10% of the initial concentration.***

[x (1.7 x 10^{-4}) < 10% x $[\ ]_i$ (0.1 x 0.100 = 0.0100)]

$$pOH = -\log[OH^-] = -\log(1.7 \times 10^{-4}) - 3.77$$

$$pH + pOH = 14.00$$

$$pH = 14.00 - 3.77 = 10.23$$

   b) The % hydrolysis.

$$\%\ \text{hydrolysis} = \frac{[OH^-]_e}{[ClO^-]_i} \times 100 = \frac{1.7 \times 10^{-4}}{0.100} \times 100 = 0.17\ \%$$

3. How many grams of NaCN (MM = 49.0) would you need to dissolve in enough water to make 250. mL of a pH 10.00 solution? [K_a (HCN) = 4.0 x 10^{-10}]

   Na^+ will not hydrolyze, but CN^- will. For every one mole of NaCN that ionizes, one mole of CN^- will be produced.

The initial concentration of NaCN = CN^- is not given; we will call it x.

	CN^-	$\underset{}{\overset{H\text{-}OH}{\rightleftharpoons}}$	HCN	+	OH^-
$[\ ]_i$:	x		0		0
$[\ ]_{change}$:	-y		+y		+y
$[\ ]_{equil}$:	x - y		y		y

y = $[OH^-]$ can be obtained from the pH.

$[H^+] = 10^{-pH} = 10^{-10.00} = 1.0 \times 10^{-10}$

$$[H^+]\,[OH^-] = K_w \quad \rightarrow \quad [OH^-] = \frac{K_w}{[H^+]} = \frac{1.0 \times 10^{-14}}{1.0 \times 10^{-10}} = 1.0 \times 10^{-4} = y$$

The equilibrium expression, is:

$$K_b = \frac{[HCN]\,[OH^-]}{[CN^-]} \qquad \text{where, } K_b = \frac{K_w}{K_a} = \frac{1.0 \times 10^{-14}}{4.0 \times 10^{-10}} = 2.5 \times 10^{-5}$$

$$K_b = \frac{(1.0 \times 10^{-4})\,(1.0 \times 10^{-4})}{(x - 1.0 \times 10^{-4})} = 2.5 \times 10^{-5}$$

$$(2.5 \times 10^{-5}\ x) - (2.5 \times 10^{-9}) = (1.0 \times 10^{-4})^2$$

$$x = \frac{(1.0 \times 10^{-4})^2 + (2.5 \times 10^{-9})}{2.5 \times 10^{-5}} = 5.0 \times 10^{-4}\ M \rightarrow [CN^-] = [NaCN]$$

$$?\ g\ NaCN - 250\ mL\ soln \left(\frac{5.0 \times 10^{-4}\ mol\ NaCN}{1000\ mL\ soln}\right)\left(\frac{49.0\ g\ NaCN}{1\ mol\ NaCN}\right) = 6.1 \times 10^{-3}\ g$$

V. **Salts in Which Both Ions Hydrolyze (pH depends on which is larger K_a or K_b)**

Salts in which both ions hydrolyze can be either acidic, basic, or neutral. A salt in which both ions hydrolyze, is one in which its:

a) **cation** is derived from a weak base [The most common weak bases are ammonia and its derivatives - amines. Cations from these weak bases have the general formula given on page 2 of this module.]

b) **anion** is derived from a weak acid [anion other than Cl^-, Br^-, I^-, ClO_4^-, ClO_3^-, NO_3^-]

In order to decipher whether a solution of a salt in which both ions hydrolyze will be acidic, basic, or neutral, we must compare the ion's K_b and K_a .

A. If $\mathbf{K_a = K_b}$, then the salt will be **neutral**.

For example -- $NH_4C_2H_3O_2$ is a salt whose cation (NH_4^+, $K_a = 5.6 \times 10^{-10}$) is derived from a weak base (NH_3) and whose anion ($C_2H_3O_2^-$, $K_b = 5.6 \times 10^{-10}$) is derived from a weak acid ($HC_2H_3O_2$).

Since $K_a = K_b$, then this salt will be neutral (pH = 7).

B. If $\mathbf{K_a > K_b}$, then the salt will be **acidic**.

For example -- NH_4F is a salt whose cation (NH_4^+, $K_a = 5.6 \times 10^{-10}$) is derived from a weak base (NH_3) and whose anion (F^-, $K_b = 1.4 \times 10^{-11}$) is derived from a weak acid (HF).

Since $K_a > K_b$, then this salt will be acidic (pH < 7).

C. If $K_a < K_b$, then the salt will be **basic**.

For example -- NH_4CN is a salt whose cation (NH_4^+, $K_a = 5.6 \times 10^{-10}$) is derived from a weak base (NH_3) and whose anion (CN^-, $K_b = 2.5 \times 10^{-5}$) is derived from a weak acid (HCN).

Since $K_a < K_b$, then this salt will be basic (pH > 7).

Example Problems

Refer to the following table of K_a and K_b.

Substance	K_a	Substance	K_b
HF	7.2×10^{-4}	CH_3NH_2	5.0×10^{-5}
HCN	4.0×10^{-10}	$C_6H_5NH_2$	4.2×10^{-10}

1. Given the above table, predict if the pH of the following salt solutions will be acidic, basic, or neutral.

   a) $CH_3NH_3^+ F^-$

   $CH_3NH_3^+F^-$ is a salt whose cation ($CH_3NH_3^+$, $K_a = 2.0 \times 10^{-10}$) is derived from a weak base (CH_3NH_2) and whose anion (F^-, $K_b = 1.4 \times 10^{-11}$) is derived from a weak acid (HF).

   Since $K_a > K_b$, then this salt will be acidic (pH < 7).

   b) $C_6H_5NH_3^+CN^-$

   $C_6H_5NH_3^+CN^-$ is a salt whose cation ($C_6H_5NH_3^+$, $K_a = 2.4 \times 10^{-5}$) is derived from a weak base ($C_6H_5NH_2$) and whose anion (CN^-, $K_b = 2.5 \times 10^{-5}$) is derived from a weak acid (HCN).

   Since $K_a < K_b$ then this salt will be basic (pH > 7).

VI. **Salts that Contain Highly Positive Cations**

Metal ions with a high positive charge (+3, +4, etc.), hydrolyze in the following simplified fashion:

$$M^{3+} \xrightleftharpoons{\text{H-OH}} MOH^{2+} + H^+ \quad \Big\} \quad K_a = \frac{[H^+]\,[MOH^{2+}]}{[M^{3+}]}$$

If a cation's $K_a < 10^{-12}$, that ion will not appreciably hydrolyze in water. Cations with a +1 charge do not hydrolyze to any great extent. For cations in group IIA only Be^{2+} hydrolyzes to any significant extent. Transition and post-transtion metal ions having a charge of +2 or higher undergo hydrolysis.

The following table gives the first hydrolysis constant for several cations:

Cation	Li^+	Ag^+	Be^{2+}	Ca^{2+}	Cr^{3+}	Fe^{3+}	Sn^{4+}
K_a	2.5×10^{-14}	1×10^{-12}	4.0×10^{-6}	1.6×10^{-13}	1×10^{-4}	4×10^{-3}	4.0
	"no" hydrolysis			"no" hydrolysis			

As can be seen from the table, for ions having the same charge, the smaller the ion (e.g., $Be^{2+} < Ca^{2+}$), the larger the K_a, the more the ion hydrolyzes, and the greater its acidity will be.

Also, as can be seen from the table that the higher the charge on the cation, the larger the K_a, the more the ion hydrolyzes, and the greater its acidity will be.

Example Problems

1. A 0.10 M solution that contains which of the following metal ions -- Ba^{2+}, Ca^{2+}, or Be^{2+} -- will hydrolyze the most?

   The higher the charge and the smaller the ion, the more the ion will hydrolyze and the greater its acidity will be. Since all the ions have the same charge this will not be a determining factor. The determining factor will be ion size. Since Be^{2+} is the smallest ion, it will hydrolyze the most.

EXERCISES

Use the following table to solve several of the problems below.

Substance	K_a	Substance	K_b
HF	7.2 x 10^{-4}	NH_3	1.8 x 10^{-5}
$HC_2H_3O_2$	1.8 x 10^{-5}	CH_3NH_2	5.0 x 10^{-5}
HCN	4.0 x 10^{-10}	$C_6H_5NH_2$	4.2 x 10^{-10}
HOCN	3.5 x 10^{-4}	$CH_3CH_2NH_2$	5.6 x 10^{-4}
HNO_2	4.5 x 10^{-4}	$(CH_3)_2NH$	7.4 x 10^{-4}
HClO	3.5 x 10^{-8}	$(CH_3)_3N$	7.4 x 10^{-5}

1. Classify each of the following salts as acidic, basic, or neutral when placed in water. (You'll need to use the above table for those salts in which both ions hydrolyze.)
   a) $CsNO_3$ b) NH_4NO_3 c) Na_2CO_3
   d) $CoCl_2$ e) NH_4OCN f) $FeCl_3$
   g) $CH_3NH_3^+F^-$ h) $NH_4C_2H_3O_2$

2. Without using the above table, rank the following in order of increasing: a) acidity and b) pH [Assume that their concentration in water is the same.]
   A. KNO_3, KCN, $Be(NO_3)_2$, $Fe(NO_3)_3$
   B. RbCl, KCl, CsF, $ZrCl_2$, $FeCl_2$

3. Complete the following table.

Acid	K_a acid ionization constant	Conjugate base	K_b base hydrolysis constant	Base	K_b base ionization constant	Conjugate Acid	K_a acid hydrolysis constant
HClO	3.5 x 10^{-8}					NH_4^+	5.6 x 10^{-10}
	1.8 x 10^{-5}	$C_2H_3O_2^-$			7.4 x 10^{-5}	$(CH_3)_3NH^+$	
HCN			2.5 x 10^{-5}	$C_6H_5NH_2$			2.4 x 10^{-5}

4. Along with the table of K_a and K_b given on the top of the page, complete the following table.

Salt	Salt Conc., M	$[H^+]$	$[OH^-]$	pH	pOH	% hydrolysis
KNO_2	0.10					
LiCN				11.35		
$Ca(C_2H_3O_2)_2$	0.10					
$CH_3NH_3^+Br^-$	0.20					
$C_6H_5NH_3^+Cl^-$			7.5 x 10^{-12}			
NH_4I		5.6 x 10^{-6}				

5. Sodium benzoate (C_6H_5COONa) is a salt of the organic acid benzoic acid ($C_6H_5COO\underline{H}$). A 0.15 M solution of sodium benzoate has a pH of 8.67. Given this information,
   a) Calculate the value for the equilibrium constant for the following reaction.

$$C_6H_5COO^- \xrightleftharpoons{\text{H-OH}} C_6H_5COOH + OH^-$$

   b) What is the acid ionization constant for benzoic acid?

6. Aspirin is a weak monoprotic acid whose acid ionization constant is 3.27 x 10^{-4}. Is an aqueous solution of the sodium salt of aspirin -- acidic, basic, or neutral?

7. Calculate the mass (in g) of NH_4Br (MM = 97.9) needed to prepare 1.00-L of a pH 5.15 solution?

MULTIPLE CHOICE PRACTICE EXAM FOR MODULE 8

1. Which of the following salts yields a neutral aqueous solution?
   1) CsI 2) $Ca(NO_3)_2$ 3) KF
   4) Two of the above.
   5) All of the above.

2. Which of the following aqueous salt solutions could not possibly have the pH (@ 25°C) that is indicated?
   1) KCN (pH = 6.48) 2) NaF (pH = 7.00) 3) $(CH_3)_3NH^+ I^-$ (pH = 8.16)
   4) Two of the above.
   5) All of the above.

3. Which response includes all of the following salts that hydrolyze to yield a solution whose pH > 7 at 25°C?
   a. $Fe(NO_3)_3$ b. $Ba(C_2H_3O_2)_2$ c. NaF d. NH_4NO_3 e. Li_2S
   1) b, e 2) b, c, e 3) d 4) a, c, e 5) c, e

4. The hydrolysis reaction that occurs when $NH_4^+Cl^-$ dissolves in water is:
   1) $NH_4^+Cl^- \xrightleftharpoons{\text{H-OH}} NH_4^+ + OH^- + Cl^- + H^+$
   2) $Cl^- \xrightleftharpoons{\text{H-OH}} HCl + OH^-$
   3) $NH_4^+ \xrightleftharpoons{\text{H-OH}} NH_3 + H_3O^+$
   4) $NH_4^+ \xrightleftharpoons{\text{H-OH}} NH_5^+ + OH^-$
   5) $NH_4^+Cl^- \xrightleftharpoons{\text{H-OH}} NH_4^+ + Cl^-$

5. The hydrolysis reaction that occurs when $RbNO_2$ is placed in water is __________ and the pH of this solution would be _________.
   1) $RbNO_2 \xrightleftharpoons{\text{H-OH}} Rb^+ + OH^- + NO_2^- + H^+$; neutral
   2) $NO_2^- \xrightleftharpoons{\text{H-OH}} HNO_2 + OH^-$; basic
   3) $Rb^+ \xrightleftharpoons{\text{H-OH}} RbOH + H^+$; acidic
   4) $RbNO_2 \xrightleftharpoons{\text{H-OH}} Rb^+ + NO_2^-$; neutral
   5) This salt does not hydrolyze in water.

The following K_a's and K_b's will be useful in solving the problems 6 - 13.

Substance	K_a	Substance	K_b
HCN	4.0×10^{-10}	NH_3	1.8×10^{-5}
HNO_2	4.5×10^{-4}	$(CH_3)_2NH$	7.4×10^{-4}
HClO	3.5×10^{-8}	C_5H_5N	1.5×10^{-9}

6. What is the base hydrolysis constant (K_b) for CN^-?
   1) 2.5×10^{-5} 2) 4.0×10^{-24} 3) 5.6×10^{-10} 4) 4.0×10^{-10} 5) 4.0×10^{4}

7. What is the acid hydrolysis constant for $(CH_3)_2NH_2^+$?
   1) 7.4×10^{-18} 2) 1.4×10^{-11} 3) 7.4×10^{10} 4) 7.4×10^{-4}
   5) It is undefined.

8. Which of the following hydrolyze to produce an <u>acidic</u> solution?
   1) $NH_4^+ ClO^-$ 2) $C_5H_5NH^+ CN^-$ 3) $(CH_3)_2NH_2^+ NO_2^-$
   4) Two of the above.
   5) None of the above.

9. Calculate the pOH of a 0.10 M KClO solution.
   1) 3.77 2) 1.00 3) 7.00 4) 5.92 5) 4.35

10. What is the pH of a 0.050 M $NH_4^+ I^-$ solution?
    1) 5.16 2) 4.62 3) 5.28 4) 4.84 5) 5.04

11. How many moles of NaCN must be present in 2.5-L of solution in order to yield a solution whose pH = 10.00?
    1) 5.0×10^{-4} 2) 1.2×10^{-3} 3) 2.5×10^{-4} 4) 8.0×10^{-14} 5) 5.2×10^{-3}

12. What concentration (in M) of $C_5H_5NH^+ Cl^-$ is required to produce an $[OH^-] = 7.5 \times 10^{-12}$ M?
    1) 8.4×10^{-18} 2) 1.1×10^{-1} 3) 3.75 4) 0.27 5) 0.16

13. Along with the information obtained in the previous question, what is the % ionization of $C_5H_5NH^+ Cl^-$ that produces an $[OH^-] = 7.5 \times 10^{-12}$ M?
    1) 0.49 2) 2.8×10^{-9} 3) 0.035 4) 0.75 5) 0.036

14. Assuming that the following salts have the same concentration, rank each salt in order of increasing pH.
    KCN, RbI, $Al(NO_3)_3$, $MgCl_2$, NaClO

    1) NaClO < KCN < RbI < $Al(NO_3)_3$ < $MgCl_2$
    2) RbI < $Al(NO_3)_3$ < $MgCl_2$ < KCN < NaClO
    3) $Al(NO_3)_3$ < $MgCl_2$ < RbI < KCN < NaClO
    4) $Al(NO_3)_3$ < $MgCl_2$ < RbI < NaClO < KCN
    5) $MgCl_2$ < $Al(NO_3)_3$ < RbI < KCN < NaClO

ANSWERS - MODULE 8

1. a) neutral b) acidic c) basic d) acidic e) acidic f) acidic g) acidic h) neutral
2. A. a) $KCN < KNO_3 < Be(NO_3)_2 < Fe(NO_3)_3$
   b) $Fe(NO_3)_3 < Be(NO_3)_2 < KNO_3 < KCN$
   B. a) $CsF < RbCl = KCl < ZrCl_2 < FeCl_2$
   b) $FeCl_2 < ZrCl_2 < RbCl = KCl < CsF$

3.

Acid	K_a	Conjugate base	K_b	Base	K_b	Conjugate Acid	K_a
HClO	3.5×10^{-8}	ClO^-	2.9×10^{-7}	NH_3	1.8×10^{-5}	NH_4^+	5.6×10^{-10}
$HC_2H_3O_2$	1.8×10^{-5}	$C_2H_3O_2^-$	5.6×10^{-10}	$(CH_3)_3N$	7.4×10^{-5}	$(CH_3)_3NH^+$	1.4×10^{-10}
HCN	4.0×10^{-10}	CN^-	2.5×10^{-5}	$C_6H_5NH_2$	4.2×10^{-10}	$C_6H_5NH_3^+$	2.4×10^{-5}

4.

Salt	Salt Conc., M	$[H^+]$	$[OH^-]$	pH	pOH	% hydrolysis
KNO_2	0.10	6.7×10^{-9}	1.5×10^{-6}	8.17	5.83	0.0015
LiCN	0.20	4.5×10^{-12}	2.2×10^{-3}	11.35	2.65	1.1
$Ca(C_2H_3O_2)_2$	0.10	9.5×10^{-10}	1.1×10^{-5}	9.02	4.98	0.0053
$CH_3NH_3^+Br^-$	0.20	6.3×10^{-6}	1.6×10^{-9}	5.20	8.80	0.0032
$C_6H_5NH_3^+Cl^-$	0.072	1.3×10^{-3}	7.5×10^{-12}	2.88	11.12	1.8
NH_4I	0.057	5.6×10^{-6}	1.8×10^{-9}	5.25	8.75	0.0099

5. a) 1.5×10^{-10} b) 6.7×10^{-5}
6. basic
7. 8.8 g

ANSWERS TO MULTIPLE CHOICE PRACTICE EXAM

1	2	3	4	5	6	7	8	9	10	11	12	13	14
4	5	2	3	2	1	2	5	1	3	2	4	1	4

MODULE 9. *Acid-Base Titrations*

I. Acid-Base Titrations

An acid-base titration is a procedure for determining the amount of acid (or base) in a solution by determining the volume of base (or acid) of known concentration that will completely react with it.

An acid-base titration curve is a plot of pH versus the volume of titrant (i.e., the substance in the buret) that is added. These curves are used to gain an awareness of the titration process: where is the **equivalence point** (point in the titration when a stoichiometric amount of reactants have been added) and what is a good indicator to use to determine the **end point** (point at which the indicator tells us the equivalence point has been reached). Ideally, the end point and the equivalence point in a titration should coincide.

At the equivalence point,

$$eq_{acid} = eq_{base}$$

An equivalence (eq) can be defined as follows:

$$eq = N \times V = (n \times M) \times V = \frac{g}{EW}$$

where,

n = # of acidic "H" that have reacted (in the acid) or n = # of "OH" that have reacted (in the base)

$$EW = \frac{MM}{n}$$

In this module you will need to recall how to distinguish between weak and strong acids and bases. The following are the strong monoprotic acids: HCl, HBr, HI, $HClO_4$, $HClO_3$ and HNO_3 and the strong monohydroxy bases: all IAOH.

In titration problems, there are basically five different types of calculations that are performed. All of these calculations will be performed with either monoprotic acids or monobasic bases.

1) Number of mL of titrant needed to reach the equivalence point
2) The pH of the initial solution
3) The pH at various points prior to the equivalence point
4) The pH at the equivalence point
5) The pH at various points past the equivalence point

Example of Individual Titration Curves that will be Studied

A) Strong Acid with Strong Base

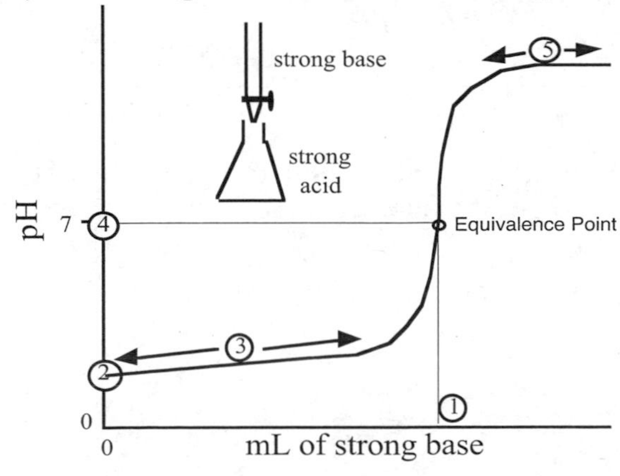

B) Strong Base with Strong Acid

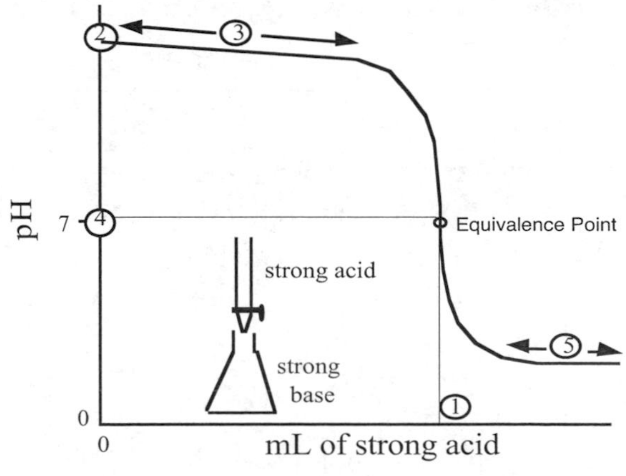

C) Weak Acid with Strong Base

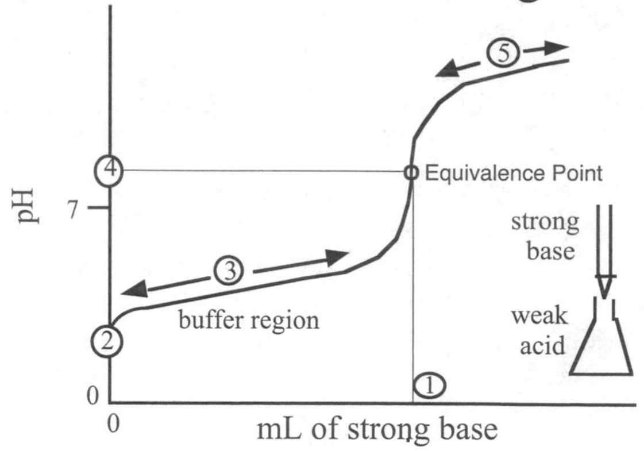

D) Weak Base with Strong Acid

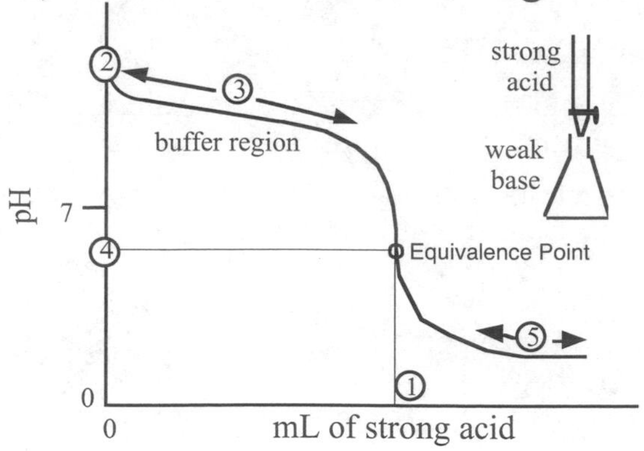

A. Titration of a Strong Acid with a Strong Base

Example: *Titration of 50.00 mL of 0.1300 M HCl with 0.1200 M NaOH.*

A1) Number of mL of titrant needed to reach the equivalence point

$$eq_{HCl} = eq_{NaOH}$$

$$(n \times M) \times V = (n \times M) \times V$$

$$\left(1 \frac{eq}{mol} \times 0.1300 \frac{mol}{L}\right) \times (50.00 \text{ mL}) = \left(1 \frac{eq}{mol} \times 0.1200 \frac{mol}{L}\right) \times V$$

$$V = 54.17 \text{ mL}$$

A2) The pH of the initial solution (Strong Acid Problem)

Since HCl is a strong acid, $[HCl] = [H^+]$

$$pH = -\log [H^+] = -\log (0.1300) = 0.89$$

A3) The pH prior to the equivalence point (Excess Strong Acid Problem)

Between 0 mL to the equivalence point (54.17 mL in this example), the calculations performed are the same. These calculations are limiting reagent problems where the acid is in excess and the base is the limiting reagent.

To illustrate this problem type, we will calculate the pH after 40.25 mL of NaOH have been added.

	HCl	+	NaOH	→	NaCl	+	H_2O
	$\left(0.1300 \frac{mol}{L}\right)(0.05000 \text{ L})$		$\left(0.1200 \frac{mol}{L}\right)(0.04025 \text{ L})$				
mol_i:	0.006500		0.004830		0		
mol_{change}:	-0.004830		-0.004830		+0.004830		
mol_{end}:	0.00167		0		0.004830		

Since NaCl is a salt derived from a strong acid and base, neither ion will hydrolyze. The pH of the solution is then strictly determined by the concentration of the unreacted HCl.

The concentration of HCl at this point is given by the moles of HCl left unreacted divided by the total volume (in L) at this point of the titration. The total volume is 50.00 + 40.25 = 90.25 mL.

$$[HCl] = [H^+] = \frac{0.00167 \text{ mol}}{0.09025 \text{ L}} = 0.01850 \text{ M}$$

$$pH = -\log [H^+] = -\log (0.01850) = 1.73$$

A4) The pH at the equivalence point (pH = 7 - Salt from Strong Base and Acid Problem)

At the equivalence point there is no acid and no base present; only the salt. Since the salt (NaCl) is derived from a strong acid and base, neither of its ions will hydrolyze in water. This being the case, *the pH at the equivalence point of a titration of a strong acid with a strong base will be 7.00.*

A5) The pH past the equivalence point (Excess Strong Base Problem)

After the equivalence point (54.17 mL in this example), the calculations performed are the same. These calculations are limiting reagent problems where the base is in excess and the acid is the limiting reagent.

To illustrate this problem type, we will calculate the pH after 55.70 mL of NaOH have been added.

	HCl	+	NaOH	→	NaCl	+	H_2O
	$\left(0.1300\ \frac{mol}{L}\right)(0.05000\ L)$		$\left(0.1200\ \frac{mol}{L}\right)(0.05570\ L)$				
mol_i:	0.006500		0.006684		0		
mol_{change}:	-0.006500		-0.006500		+0.006500		
mol_{end}:	0		0.000184		0.006500		

Since NaCl is a salt derived from a strong acid and base, neither ion will hydrolyze. The pH of the solution is then strictly determined by the concentration of the NaOH that is in excess.

The concentration of NaOH at this point is given by the moles of NaOH in excess divided by the total volume (in L) at this point of the titration. The total volume is 50.00 + 55.70 = 105.70 mL.

$$[NaOH] = [OH^-] = \frac{0.000184\ mol}{0.10570\ L} = 0.001741\ M$$

$$pOH = -\log[OH^-] = -\log(0.01741) = 2.76$$

$$pH + pOH = 14.00$$

$$pH = 14.00 - 2.76 = 11.24$$

B. Titration of a Strong Base with a Strong Acid

Example: *Titration of 35.00 mL of 0.175 M KOH with 0.125 M HBr.*

B1) Number of mL of titrant needed to reach the equivalence point

$$eq_{HBr} = eq_{KOH}$$

$$(n \times M) \times V = (n \times M) \times V$$

$$\left(1\ \frac{eq}{mol} \times 0.125\ \frac{mol}{L}\right) \times V = \left(1\ \frac{eq}{mol} \times 0.175\ \frac{mol}{L}\right) \times (35.00\ mL)$$

$$V = 49.00\ mL$$

B2) The pH of the initial solution (Strong Base Problem)

Since KOH is a strong base, $[KOH] = [OH^-]$

$$pOH = -\log[OH^-] = -\log(0.175) = 0.76$$

$$pH + pOH = 14.00$$

$$pH = 14.00 - 0.76 = 13.24$$

B3) The pH prior to the equivalence point (Excess Strong Base Problem)

Between 0 mL to the equivalence point (49.00 mL in this example), the calculations performed are the same. These calculations are limiting reagent problems where the base is in excess and the acid is the limiting reagent.

To illustrate this problem type, we will calculate the pH after 44.00 mL of HBr have been added.

	HBr	+ KOH	→ KBr + H_2O
	$\left(0.125\ \frac{mol}{L}\right)(0.04400\ L)$	$\left(0.175\ \frac{mol}{L}\right)(0.03500L)$	
mol_i:	0.00550	0.00612	0
mol_{change}:	-0.00550	-0.00550	+0.00550
mol_{end}:	0	0.00062	0.00550

Since KBr is a salt derived from a strong acid and base, neither ion will hydrolyze. The pH of the solution is then strictly determined by the concentration of the unreacted KOH.

The concentration of KOH at this point is given by the moles of KOH left unreacted divided by the total volume (in L) at this point of the titration. The total volume is 44.00 + 35.00 = 79.00 mL.

$$[KOH] = [OH^-] = \frac{0.00062\ mol}{0.07900\ L} = 0.00785\ M$$

$$pOH = -\log[OH^-] = -\log(0.00785) = 2.11$$

$$pH + pOH = 14.00$$

$$pH = 14.00 - 2.11 = 11.89$$

B4) The pH at the equivalence point (pH = 7 - Salt from Strong Base and Acid Problem)

At the equivalence point there is no acid and no base present; only the salt. Since the salt (KBr) is derived from a strong acid and base, neither of its ions will hydrolyze in water. This being the case, *the pH at the equivalence point of a titration of a strong base with a strong acid will be 7.00.*

B5) The pH past the equivalence point (Excess Strong Acid Problem)

After the equivalence point (49.00 mL in this example), the calculations performed are the same. These calculations are limiting reagent problems where the acid is in excess and the base is the limiting reagent.

To illustrate this problem type, we will calculate the pH after 52.00 mL of HBr have been added.

	HBr	+ KOH	→ KBr + H_2O
	$\left(0.125\ \frac{mol}{L}\right)(0.05200\ L)$	$\left(0.175\ \frac{mol}{L}\right)(0.03500\ L)$	
mol_i:	0.006500	0.00612	0
mol_{change}:	-0.00612	-0.00612	+0.00612
mol_{end}:	0.00038	0	0.00612

Since KBr is a salt derived from a strong acid and base, neither ion will hydrolyze. The pH of the solution is then strictly determined by the concentration of the HBr that is in excess.

The concentration of HBr at this point is given by the moles of HBr in excess divided by the total volume (in L) at this point of the titration. The total volume is 35.00 + 52.00 = 87.00 mL.

$$[HBr] = [H^+] = \frac{0.00038\ mol}{0.08700\ L} = 0.00437\ M$$

$$pH = -\log[H^+] = -\log(0.00437) = 2.36$$

C. Titration of a Weak Acid with a Strong Base

Example: *Titration of 50.00 mL of 0.1300 M HF ($K_a = 7.2 \times 10^{-4}$) with 0.1200 M NaOH.*

C1) Number of mL of titrant needed to reach the equivalence point

$$eq_{HF} = eq_{NaOH}$$

$$(n \times M) \times V = (n \times M) \times V$$

$$\left(1\ \frac{eq}{mol} \times 0.1300\ \frac{mol}{L}\right) \times (50.00\ mL) = \left(1\ \frac{eq}{mol} \times 0.1200\ \frac{mol}{L}\right) \times V$$

$$V = 54.17\ mL$$

C2) The pH of the initial solution (Weak Acid Equilibrium Problem)

Since HF is a weak acid, the [HF] ≠ [H^+]. To find the initial pH we must set up a weak acid equilibrium.

$$HF_{(aq)} \overset{H\text{-}OH}{\rightleftharpoons} H^+_{(aq)} + F^-_{(aq)}$$

	$HF_{(aq)}$	$H^+_{(aq)}$	$F^-_{(aq)}$
$[\ ]_i$:	0.1300	0	0
$[\ ]_{change}$:	-x	+x	+x
$[\ ]_{equil}$:	0.1300 - x	x	x

$$K_a = \frac{[H^+][F^-]}{[HF]}$$

$$7.2 \times 10^{-4} = \frac{(x)\ (x)}{(0.1300 - x)}$$

Assume that x is small

Since K_a (7.2×10^{-4}) < $[\ ]_i \times 10^{-2}$ ($0.1300 \times 10^{-2} = 1.3 \times 10^{-3}$), x will be assumed to be small in comparison to the initial concentration of 0.1300 and as such will be neglected.

$$9.4 \times 10^{-5} = x^2$$

$$x = \sqrt{9.4 \times 10^{-5}} = 9.7 \times 10^{-3}$$

$$x = [H^+] = 9.7 \times 10^{-3}$$

Our assumption that x was small in comparison to the initial concentration was correct. ***A small x is considered one that is less than 10% of the initial concentration.***

[x (9.7×10^{-3}) < 10% x $[\ ]_i$ ($0.1 \times 0.1300 = 0.0130$)]

$$pH = -\log [H^+] = -\log (9.7 \times 10^{-3}) = 2.01$$

C3) The pH prior to the equivalence point (Weak Acid Buffer Problem)

Between 0 mL and the equivalence point (54.17 mL in this example), the calculations performed are the same. These calculations are limiting reagent problems where the acid is in excess and the base is the limiting reagent.

To illustrate this problem type, we will calculate the pH after 40.25 mL of NaOH have been added.

	HF	+	NaOH	→	NaF	+	H_2O
	$\left(0.1300\ \frac{mol}{L}\right)(0.05000\ L)$		$\left(0.1200\ \frac{mol}{L}\right)(0.04025\ L)$				
mol_i:	0.006500		0.004830		0		
mol_{change}:	-0.004830		-0.004830		+0.004830		
mol_{end}:	0.00167		0		0.004830		

In this particular case, *this is a buffer problem because we have a weak acid (HF) and its salt (NaF).*

We will use the weak acid buffer formula to find [H⁺], and then the pH.

$$[H^+] = \frac{a}{s} K_a = \frac{0.00167}{0.00483} \times 7.2 \times 10^{-4} = 2.5 \times 10^{-4}$$

$$pH = -\log [H^+] = -\log (2.5 \times 10^{-4}) = 3.60$$

It should be noted, that one way that one can obtain the pK_a of a weak acid is by obtaining the pH at the titration's halfway point. At the halfway point, an equimolar amount of acid (a) and salt (s) is present and thus, $[H^+] = K_a$ or $pH = pK_a$. In this particular example, the halfway point of the titration occurs at 27.08 mL (54.17 mL / 2). Thus, to obtain the pK_a (or K_a) of any weak acid, one would need to know the pH at the halfway point of the titration.

C4) The pH at the equivalence point (pH > 7 - Hydrolysis Problem of Salt Derived from Strong Base and Weak Acid)

At the equivalence point (54.17 mL in this case) there is no acid and no base present only the salt.

	HF	+	NaOH	→	NaF	+	H_2O
	$\left(0.1300 \frac{mol}{L}\right)(0.05000\ L)$		$\left(0.1200 \frac{mol}{L}\right)(0.05417\ L)$				
mol_i:	0.006500		0.006500		0		
mol_{change}:	-0.006500		-0.006500		+0.006500		
mol_{end}:	0		0		0.006500		

Since Na^+ is derived from a strong base (NaOH) and F^- is derived from a weak acid (HF), only the F^- ion will hydrolyze in water. This being the case, *the pH at the equivalence point of a weak acid with a strong base will be* *__basic__* *and is determined by the hydrolysis of the anion.*

The concentration of F^- at this point is given by the moles of NaF produced divided by the total volume (in L) at this point of the titration. The total volume is 50.00 + 54.17 = 104.17 mL.

	F^-	$\xrightleftharpoons{H\text{-}OH}$	HF	+	OH^-
	$\frac{0.006500\ mol}{0.10417\ L}$				
$[\ ]_i$:	0.06240		0		0
$[\ ]_{change}$:	-x		+x		+x
$[\ ]_{equil}$:	0.06240 - x		x		x

The equilibrium expression, is:

$$K_b = \frac{[HF][OH^-]}{[F^-]} \quad \text{where,} \quad K_b = \frac{K_w}{K_a} = \frac{1.0 \times 10^{-14}}{7.2 \times 10^{-4}} = 1.4 \times 10^{-11}$$

$$1.4 \times 10^{-11} = \frac{(x)\ (x)}{(0.06240 - x)}$$

Assume that x is small

Since K_b (1.4×10^{-11}) < $[\ ]_i \times 10^{-2}$ (0.06240×10^{-2}), x will be assumed to be small in comparison to the initial concentration of 0.06240 and as such will be neglected.

$$8.7 \times 10^{-13} = x^2$$

$$x = \sqrt{8.7 \times 10^{-13}} = 9.3 \times 10^{-7}$$

Our assumption that x was small in comparison to the initial concentration was correct. ***A small x is considered one that is less than 10% of the initial concentration.***

[x (9.3×10^{-7}) < 10% x $[\ ]_i$ (0.1 x 0.06240= 0.006240)]

$$x = [OH^-] = 9.3 \times 10^{-7}$$

$$pOH = -\log[OH^-] = -\log (9.3 \times 10^{-7}) = 6.03$$

$$pH + pOH = 14.00$$

$$pH = 14.00 - 6.03 = 7.97$$

C5) The pH past the equivalence point (Excess Strong Base Problem)

After the equivalence point (54.17 mL in this example), the calculations performed are the same. These calculations are limiting reagent problems where the base is in excess and the acid is the limiting reagent.

To illustrate this problem type, we will calculate the pH after 55.70 mL of NaOH have been added.

	HF	+	NaOH	→	NaF	+	H_2O
	$\left(0.1300\ \frac{mol}{L}\right)(0.05000\ L)$		$\left(0.1200\ \frac{mol}{L}\right)(0.05570\ L)$				
mol_i:	0.006500		0.006684		0		
mol_{change}:	-0.006500		-0.006500		+0.006500		
mol_{end}:	0		0.000184		0.006500		

At this stage of the titration, we have two species responsible for making the pH basic, OH^-(NaOH) and F^-. *Since OH^- is a much stronger base than F^-, we can safely neglect the F^- in our pH calculation.*

The concentration of NaOH at this point is given by the moles of NaOH in excess divided by the total volume (in L) at this point of the titration. The total volume is 50.00 + 55.70 = 105.70 mL.

$$[NaOH] = [OH^-] = \frac{0.000184\ mol}{0.10570\ L} = 0.001741\ M$$

$$pOH = -\log[OH^-] = -\log(0.001741) = 2.76$$

$$pH + pOH = 14.00$$

$$pH = 14.00 - 2.76 = 11.24$$

D. Titration of a Weak Base with a Strong Acid

Example: *Titration of 35.00 mL of 0.175 M NH_3 ($K_b = 1.8 \times 10^{-5}$) with 0.125 M HBr.*

D1) Number of mL of titrant needed to reach the equivalence point

$$eq_{HBr} = eq_{NH_3}$$

$$(n \times M) \times V = (n \times M) \times V$$

$$\left(1\ \frac{eq}{mol} \times 0.125\ \frac{mol}{L}\right) \times V = \left(1\ \frac{eq}{mol} \times 0.175\ \frac{mol}{L}\right) \times (35.00\ mL) \rightarrow V = 49.00\ mL$$

D2) The pH of the initial solution (Weak Base Equilibrium Problem)

Since NH_3 is a weak base, the $[NH_3] \neq [OH^-]$. To find the initial pH we must set up a weak base equilibrium.

	NH_3	$\xrightleftharpoons{H\text{-}OH}$	NH_4^+	+	OH^-
$[\ ]_i$:	0.175		0		0
$[\ ]_{change}$:	-x		+x		+x
$[\ ]_{equil}$:	0.175 - x		x		x

$$K_b = \frac{[NH_4^+][OH^-]}{[NH_3]}$$

$$1.8 \times 10^{-5} = \frac{(x)(x)}{(0.175 - \cancel{x})}$$

Assume that x is small

Since K_a (1.8×10^{-5}) < $[\ ]_i \times 10^{-2}$ (0.175×10^{-2}), x will be assumed to be small in comparison to the initial concentration of 0.175 and as such will be neglected.

$3.2 \times 10^{-6} = x^2$

$x = \sqrt{3.2 \times 10^{-6}} = 1.8 \times 10^{-3}$

$x = [OH^-] = 1.8 \times 10^{-3}$

Our assumption that x was small in comparison to the initial concentration was correct. ***A small x is considered one that is less than 10% of the initial concentration.***

$[x\ (1.8 \times 10^{-3}) < 10\% \times [\ ]_i\ (0.1 \times 0.175 = 0.0175)]$

$pOH = -\log[OH^-] = -\log(1.8 \times 10^{-3}) = 2.75$

$pH + pOH = 14.00 \rightarrow pH = 14.00 - 2.75 = 11.25$

D3) The pH prior to the equivalence point (Weak Base Buffer Problem)

Between 0 mL and the equivalence point (49.00 mL in this example), the calculations performed are the same. These calculations are limiting reagent problems where the base is in excess and the acid is the limiting reagent.

To illustrate this problem type, we will calculate the pH after 44.00 mL of HBr have been added.

	HBr	+ NH_3	→ NH_4Br
	$\left(0.125\ \frac{mol}{L}\right)(0.04400\ L)$	$\left(0.175\ \frac{mol}{L}\right)(0.03500L)$	
mol_i:	0.00550	0.00612	0
mol_{change}:	-0.00550	-0.00550	+0.00550
mol_{end}:	0	0.00062	0.00550

In this particular case, *this is a buffer problem because we have a weak base (NH_3) and its salt (NH_4Br).*

We will use the weak base buffer formula to find $[OH^-]$, and then the pH.

$$[OH^-] = \frac{b}{s} K_b = \frac{0.00062}{0.0055} \times 1.8 \times 10^{-5} = 2.0 \times 10^{-6}$$

$pOH = -\log[OH^-] = -\log(2.0 \times 10^{-6}) = 5.69$

$pH + pOH = 14.00$

$pH = 14.00 - 5.69 = 8.31$

It should be noted, that one way that one can obtain the pK_b of a weak base is by obtaining the pOH at the titration's halfway point. At the halfway point, an equimolar amount of base (b) and salt (s) is present and thus, $[OH^-] = K_b$ or $pOH = pK_b$. In this particular example, the halfway point of the titration occurs at 24.50 mL (49.00 mL / 2). Thus, to obtain the pK_b (or K_b) of any weak base, one would need to know the pOH at the halfway point of the titration. [NOTE: pH is what is measured in a titration, so to get the pOH you need to subtract the pH from 14.]

D4) The pH at the equivalence point (pH < 7 - Hydrolysis Problem of Salt Derived from Weak Base and Strong Acid)

At the equivalence point (@ 49.00 mL of HBr) there is no acid and no base present; only the salt.

	HBr	+ NH_3	→ NH_4Br
	$\left(0.125\ \frac{mol}{L}\right)(0.04900\ L)$	$\left(0.175\ \frac{mol}{L}\right)(0.03500\ L)$	
mol_i:	0.00612	0.00612	0
mol_{change}:	-0.00612	-0.00612	+0.00612
mol_{end}:	0	0	0.00612

Since Br^- is derived from a strong acid and NH_4^+ is derived from a weak base, only the NH_4^+ ion will hydrolyze in water. This being the case, *the pH at the equivalence point of a weak base with a strong acid will be* _acidic_ *and is determined by the hydrolysis of the cation.*

The concentration of NH_4^+ at this point is given by the moles of NH_4Br produced divided by the total volume (in L) at this point of the titration. The total volume is 49.00 + 35.00 = 84.00 mL.

$$NH_4^+ \overset{\text{H-OH}}{\rightleftharpoons} NH_3 + H_3O^+$$

	NH_4^+	NH_3	H_3O^+
	$\frac{0.00612 \text{ mol}}{0.08400 \text{ L}}$		
$[\,]_i$:	0.0729	0	0
$[\,]_{change}$:	-x	+x	+x
$[\,]_{equil}$:	0.0729 - x	x	x

The equilibrium expression, is:

$$K_a = \frac{[NH_3][H_3O^+]}{[NH_4^+]} \quad \text{where,} \quad K_a = \frac{K_w}{K_b} = \frac{1.0 \times 10^{-14}}{1.8 \times 10^{-5}} = 5.6 \times 10^{-10}$$

$$5.6 \times 10^{-10} = \frac{(x)\ (x)}{(0.0729 - x)}$$

Assume that x is small

Since K_b (5.6×10^{-10}) < $[\,]_i \times 10^{-2}$ (0.0729×10^{-2}), x will be assumed to be small in comparison to the initial concentration of 0.0729 and as such will be neglected.

$$4.1 \times 10^{-11} = x^2$$

$$x = \sqrt{4.1 \times 10^{-11}} = 6.4 \times 10^{-6}$$

Our assumption that x was small in comparison to the initial concentration was correct. ***A small x is considered one that is less than 10% of the initial concentration.***

[x (6.4×10^{-6}) < 10% x $[\,]_i$ (0.1 x 0.0729= 0.00729)]

$$x = [H_3O^+] = [H^+] = 6.4 \times 10^{-6}$$

$$pH = -\log[H^+] = -\log(6.4 \times 10^{-6}) = 5.19$$

D5) The pH past the equivalence point (Excess Strong Acid Problem)

After the equivalence point (49.00 mL in this example), the calculations performed are the same. These calculations are limiting reagent problems where the acid is in excess and the base is the limiting reagent.

To illustrate this problem type, we will calculate the pH after 52.00 mL of HBr have been added.

$$HBr + NH_3 \rightarrow NH_4Br$$

	HBr	NH_3	NH_4Br
	$\left(0.125 \frac{\text{mol}}{\text{L}}\right)(0.05200 \text{ L})$	$\left(0.175 \frac{\text{mol}}{\text{L}}\right)(0.03500 \text{ L})$	
mol_i:	0.006500	0.00612	0
mol_{change}:	-0.00612	-0.00612	+0.00612
mol_{end}:	0.00038	0	0.00612

At this stage of the titration, we have two species responsible for making the pH acidic, H^+ (HBr) and NH_4^+ (NH_4Br). *Since H^+ is a much stronger acid than NH_4^+, we can safely neglect the NH_4^+ in our pH calculation.*

The concentration of HBr at this point is given by the moles of HBr in excess divided by the total volume (in L) at this point of the titration. The total volume is 35.00 + 52.00 = 87.00 mL.

$$[HBr] = [H^+] = \frac{0.00038 \text{ mol}}{0.08700 \text{ L}} = 0.00437 \text{ M}$$

$$pH = -\log[H^+] = -\log(0.00437) = 2.36$$

II. Side-By-Side Comparison of Titration Curves

The following are superimposed titration curves of a strong acid (SA) with a strong base (SB) titrant and a weak acid (WA) with a strong base (SB) titrant. Both the initial volume and molarity of acid are the same.

$$HA \quad + \quad NaOH \quad \rightarrow \quad NaA \quad + \quad H_2O$$

- Titration of a Strong Acid (**10.0 mL of 0.100 M**) with a Strong Base (**0.100 M**)
- Titration of a Weak Acid (**10.0 mL of 0.100 M**) with a Strong Base (**0.100 M**)

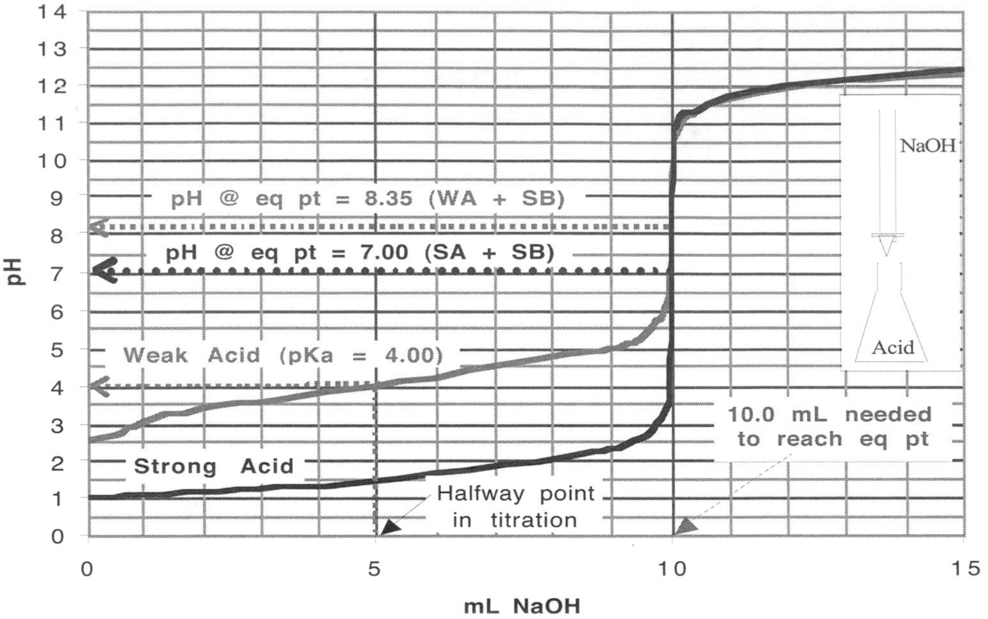

mL titrant	pH (WA)	pH (SA)
0.00	2.50	1.00
0.50	2.72	1.04
1.00	3.05	1.09
2.00	3.40	1.18
5.00	4.00	1.48
9.00	4.95	2.28
9.50	5.28	2.59
10.00	8.35	7.00
10.20	11.00	11.00
10.30	11.17	11.17
10.50	11.39	11.39
11.00	11.68	11.68
12.00	11.96	11.96
13.00	12.12	12.12
14.00	12.22	12.22
15.00	12.30	12.30

The following are superimposed titration curves of a strong base (SB) with a strong acid (SA) titrant and a weak base (WB) with a strong acid (SA) titrant. Both the initial volume and molarity of base are the same.

$$IAOH \quad + \quad HCl \quad \rightarrow \quad IACl \quad + \quad H_2O$$

$$B: \quad + \quad HCl \quad \rightarrow \quad BH^+ Cl^-$$

- Titration of a Strong Base (**15.0 mL of 0.100 M**) with a Strong Acid (**0.100 M**)
- Titration of a Weak Base (**15.0 mL of 0.100 M**) with a Strong Acid (**0.100 M**)

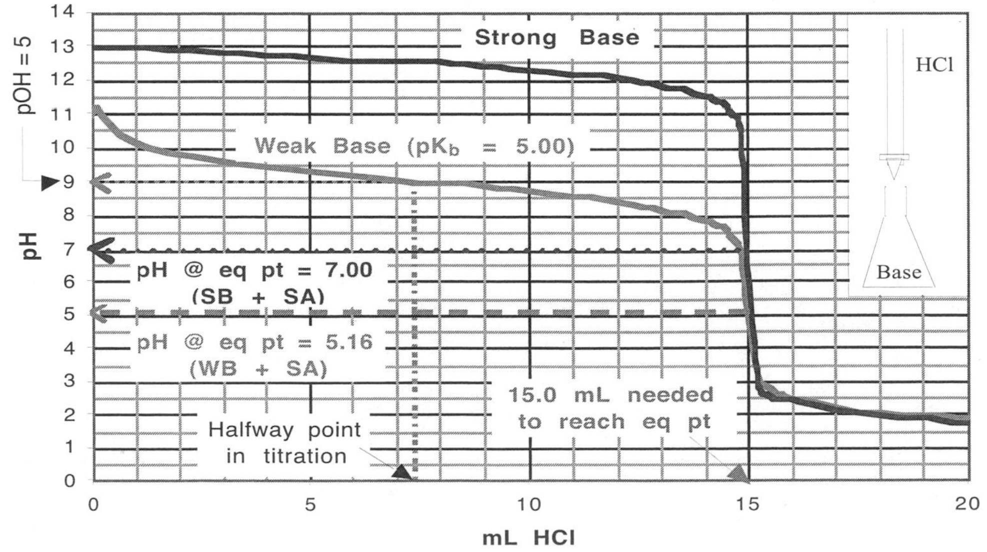

mL titrant	pH (WB)	pH (SB)
0.00	11.00	13.00
0.10	11.17	12.99
1.00	10.15	12.94
3.00	9.60	12.82
7.50	9.00	12.52
9.00	8.82	12.40
12.00	8.40	12.05
13.00	8.19	11.85
14.80	7.13	10.83
14.90	6.83	10.52
15.00	5.15	7.00
15.40	2.88	2.88
16.00	2.49	2.49
17.00	2.20	2.20
18.00	2.04	2.04
19.00	1.93	1.93
20.00	1.85	1.85
25.00	1.60	1.60

III. Acid-Base Indicators

An *indicator* is merely a substance whose color changes as a result of pH changes. Indicators do not all change color in the same pH range, so the choice of an indicator for a particular titration basically depends on the nature of the acid and base used in the titration. Let's consider a weak monoprotic acid, HIn, which acts as an indicator.

$$HIn \underset{}{\overset{H_2O}{\rightleftharpoons}} H^+ + In^- \qquad K_a = \frac{[H^+][In^-]}{[HIn]}$$

In a very acidic solution (high $[H^+]$), according to the LeChatelier Principle the equilibrium shifts to the left and the color of HIn will predominate. In a very basic solution (low $[H^+]$), according to the LeChatelier Principle the equilibrium shifts to the right and the color of In^- will predominate.

The following table gives some commonly used indicators used in acid-base titrations.

Indicator	Color		pH range*
	In acid	In base	
methyl violet	yellow	blue	0.0 - 1.6
thymol blue‡	red	yellow	1.2 - 2.8
methyl orange	red	yellow	3.2 - 4.4
methyl red	red	yellow	4.2 - 6.3
bromocresol purple	yellow	purple	5.2 - 6.8
bromothymol blue	yellow	blue	6.2 - 7.6
litmus	red	blue	4.7 - 8.3
cresol red	yellow	red	7.0 - 8.8
thymol blue ‡	yellow	blue	8.0 - 9.6
phenolphthalein	colorless	pink	8.2 - 10.0
thymolphthalein	colorless	blue	9.4 - 10.6
alizarin yellow R	yellow	red	10.5 - 12.3

The criteria for choosing an appropriate indicator, is whether the pH range over which the indicator changes color corresponds with the steep portion of the titration curve. If this criteria is not met, then the indicator will not accurately identify the equivalence point.

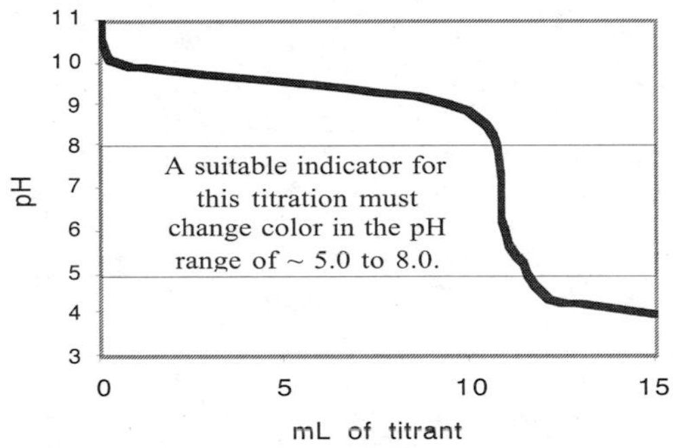

A suitable indicator for this titration must change color in the pH range of ~ 5.0 to 8.0.
pH
mL of titrant

* The pH range is the range over which the indicator changes from its acid (HIn) to its base (In^-) color. Generally, an indicator's pH range is within ±1 of its pK_a. Therefore, if an indicator has a $pK_a = 5$, it changes color in the pH range of 4 (from its acid color) to 6 (to its base color). When $pH = pK_a$, the ratio of HIn : In^- is 1 : 1. A decrease in pH by one unit (relative to the pK_a of the indicator) causes this ratio to increase to 10 : 1 (i.e., 10 out of 11 or over 90% of the indicator molecules are present in its acidic form).

‡ Thymol blue has two pH ranges over which it changes color.

Example Problems

1. What would be a good indicator to use in a titration whose curve is shown to your right?

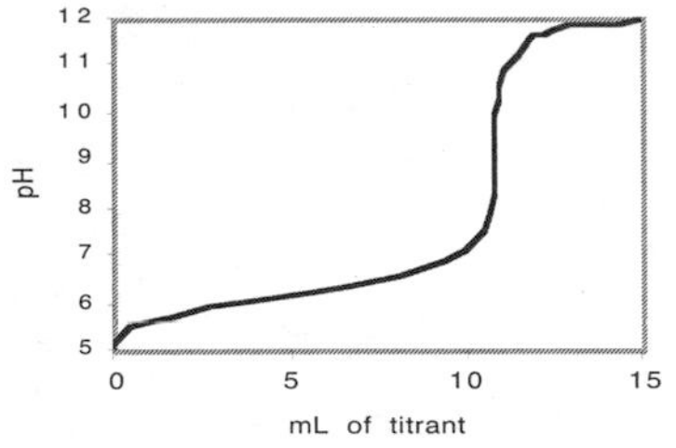

pH
mL of titrant

The steep part of this titration curve occurs from pH ~7.5 - 11 so the appropriate indicator must change pH in this range. Thus, the following indicators would suitably identify the equivalence point: thymol blue, phenolphthalein, and thymolphthalein.

2. The pK_a for methyl red ($C_{14}H_{14}N_3COOH$) is 5.1. At what pH will over 90% of its molecules exist as $C_{14}H_{14}N_3COO^-$? **[OPTIONAL]**

6.1 [An increase in pH by 1 unit relative to the indicator's pK_a causes over 90% of its molecules (or 1 HIn : 10 In^- ratio) to exist in its basic (In^-) form.

IV. Titrations of Weak Acids with Weak Bases (or vice-versa)

The titration of weak acids with weak bases, and vice-versa, are not normally done using indicators because the steep rise that occurs close to the equivalence point is very small. This being the case, it is very difficult for an indicator to appropriately change colors in the range where the equivalence point occurs.

V. Titration Curve of Polyprotic Acids

The most striking evidence that a polyprotic acid ionizes in more than one step can be ascertained by analysis of their titration curve. While complete analysis of the titration curve of polyprotic acids is beyond the scope of this course, the following titration curve of a diprotic acid gives you several points of interest that you could build upon should the need arise.

Titration Curve of 0.1 M H_2A (a diprotic acid) with 0.1 M NaOH

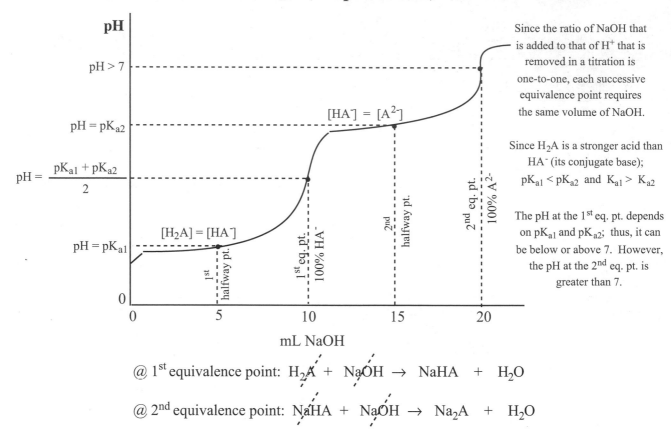

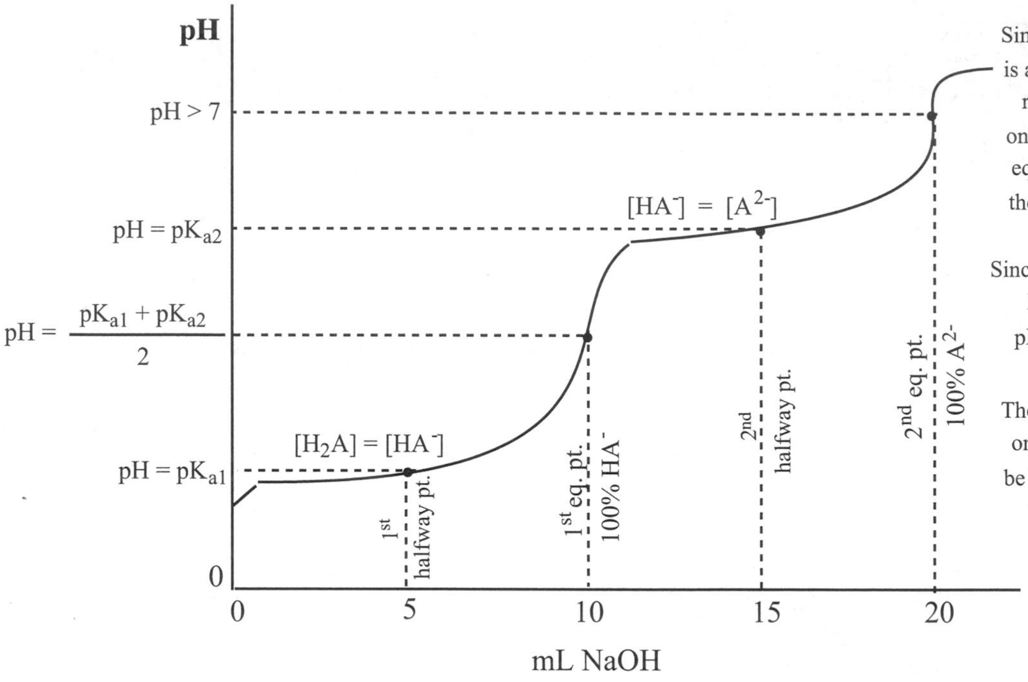

Since the ratio of NaOH that is added to that of H^+ that is removed in a titration is one-to-one, each successive equivalence point requires the same volume of NaOH.

Since H_2A is a stronger acid than HA^- (its conjugate base); $pK_{a1} < pK_{a2}$ and $K_{a1} > K_{a2}$

The pH at the 1st eq. pt. depends on pK_{a1} and pK_{a2}; thus, it can be below or above 7. However, the pH at the 2nd eq. pt. is greater than 7.

@ 1st equivalence point: $H_2A + NaOH \rightarrow NaHA + H_2O$

@ 2nd equivalence point: $NaHA + NaOH \rightarrow Na_2A + H_2O$

EXERCISES

1. Complete the following table in reference to the titration of 25.00 mL of 0.1000 M HCl with 0.1000 M NaOH.

mL NaOH	0.00	12.50	21.00	24.00	25.00	26.00	35.00
pH							

2. Complete the following table in reference to the titration of 25.00 mL of 0.1000 M nicotinic acid ($K_a = 1.4 \times 10^{-5}$) with 0.1000 M NaOH. Nicotinic acid is a monoprotic acid (i.e., HA).

mL NaOH	0.00	12.50	21.00	24.00	25.00	26.00	35.00
pH							

3. Complete the following table in reference to the titration of 25.00 mL of 0.1000 M NH_3 ($K_b = 1.8 \times 10^{-5}$) with 0.1000 M HCl.

mL HCl	0.00	12.50	21.00	24.00	25.00	26.00	35.00
pH							

4. Complete the following table in reference to the titration of 25.00 mL of 0.1000 M NaOH with 0.1000 M HCl.

mL HCl	0.00	12.50	21.00	24.00	25.00	26.00	35.00
pH							

5. Will the titration of the following have a pH above, equal to, or below 7 at the equivalence point?
   a) KOH with HCl   b) HF with NaOH   c) CH_3NH_2 with $HClO_4$

6. What is the pH at the equivalence point when 35.0 mL of 0.200 M NH_3 ($K_b = 1.8 \times 10^{-5}$) are titrated with 0.120 M HCl?

7. What is the pH at the equivalence point when 32.0 mL of 0.087 M $CH_3CH_2NH_2$ ($K_b = 4.7 \times 10^{-4}$) are titrated with 0.150 M HCl?

8. What is the pH at the equivalence point when a 1.24 g sample of the weak organic acid, benzoic acid, C_6H_5COOH ($K_a = 6.6 \times 10^{-5}$, MM = 121) are titrated with 0.180 M LiOH? [HINT: First find the volume of LiOH required to neutralize the acid and then assume that this volume is the volume of the solution at the equivalence point.]

9. What is the molarity of an HBr solution in which a volume of 12.50 mL of it neutralizes 14.75 mL of 0.250 M NaOH?

10. A 0.2688 g sample of a monoprotic acid neutralizes 16.40 mL of a 0.08990 M NaOH solution. Given this information, what is:
    a) The equivalent weight (in g/eq) of the acid.   b) The molar mass (in g) of the acid.

11. A sample of 0.1276 g of an unknown monoprotic acid was dissolved in 25.00 mL of water and titrated with 0.0633 M KOH. The volume of the base required to neutralize the acid was 18.40 mL.
    a) What is the molar mass of the unknown acid?
    b) Given that after 10.00 mL of base had been added to the acid, the pH was found to be 5.87, then calculate the K_a for the acid.

12. Answer the following questions about the following titration curve.
    a) What kind of titration does it represent?
    b) Using the table of indicators found in this module, which indicator would be appropriate to use to signal the correct end point to this titration?

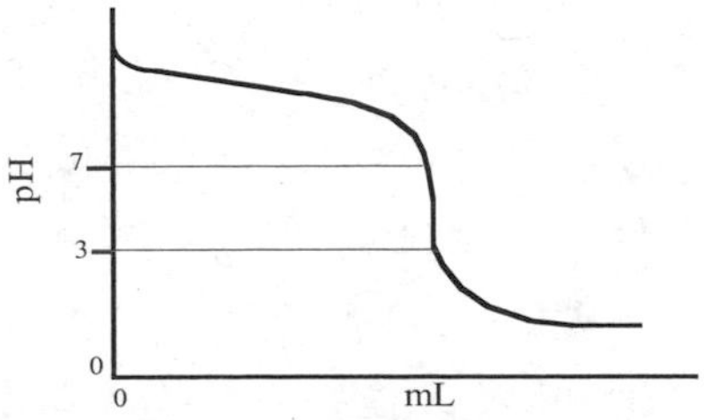

13. Consider the titration curve of a weak acid (HA) with a strong base (MOH) to your right.

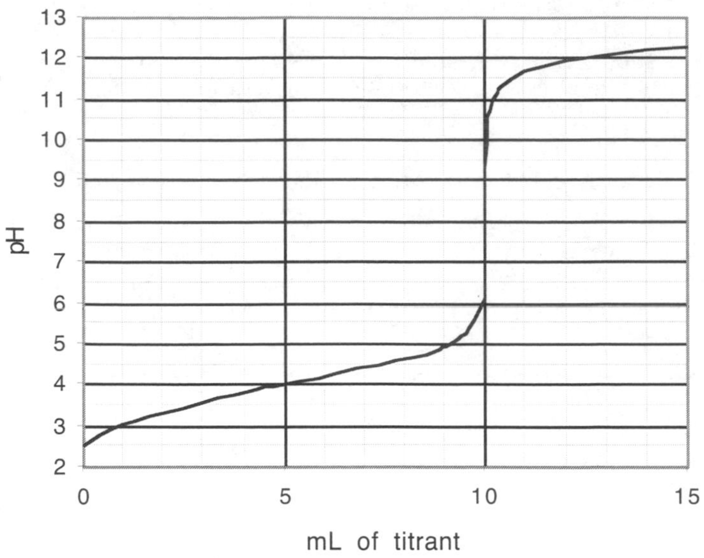

a) Would methyl orange, which changes color in the pH range of 3.2 - 4.4, be a suitable indicator to use in this titration? EXPLAIN.

b) How many mL of titrant were added when the equivalence point of the titration was reached?

c) What is the (approximate) pH at the equivalence point of the titration?

d) In what region of the titration curve is there maximum buffering?

e) Where is the pH = pK_a?

f) What is the K_a for the weak acid used in this titration?

g) A very crude approximation of the $[HA]_i$ (in M) is ______________ .

h) In what region of the titration curve is the pH only dependent on the [HA]?

i) In what region of the titration curve is the pH only dependent on the $[A^-]$?

j) In what region of the titration curve is the pH only dependent on the amount of excess base added?

k) At what approximate pH and volume of titrant is $[HA] = [A^-]$?

l) At what approximate pH and volume of titrant is $[A^-]$ at a maximum?

14. Consider the titration curve of a weak base (B:) with a strong acid (HA) to your right.

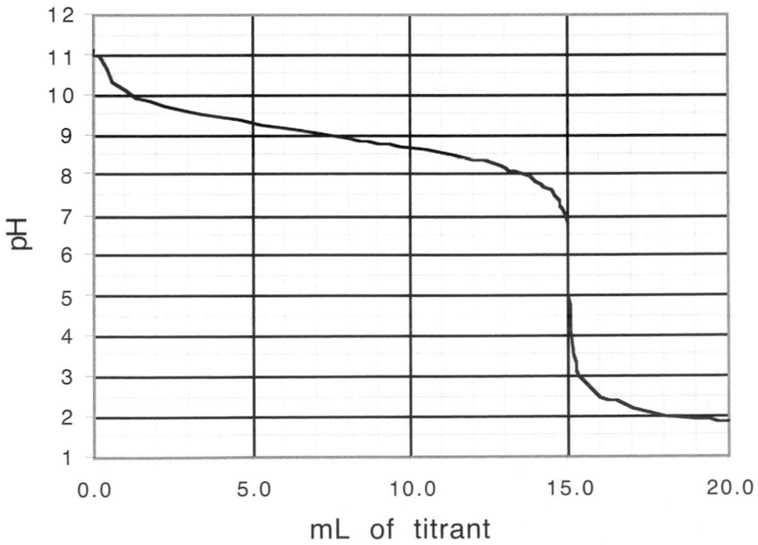

a) Would methyl red, which has a $pK_a = 5.1$, be a suitable indicator to use in this titration? EXPLAIN.

b) How many mL of titrant were added when the equivalence point of the titration was reached?

c) What is the (approximate) pH at the equivalence point of the titration?

d) In what region of the titration curve is there maximum buffering?

e) Where is the pOH = pK_b?

f) What is the K_b for the weak base used in this titration?

g) A very crude approximation of the $[B:]_i$ (in M) is ______________ .

h) In what region of the titration curve is the pH only dependent on the [B:]?

i) In what region of the titration curve is the pH only dependent on the concentration of $[BH^+]$?

j) In what region of the titration curve is the pH only dependent on the amount of excess acid added?

k) At what approximate pH and volume of titrant is $[B:] = [BH^+]$?

15. Consider the stylized titration curve of fictitious weak acid H_2A with 0.100 M NaOH shown to your right.

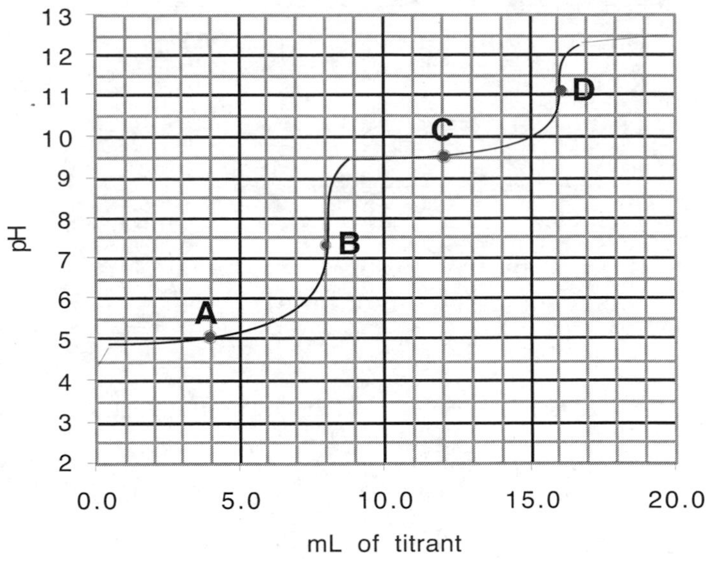

a) The pK_{a1} of H_2A is ________.

b) The pK_{a2} of H_2A is ________.

c) At what point (A, B, C, or D) in the titration is $[H_2A] = [HA^-]$?

d) At what point (A, B, C, or D) in the titration is $[HA^-] = [A^{2-}]$?

e) At what point (A, B, C, or D) in the titration is the $[HA^-]$ at a maximum?

f) At what point (A, B, C, or D) in the titration is the $[A^{2-}]$ at a maximum?

g) How many mL of NaOH are required to reach the first equivalence point?

h) How many mL of NaOH are required to reach the second equivalence point?

i) At what point in the titration (A, B, C, or D) is the $pH = (pK_{a1} + pK_{a2}) / 2$?

j) Would methyl red, which has a $pK_a = 5.1$, be a suitable indicator to use to signal when the first equivalence point has been reached? EXPLAIN.

MULTIPLE CHOICE PRACTICE EXAM FOR MODULE 9

1. How many mL of 0.4067 M NaOH are required to neutralize 1.673 g of CH_3COOH? (MM = 60.0, $K_a = 1.8 \times 10^{-5}$)
   1) 0.06856 2) 11.34 3) 26.37 4) 14.59 5) 68.56
2. What is the pH at the start of the titration of 45.00 mL of 0.3967 M LiOH with 0.4670 M HCl?
   1) 0.40 2) 13.60 3) 0.33 4) 13.67 5) 12.25
3. If 25.00 mL of 0.1005 M HNO_3 are titrated with 0.2010 M LiOH, then what is the pH after the addition of 12.50 mL of LiOH?
   1) 4.60 2) 5.70 3) 7.00 4) 10.10 5) 9.40
4. What is the $[H^+]$, in M, of a solution resulting from the addition of 46.0 mL of 0.137 M LiOH to 47.0 mL of 0.137 M HI?
   1) 1.50×10^{-3} 2) 1.00×10^{-7} 3) 2.97×10^{-6} 4) 1.40×10^{-4} 5) 8.63×10^{-1}
5. What is the pH at the equivalence point of the titration of 50.00 mL of 0.2311 M $HC_2H_3O_2$ ($K_a = 1.8 \times 10^{-5}$) with 0.2311 M KOH?
   1) 5.10 2) 5.60 3) 7.00 4) 8.90 5) 8.40
6. If 50.00 mL of 0.2311 M $HC_2H_3O_2$ ($K_a = 1.8 \times 10^{-5}$) are titrated with 0.2311 M CsOH, then what is the pH after the addition of 50.00 mL of CsOH?
   1) 5.10 2) 5.60 3) 7.00 4) 8.90 5) 8.40
7. What is the pH of a solution resulting from the addition of 15.0 mL of 0.250 M HBr to 25.0 mL of 0.150 M weak base (B:) whose base ionization constant is 3.00×10^{-5}?
   1) 7.00 2) 5.95 3) 5.43 4) 4.73 5) 5.25
8. What is the $[OH^-]$, in M, of a solution in which 22.00 mL of 0.3673 M NH_3 ($K_b = 1.8 \times 10^{-5}$) has been reacted with 13.67 mL of 0.2596 M HCl?
   1) 2.30×10^{-5} 2) 4.35×10^{-10} 3) 1.41×10^{-8} 4) 2.55×10^{-5} 5) 1.27×10^{-5}
9. What is the pH of a solution in which 50.00 mL of 0.1234 M HNO_2 ($K_a = 4.5 \times 10^{-8}$) has been titrated with 50.00 mL of 0.1399 M LiOH?
   1) 2.08 2) 11.92 3) 3.08 4) 10.92 5) 7.40
10. What is the pH of a solution resulting from the addition of 20.0 mL of 0.100 M NaOH to 30.0 mL of 0.100 M $HC_2H_3O_2$ ($K_a = 1.8 \times 10^{-5}$)?
    1) 4.88 2) 4.96 3) 5.05 4) 4.73 5) 4.56
11. In which of the following titrations is the pH at the equivalence point correctly identified?
    1) HClO + CsOH ($pH_{eq\ pt}$ - basic) 2) NH_3 + HCl ($pH_{eq\ pt}$ - acidic)
    3) NaOH + $HClO_4$ ($pH_{eq\ pt}$ - basic)
    4) Two of the above choices. 5) All of the above choices.
12. Which of the following titrations could the following curve describe?
    1) Titration of $HClO_2$ *with* KOH
    2) Titration of HNO_3 *with* CsOH
    3) Titration of $HC_2H_3O_2$ *with* NaOH
    4) Two of the above choices.
    5) All of the above choices.

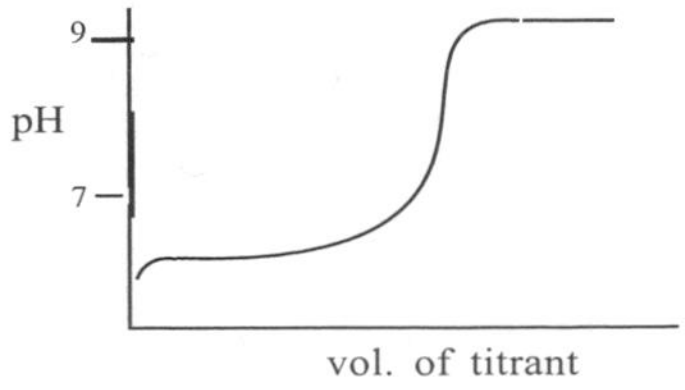

13. A suitable indicator to use in the titration whose curve is shown in problem 12 has a K_a of _______ .

1) 10^{-2} 2) 10^{-8} 3) 10^{-9} 4) 10^{-7} 5) 10^{8}

Consider the following titration curve in which the titrant is NaOH, as well as, the table of indicators when answering questions 14 - 17.

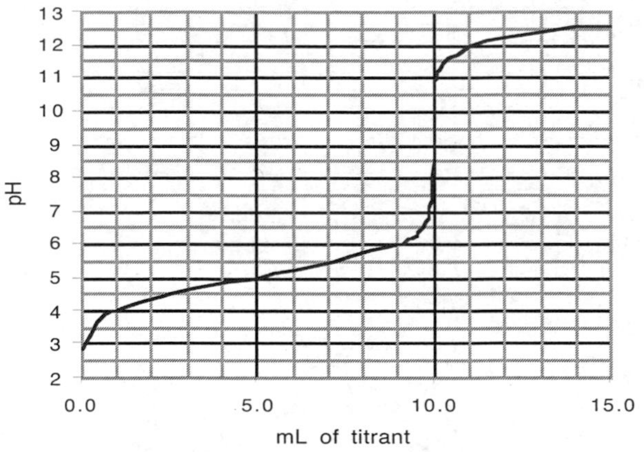

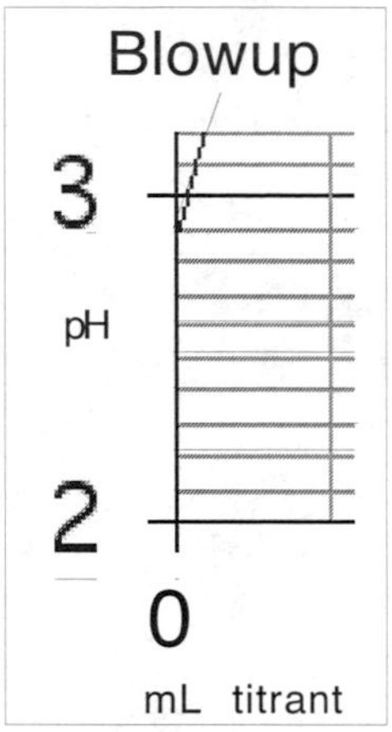

	Color		
Indicator	In acid	In base	pH range*
methyl violet	yellow	blue	0.0 - 1.6
thymol blue‡	red	yellow	1.2 - 2.8
methyl orange	red	yellow	3.2 - 4.4
methyl red	red	yellow	4.2 - 6.3
bromocresol purple	yellow	purple	5.2 - 6.8
bromothymol blue	yellow	blue	6.2 - 7.6
litmus	red	blue	4.7 - 8.3
cresol red	yellow	red	7.0 - 8.8
thymol blue ‡	yellow	blue	8.0 - 9.6
phenolphthalein	colorless	pink	8.2 - 10.0
thymolphthalein	colorless	blue	9.4 - 10.6
alizarin yellow R	yellow	red	10.5 - 12.3

14. Which of the following best approximates what the pK_a of the acid, HA, being used in this titration is?

1) 3. 2) 7. 3) 4. 4) 5.

5) There is not enough information to be able to answer this question.

15. Which of the following statements is/are correct?

1) If thymolphthalcin was used as an indicator, it would start to turn blue at the half-way point in the titration.

2) The approximate $[H^+]$ at the start of the titration is equal to 1.3×10^{-3} M.

3) The weak acid used in the titration could be HCN whose acid ionization constant is 4.9×10^{-10}.

4) Two of the above statements are correct.

5) None of the above statements are correct.

16. Which of the following best approximates what the pH after 10.0 mL of titrant have been added is?

1) 9. 2) 7. 3) 11. 4) 8. 5) 10.

17. Which of the following would be a suitable indicator to use?

1) cresol red 2) bromocresol purple 3) litmus

4) Two of the above. 5) None of the above.

18. Which of the following statements is/are true regarding the titration curve to your right?

1) The initial molarity of the weak base being titrated is 3.0 M.

2) The approximate pK_b of the base used in the titration is 9.

3) An indicator whose pK_a = 6.3, could be used as an indicator in this titration.

4) This titration curve is illustrative of what the titration of NaOH with HCl would look like.

5) More than one of the above statements are correct.

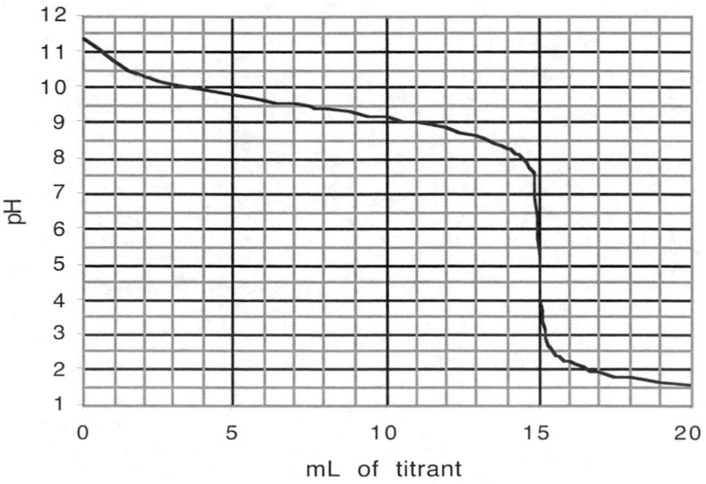

19. Which of the following statements is/are **false** in regard to the titration curve of the weak acid H_2A with NaOH that is depicted below?

A. Point D is where $[HA^-] = [A^{2-}]$.

B. An indicator whose pKa is10.2 would be a suitable indicator to signal when the second equivalence point has been reached.

C. At Point B and beyond of the titration, the $[H_2A]$ is equal to zero.

D. $K_{a1} \approx 4.1$

E. Point B is where the first equivalence point has been reached.

F. pK_{a2} $(H_2A) \approx 8.6$

G. Point A is where $[H_2A] = [HA^-]$.

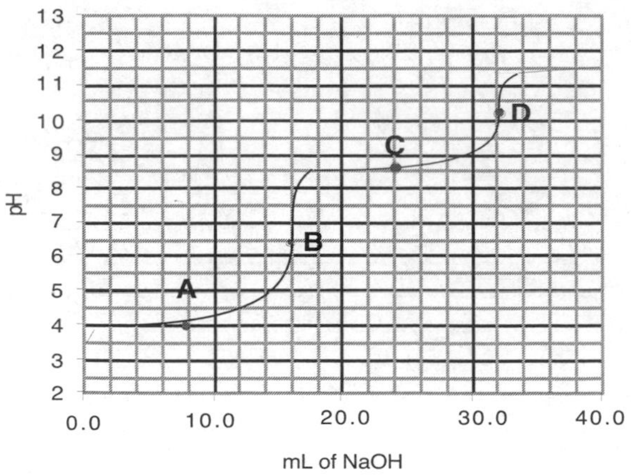

1) only A and D
2) only D
3) only D and G
4) only B and D
5) None of the above is false.

MODULE 9 - ANSWERS

1.

mL NaOH	0.00	12.50	21.00	24.00	25.00	26.00	35.00
pH	1.00	1.48	2.06	2.69	7.00	11.29	12.22

2.

mL NaOH	0.00	12.50	21.00	24.00	25.00	26.00	35.00
pH	2.93	4.85	5.57	6.23	8.78	11.29	12.22

3.

mL HCl	0.00	12.50	21.00	24.00	25.00	26.00	35.00
pH	11.13	9.26	8.54	7.88	5.28	2.71	1.78

4.

mL HCl	0.00	12.50	21.00	24.00	25.00	26.00	35.00
pH	13.00	12.52	11.94	11.31	7.00	2.71	1.78

5. a) equal to 7 b) above 7 c) below 7
6. 5.19
7. 5.97
8. 8.72
9. 0.295
10. a) 182.3 g/eq b) 182.3 g/mol
11. a) 110 g/mol b) 1.6×10^{-6}
12. a) weak base with strong acid
    b) methyl orange, methyl red, bromocresol purple
13. a) No. The criteria for choosing an appropriate indicator, is whether the pH range over which the indicator changes color corresponds with the steep portion of the titration curve. The steep part of this titration curve is from a pH of ~ 6.0 to 10.5 and methyl orange changes color from a pH of 3.2 to 4.4.
    b) 10.0 mL. The volume of titrant added at the equivalence point is the volume where you see a steep rise in pH.
    c) ~ 8.2. The pH halfway between the steep part of the curve is where the equivalence point occurs (i.e., 1/2 (6.0 + 10.5) = 8.25 → 8.2).
    d) Maximum buffering occurs where the pH does not change drastically with the addition of base, this occurs when ~ 1 to 9 mL of titrant have been added. Also, the pH is not changing drastically at the end of the titration $V_{titrant} > 12$ mL.
    e) pH is equal to pK_a when an equimolar amount of [acid] and [salt] are present (i.e., [acid] = [salt] or [HA] = [MA]). This occurs halfway before the endpoint (equivalence) point (10.0 mL). The halfway point of the titration occurs when 5.0 mL of titrant have been added at a pH ~ 4.0.
    f) 1.0×10^{-4} ($K_a = 10^{-pKa}$)
    g) 0.10 M (Considering an initial pH = 2.5 and $K_a = 1.0 \times 10^{-4}$)
    h) The only region of a titration where the pH is dependent only on the concentration of the acid is before you start the titration (0 mL of titrant added).
    i) The only region of a titration where the pH is dependent only on the concentration of the [A^-] is when all the acid (HA) has been neutralized by the base (MOH), at this point only a salt (MA or A^-) is present; this occurs at the equivalence point of the titration when 10.0 mL of titrant have been added.
    j) The region of a titration where the pH is dependent only on the concentration of excess [OH^-] that is added is past the equivalence point. This occurs when more 10.0 mL of titrant have been added.
    k) This occurs at the halfway point of the titration → pH = 4.0 and 5.0 mL of titrant
    l) This occurs at the equivalence point → pH ~ 8.2 and 10.0 mL of titrant
14. a) Yes. The criteria for choosing an appropriate indicator, is whether the pH range over which the indicator changes color corresponds with the steep portion of the titration curve. The steep part of this titration curve is from pH 3.5 to pH 7.0. Generally, an indicator's pH range is within ± 1 of its pKa; therefore, methyl red is expected to change color in the pH region from ~4.1 - 6.1.

b) 15.0 mL. The volume of titrant added at the equivalence point is the volume where you see a steep rise in pH.

c) ~ 5.2. The pH halfway between the steep part of the curve is where the equivalence point occurs (i.e., 1/2 (7.0 + 3.5) = 5.25 → 5.2).

d) Maximum buffering occurs where the pH does not change drastically with the addition of base, this occurs when ~ 1 to 14 mL of titrant have been added. Also, the pH is not changing drastically at the end of the titration $V_{titrant}$ > 17 mL.

e) pOH is equal to pK_b when an equimolar amount of [base] and [salt] are present (i.e., [base] = [salt] or [B:] = $[BH^+]$). This occurs halfway before the endpoint (equivalence) point (15.0 mL). The halfway point of the titration occurs when 7.5 mL of titrant have been added at a pH ~ 9.0 or pOH ~ 5.0 thus, pK_b ~ 5.0.

f) 1.0×10^{-5} $(K_b = 10^{-pKb})$

g) 0.10 M (Considering an initial pH = 11.0 and $K_b = 1.0 \times 10^{-5}$)

h) The only region of a titration where the pH is dependent only on the concentration of the base is before you start the titration (0 mL of titrant added).

i) The only region of a titration where the pH is dependent only on the concentration of the $[BH^+]$ is when all the base (B) has been neutralized by the acid (HA), at this point only a salt (BH^+A^- or BH^+) is present; this occurs at the equivalence point of the titration when 15.0 mL of titrant have been added.

j) The region of a titration where the pH is dependent only on the concentration of excess $[H^+]$ that is added is past the equivalence point. This occurs when more 15.0 mL of titrant have been added.

k) This occurs at the halfway point of the titration → pH = 9.0 and 7.5 mL of titrant

14. a) 5.1 b) 9.5 c) A d) C e) B f) D g) 8.0 mL h) 16.0 mL i) B

i) No. The criteria for choosing an appropriate indicator, is whether the pH range over which the indicator changes color corresponds with the steep portion of the titration curve. The steep portion of the titration curve for the first equivalence point is from pH 6.5 to pH 8.5. Generally, an indicator's pH range is within ± 1 of its pKa; therefore, methyl red is expected to change color in the pH region from ~4.1 - 6.1 - this pH range is not within the steep portion of the titration curve.

ANSWERS TO MULTIPLE CHOICE PRACTICE EXAM

1	2	3	4	5	6	7	8	9	10	11	12	13	14	15	16	17	18	19
5	2	3	1	4	4	5	1	2	3	4	4	2	4	2	1	1	3	1

MODULE 10. *Solubility Product (K_{sp}) of Slightly Soluble and Insoluble Salts*

I. Solubility Product of Slightly Soluble and Insoluble Salts

For the last couple of modules we have been studying equilibrium reactions of soluble substances. In this module we will be studying equilibrium reactions of slightly soluble and insoluble salts. A brief and truncated review of the solubility rules of those salts that are soluble is given below.

a) All IA^+, NH_4^+, NO_3^-, ClO_3^-, ClO_4^-, $C_2H_3O_2^-$ salts are soluble in water.

b) All Cl^-, Br^-, and I^- salts (except Ag^+, Pb^{2+}, and Hg_2^{2+}) are soluble in water.

c) All SO_4^{2-} are soluble except for Ba^{2+}, Pb^{2+} and Sr^{2+}.

Suppose that we added one gram of $BaSO_4$ (MM = 233) to one liter of water at 25°C - since barium sulfate is not soluble in water we would find that very little of the one gram that was added dissolved in one liter of water. As a matter of fact, only 0.0025 grams of it dissolves in one liter of water at 25°C. The molarity of $BaSO_4$ present in a saturated solution (i.e., the maximum amount of moles that will dissolve / ionize in 1 L of solution), which is also known as its *molar solubility*, can be obtained as follows:

$$? \text{ M BaSO}_4 = \left(\frac{0.0025 \text{ g BaSO}_4}{1 \text{ L soln}}\right)\left(\frac{1 \text{ mol BaSO}_4}{233 \text{ g BaSO}_4}\right) = 1.1 \times 10^{-5} \frac{\text{mol}}{\text{L}}$$

The equilibrium that is considered in this case is as follows.

The initial concentration used in problems involving "insoluble" salts is the salt's molar solubility (i.e., the maximum number of mol that will dissolve in 1 L of solution).

$$BaSO_{4\,(s)} \overset{H_2O}{\rightleftharpoons} Ba^{2+}_{(aq)} + SO_4^{2-}{}_{(aq)}$$

	$BaSO_{4\,(s)}$	$Ba^{2+}_{(aq)}$	$SO_4^{2-}{}_{(aq)}$
$[\,]_i$:	1.1×10^{-5}	0	0
$[\,]_{change}$:	-1.1×10^{-5}	$+1.1 \times 10^{-5}$	$+1.1 \times 10^{-5}$
$[\,]_{equil}$:	0	1.1×10^{-5}	1.1×10^{-5}

The equilibrium expression obtained in the case of slightly soluble salts is known as the *solubility product expression.* The equilibrium constant associated with this equilibrium expression is called the *solubility product equilibrium constant,* K_{sp}. Its value is constant at a particular temperature for a *saturated* solution of a compound. You may recall from a previous module, that pure liquids and solids do not enter into equilibrium expressions. Therefore, the solubility product expression and constant for $BaSO_4$ is defined as follows:

$$K_{sp} = [Ba^{2+}]\,[SO_4^{2-}]$$

$$K_{sp} = (1.1 \times 10^{-5})\,(1.1 \times 10^{-5}) = 1.2 \times 10^{-10}$$

Unless otherwise stated, assume that all the problems that we will be doing are at 25°C.

The following table gives the Solubility Product Constant (K_{sp}) for select inorganic compounds.

Substance	K_{sp}	Substance	K_{sp}	Substance	K_{sp}	Substance	K_{sp}
$Ca_3(AsO_4)_2$	6.8×10^{-19}	AgBr	3.3×10^{-13}	$Cd(CN)_2$	1.0×10^{-8}	$Ba_3(PO_4)_2$	1.3×10^{-29}
$Cd_3(AsO_4)_2$	2.2×10^{-32}	$PbBr_2$	8.7×10^{-9}	$Zn(CN)_2$	8.0×10^{-12}	$Ca_3(PO_4)_2$	1.0×10^{-25}
$Mg_3(AsO_4)_2$	2.1×10^{-20}	AgI	1.5×10^{-16}	$BaCrO_4$	2.0×10^{-10}	Ag_2S	1.0×10^{-49}
$Pb_3(AsO_4)_2$	4.1×10^{-36}	PbI_2	8.7×10^{-9}	$CaCrO_4$	7.1×10^{-4}	Bi_2S_3	1.6×10^{-72}
AgCl	1.8×10^{-10}	Ag_2CO_3	8.1×10^{-12}	BaF_2	1.7×10^{-6}	Fe_2S_3	1.4×10^{-88}
Hg_2Cl_2	1.1×10^{-18}	$BaCO_3$	8.1×10^{-9}	CaF_2	3.9×10^{-11}	$BaSO_4$	1.1×10^{-10}
$PbCl_2$	1.7×10^{-5}	$CaCO_3$	4.8×10^{-9}	PbF_2	3.7×10^{-8}	$PbSO_4$	1.8×10^{-8}

Example Problems:

1. If the molar solubility of $La(IO_3)_3$ is 6.9×10^{-4} mol/L, then calculate its K_{sp}.

   The following is the equilibria under study.

	$La(IO_3)_3$ (s)	$\xrightleftharpoons{H_2O}$	La^{3+} (aq)	+	$3\ IO_3^-$ (aq)
[ ]i:	6.9×10^{-4}		0		0
[ ]change:	-6.9×10^{-4}		$+6.9 \times 10^{-4}$		$+ 3(6.9 \times 10^{-4})$
[ ]equil:	0		6.9×10^{-4}		2.1×10^{-3}

   $K_{sp} = [La^{3+}]\,[IO_3^-]^3$

   $K_{sp} = (6.9 \times 10^{-4})\,(2.1 \times 10^{-3})^3 = 6.4 \times 10^{-12}$

2. If the K_{sp} for MgF_2 is 6.4×10^{-9}, then calculate:

   a) Its molar solubility.

   The following is the equilibria under study. Let x = molar solubility of MgF_2 (i.e., the amount that dissolves in water).

	MgF_2 (s)	$\xrightleftharpoons{H_2O}$	Mg^{2+} (aq)	+	$2\ F^-$ (aq)
[ ]i:	x		0		0
[ ]change:	-x		+x		+ 2x
[ ]equil:	0		x		2x

   $K_{sp} = [Mg^{2+}]\,[F^-]^2$

   $6.4 \times 10^{-9} = (x)\,(2x)^2$

   $6.4 \times 10^{-9} = 4x^3$

   $x = \sqrt[3]{1.6 \times 10^{-9}} = 1.2 \times 10^{-3}$ mol/L

   b) The concentration of each ion present in a saturated solution.

   For every one mol of MgF_2 (x) that dissolves , 1 mol of Mg^{2+} (x) is produced and 2 mol of F^- (2x) are produced. Thus,

   $x = [MgF_2] = [Mg^{2+}]$ and $[F^-] = 2x$

   $[Mg^{2+}] = 1.2 \times 10^{-3}$ and $[F^-] = 2.4 \times 10^{-3}$

   c) The number of grams of MgF_2 (MM = 62.3) that will dissolve in 2.5 liter of solution.

   $$? \text{ g } MgF_2 = 2.5 \text{ L} \left(1.2 \times 10^{-3} \frac{\text{mol } MgF_2}{\text{L}}\right)\left(\frac{62.3 \text{ g } MgF_2}{1 \text{ mol } MgF_2}\right) = 1.9 \times 10^{-1} \text{ g}$$

3. Which of the following is more soluble in water?

   a) AgBr ($K_{sp} = 5.0 \times 10^{-13}$) or AgCl ($K_{sp} = 1.8 \times 10^{-10}$)

   If we compare two compounds that give the same ratio of ions then the compound with the higher K_{sp} is more soluble. In this particular case the two compounds have the same ratio of ions (1:1); therefore, AgCl is more soluble because it has the higher K_{sp}.

   b) AgCl ($K_{sp} = 1.8 \times 10^{-10}$) or Ag_2CO_3 ($K_{sp} = 8.1 \times 10^{-12}$)

   In this case, we can't compare the K_{sp}'s outright because the ratio of ions is not the same.

   The molar solubility for AgCl can be obtained as follows. Where, x = mol of AgCl that dissolve in 1-L of aqueous solution.

$K_{sp} = [Ag^+] [Cl^-]$

$1.8 \times 10^{-10} = (x)(x)$

$x = 1.3 \times 10^{-5}$ mol AgCl that will dissolve per liter of solution

The molar solubility of Ag_2CO_3 can be obtained as follows. Where, x = mol of Ag_2CO_3 that dissolve in 1-L of aqueous solution.

$K_{sp} = [Ag^+]^2 [CO_3^{2-}]$

$8.1 \times 10^{-12} = (2x)^2 (x)$

$x = 1.3 \times 10^{-4}$ mol Ag_2CO_3 that will dissolve per liter of solution

Since the molar solubility (x) for Ag_2CO_3 is greater, it will be more soluble in water than AgCl.

4. If a saturated solution of $Zn(OH)_2$ has a pH of 8.65, what is its solubility product equilibrium constant?

$$Zn(OH)_{2\,(s)} \xrightleftharpoons{H_2O} Zn^{2+}{}_{(aq)} + 2\,OH^-{}_{(aq)}$$

	$Zn(OH)_{2\,(s)}$	$Zn^{2+}{}_{(aq)}$	$2\,OH^-{}_{(aq)}$	
$[\,]_i$:	x	0	0	x = $[Zn(OH)_2]$ in a sat soln = molar solubility
$[\,]_{change}$:	-x	+x	+ 2x	
$[\,]_{equil}$:	0	x	2x	

$$[OH^-] = 10^{-pOH} = 10^{-(14 - 8.65)} = 4.47 \times 10^{-6}\ M \rightarrow 2x$$

$$[Zn^{2+}] = x = \frac{4.47 \times 10^{-6}}{2} = 2.23 \times 10^{-6}\ M$$

$$K_{sp} = [Zn^{2+}] [OH^-]^2 = (2.23 \times 10^{-6}) (4.47 \times 10^{-6})^2 = 4.46 \times 10^{-17}$$

II. The Common Ion Effect in Solubility Calculations

The common ion effect is defined as the suppression of ionization of a weak electrolyte by the presence of a common ion in solution coming from a strong electrolyte. We have seen the common ion effect before. A buffer solution was an example of a common ion effect. For example, in a weak acid buffer, the ionization of the weak acid (i.e., HA) is suppressed by the presence of its conjugate base, A^-, which can be obtained from the acid's common ion salt (e.g., NaA).

This common ion effect is a result of the LeChatelier Principle. For example, lets suppose that we have the following equilibrium for a slightly soluble or insoluble salt (MX) where a common ion (X^-) is then added:

$$MX_{(s)} \xrightleftharpoons{H_2O} M^+{}_{(aq)} + X^-{}_{(aq)}$$
$$\downarrow$$

Addition of X^- from a soluble salt (e.g., NaX) will drive the equilibrium to the left which leads to a suppression of ionization (i.e., lowering the solubility of MX).

Complications with K_{sp} problems involving common ions that are beyond the scope of this course include:

- Problems dealing with very insoluble hydroxides derived from metal ions having charges greater than +2, where the contribution from the hydroxide ion concentration from the autoionization of water can't be ignored.
- Problems in which highly charged ions undergo hydrolysis.

Example Problems:

1. The molar solubility of MgF_2 in water is 1.2×10^{-3} M. If the K_{sp} for MgF_2 is 6.4×10^{-9}, then calculate its molar solubility in the presence of a 0.300 M NaF solution.

   In this particular case, this is a common ion problem. As a result of having a common ion in solution (i.e., F^- -- from NaF), this will lower the solubility of MgF_2. Thus, we expect that its molar solubility will be less than 1.2×10^{-3} mol/L.

   For every 1 mol of NaF that ionizes, 1 mol F^- is produced. Thus, the initial concentration of F^- present (due to NaF) is 0.300 M.

   Let x = molar solubility of MgF_2 in 0.300 M Na F.

$$MgF_{2\,(s)} \overset{H_2O}{\rightleftharpoons} Mg^{2+}{}_{(aq)} + 2\,F^-{}_{(aq)}$$

	$MgF_{2\,(s)}$	$Mg^{2+}{}_{(aq)}$	$2\,F^-{}_{(aq)}$
[ ]i:	x	0	0.300
[ ]change:	-x	+x	+ 2x
[ ]equil:	0	x	0.300 + 2x

$K_{sp} = [Mg^{2+}][F^-]^2$

$6.4 \times 10^{-9} = (x)(0.300 + 2x)^2$

assume that 2x is small

$6.4 \times 10^{-9} = 0.0900\,x$

$x = \dfrac{6.4 \times 10^{-9}}{0.0900} = 7.1 \times 10^{-8}$ mol/L {Our assumption that 2x (1.4×10^{-7}) was small was correct.}

   Notice that solubility of MgF_2 in 0.300 M NaF (i.e., 7.1×10^{-8}) is ~16,900 times less than that in pure water (i.e., 1.2×10^{-3}).

2. MgF_2 would be least soluble in which of the following -- H_2O, 0.1 M NaF, 2.7 M NaBr, or 1.0 M KF.

   MgF_2 would be least soluble in a 1.0 M KF solution. The more of a common ion (in the case of 1.0 M KF, $[F^-] = 1.0$ M) that is present in solution, the less soluble a salt will be.

III. Predicting Precipitation Formation

Another application of solubility products is in the calculation of the maximum concentration of ions that can coexist in solution without incurring precipitation. From these calculations we can determine whether a precipitate will form in a given solution. By comparing the solubility product reaction quotient (Q_{sp}) with the solubility product constant (K_{sp}), we can predict whether or not precipitation will occur.

In order to determine whether a precipitate will form from the combination of two particular ion concentrations:

a) Find the initial concentration of the two ions, if they are not given.

b) Plug each initial ion concentration into Q_{sp} expression which has the same form as K_{sp} expression and find the Q_{sp}.

If $Q_{sp} < K_{sp}$ then solution is ***unsaturated*** more solid can dissolve

If $Q_{sp} = K_{sp}$ then solution is ***saturated***

If $Q_{sp} > K_{sp}$ then ***precipitation*** occurs

c) Compare K_{sp} and Q_{sp} with the above scenarios to make a judgement as to whether or not these initial ion concentrations are sufficiently large to produce a precipitate.

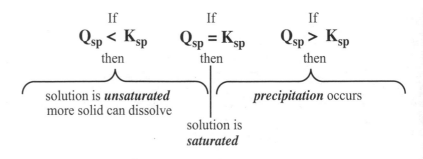

Example Problems:

1. The K_{sp} for BaF_2 is 1.0 x 10^{-6}. If $[Ba^{2+}]$ = 0.025 M and that of $[F^-]$ = 0.010 M, would precipitation occur? EXPLAIN.

$$BaF_{2\,(s)} \xrightleftharpoons{H_2O} Ba^{2+}_{(aq)} + 2\,F^-_{(aq)}$$

	$BaF_{2\,(s)}$	$Ba^{2+}_{(aq)}$	$2\,F^-_{(aq)}$
[ ]i:	0	0.025	0.010

$Q_{sp} = [Ba^{2+}]\,[F^-]^2$

$Q_{sp} = (0.025)\,(0.010)^2 = 2.5 \times 10^{-6}$

Since Q_{sp} (2.5 x 10^{-6}) > K_{sp} (1.0 x 10^{-6}), precipitation occurs.

2. What $[Ba^{2+}]$ is necessary to start the precipitation of $BaSO_4$ (K_{sp} = 1.1x 10^{-10}) in a solution that is 0.0025 M in Na_2SO_4?

$[Na_2SO_4] = [SO_4^{2-}] = 0.0025$ M

Substitution into the K_{sp} expression gives us the $[Ba^{2+}]$ in a saturated solution.

$$BaSO_{4\,(s)} \xrightleftharpoons{H_2O} Ba^{2+}_{(aq)} + SO_4^{2-}{}_{(aq)}$$

$K_{sp} = [Ba^{2+}]\,[SO_4^{2-}]$

$1.1 \times 10^{-10} = [Ba^{2+}]\,(0.0025)$

$$[Ba^{2+}] = \frac{1.1 \times 10^{-10}}{0.0025} = 4.4 \times 10^{-8}\ M$$

To start precipitation, $[Ba^{2+}] > 4.4 \times 10^{-8}$ M

3. Will a precipitate of MgF_2 (K_{sp} = 6.4 x 10^{-9}) form when 300. mL of 1.1 x 10^{-3} M $MgCl_2$ is added to 500. mL of 1.2 x 10^{-3} M NaF? EXPLAIN.

First we must find the moles of each reactant from the given volume and molarity.

$$?\ mol\ MgCl_2 = 300.\ mL\left(\frac{1.1 \times 10^{-3}\ mol}{1000\ mL}\right) = 3.3 \times 10^{-4}\ mol$$

$$?\ mol\ NaF = 500.\ mL\left(\frac{1.2 \times 10^{-3}\ mol}{1000\ mL}\right) = 6.0 \times 10^{-4}\ mol$$

Secondly, we need to find the molarity of each reactant at the instant they are mixed (the volume at that point is 300 + 500 = 800 mL). Furthermore, these two reactants are soluble in water and thus completely ionize.

$$?\ M\ MgCl_2 = \ = \frac{3.3 \times 10^{-4}\ mol}{0.800\ L} = 4.1 \times 10^{-4}\ M \rightarrow [Mg^{2+}]$$

$$?\ M\ NaF = \ = \frac{6.0 \times 10^{-4}\ mol}{0.800\ L} = 7.5 \times 10^{-4}\ M \rightarrow [F^-]$$

$$MgCl_{2\,(aq)} + 2\,NaF_{(aq)} \longrightarrow MgF_{2\,(s\ or\ aq)} + 2\,NaCl_{(aq)}$$

If $Q_{sp} > K_{sp}$, then MgF_2 will precipitate
If $Q_{sp} < K_{sp}$, then MgF_2 will stay in solution

Q_{sp} [$MgF_{2\,(s)} \xrightleftharpoons{H_2O} Mg^{2+}{}_{(aq)} + 2\,F^{-}{}_{(aq)}$] is obtained as follows:

$$Q_{sp} = [Mg^{2+}]\,[F^{-}]^2 = (4.1 \times 10^{-4})\,(7.5 \times 10^{-4})^2 = 2.3 \times 10^{-10}$$

Since Q_{sp} (2.3×10^{-10}) < K_{sp} (6.4×10^{-9}), no precipitation will occur.

IV. **The Effect of pH on Solubility**

In addition to depending on the presence of a common ion, the solubility of many substances also depends on the pH of the solution.

In general, slightly soluble salts in which the anion is derived from a weak acid is significantly more soluble in an acidic solution than it will be in pure water. For example,

$$CaF_{2\,(s)} \xrightleftharpoons{H_2O} Ca^{2+}\,(aq) + 2\;F^{-}\,(aq)$$
$$\Downarrow$$

F^- reacts with H^+ from the acid that is being added. As a result, HF forms. HF is a weak acid that does not completely ionize. Since F^- in effect is being removed from the solution, the equilibrium will shift to the right, causing more salt (i.e., CaF_2) to dissolve when the solution's pH is decreased.

The dissolution of insoluble hydroxides can be increased by decreasing the pH of the solution via the addition of H^+ (from a strong acid). For example,

$$Al(OH)_{3\,(s)} \xrightleftharpoons{H_2O} Al^{3+}{}_{(aq)} + 3\;OH^{-}{}_{(aq)}$$
$$\Downarrow$$

Addition of H^+ causes OH^- to react. As a result H_2O, which is a weak electrolyte, forms. Since OH^- is removed from the solution, the equilibrium will shift to the right, thus causing more $Al(OH)_3$ to dissolve.

In a basic solution, the slightly soluble salt's cation can react with the hydroxide ion to form a precipitate.

Example Problems:

1. Which of the following -- AgCl or Ag_2S -- is expected to be more soluble in acidic solution than in pure water?

   Since S^{2-} is derived from a weak acid, AgS will be more soluble in acidic solution than in pure water. Since Cl^- is derived from a strong acid; AgCl will not be expected to be more soluble in an acidic solution than in pure water.

2. Will a precipitate of $Mg(OH)_2$ ($K_{sp} = 1.5 \times 10^{-11}$) form in a 1.0×10^{-3} M $Mg(NO_3)_2$ solution whose pH has been adjusted to 9.00?

   From the pH of the solution we can find the $[OH^-]$

   $pH + pOH = 14.00$

   $pOH = 14.00 - 9.00 = 5.00$

   $[OH^-] = 10^{-pOH} = 10^{-5}$

   The concentration of $[Mg^{2+}] = [Mg(NO_3)_2] = 1.0 \times 10^{-3}$ M

   Q_{sp} [$Mg(OH)_{2\,(s)} \xrightleftharpoons{H_2O} Mg^{2+}{}_{(aq)} + 2\,OH^{-}{}_{(aq)}$] is obtained as follows:

$$Q_{sp} = [Mg^{2+}]\,[OH^-]^2 = (1.0 \times 10^{-3})\,(10^{-5})^2 = 1.0 \times 10^{-13}$$

Since Q_{sp} $(1.0 \times 10^{-13}) < K_{sp}$ (1.5×10^{-11}), no precipitation will occur.

[NOTE: While with this particular Mg^{2+} concentration, $Mg(OH)_2$ does not precipitate at pH = 9.00, it will precipitate at a pH > 10.1. You may want to try this problem for yourself.]

EXERCISES

1. Complete the following table.

Compound	MM	Solubility (g/L)	Molar Solubility (mol/L)	K_{sp} (Solubility Product)
$AgBrO_3$	235.8	0.0072		
$Cu(IO_3)_2$	413.3			1.2×10^{-7}
$Co_3(AsO_4)_2$	454.5		9.3×10^{-7}	
PbF_2	245.2	0.46		

2. The K_{sp} for Ag_3PO_4 (MM = 418.7) is 1.8×10^{-18}.
   a) What is the $[Ag^+]$ in a saturated solution?
   b) How many grams of Ag_3PO_4 will dissolve in 500 mL of water?
3. How many moles of $Mg(OH)_2$ ($K_{sp} = 1.5 \times 10^{-11}$) will dissolve in 400 mL of a solution having a pH of 12.70?
4. The pH of a saturated solution of a base having the general formula $M(OH)_2$ was found to be 10.52. What is the K_{sp} for this compound?
5. The K_{sp} for MgC_2O_4 is 8.6×10^{-5}. If $[Mg^{2+}] = 0.0017$ M and that of $[C_2O_4^{2-}] = 0.038$ M, would precipitation occur?
6. Which compound is more soluble in water?
   a) CuS ($K_{sp} = 6 \times 10^{-36}$) or CoS ($K_{sp} = 4 \times 10^{-21}$)
   b) AgBr ($K_{sp} = 5.0 \times 10^{-13}$) or Ag_3PO_4 ($K_{sp} = 1.8 \times 10^{-18}$)
7. What is the molar solubility of CaC_2O_4 ($K_{sp} = 2.3 \times 10^{-9}$) in:
   a) pure water b) 0.15 M $CaCl_2$
8. What is the molar solubility of $Mg(OH)_2$ ($K_{sp} = 1.5 \times 10^{-11}$) in:
   a) pure water b) 0.015 M NaOH c) 0.015 M $MgCl_2$
9. What is the molar solubility of $PbBr_2$ ($K_{sp} = 8.7 \times 10^{-9}$) in:
   a) pure water b) 0.100 M $CaBr_2$
10. What is the solubility (in g/L) of $SrSO_4$ (MM = 183.7, $K_{sp} = 2.5 \times 10^{-7}$) in 0.15 M Na_2SO_4?
11. The solubility of MgF_2 (MM = 62.3) in water is 7.6×10^{-3} g/L. What is its solubility (in g/L) in 0.020 M NaF?
12. How many moles of $CaCl_2$ can be added to 1.5 L of 0.020 M K_2SO_4 before $CaSO_4$ ($K_{sp} = 2.4 \times 10^{-5}$) precipitates? Assume that solution volumes do not change.
13. If 255 mL of a 0.0016 M $Pb(NO_3)_2$ solution are mixed with 456 mL of a 0.0023 M Na_2SO_4 solution, would $PbSO_4$ precipitate ($K_{sp} = 1.7 \times 10^{-8}$)?
14. If 50.0 mL of a 0.0010 M $BaCl_2$ solution are mixed with 50.0 mL of a 0.00010 M Na_2SO_4 solution, would $BaSO_4$ precipitate ($K_{sp} = 1.1 \times 10^{-10}$)?
15. Which of the following salts -- PbI_2, $PbCO_3$, PbF_2, $PbBr_2$, $PbCl_2$ -- would be expected to be significantly more soluble in an acidic solution than in pure water?
16. Explain whether or not a precipitate is expected to form when each of the following is mixed. [NOTE: You may need to use the table of solubility product constants on page 1 of this module.]
   a) 500. mL of 0.10 M KNO_3 + 500. mL of 0.10 M $AgC_2H_3O_2$
   b) 500. mL of 1.0×10^{-6} M KCl + 500. mL of 1.0×10^{-5} M $AgNO_3$

MULTIPLE CHOICE PRACTICE EXAM FOR MODULE 10

1. The solubility product for $Ag_2C_2O_4$ is 1.10×10^{-11}. Given this information, what is its molar solubility?
   1) 2.22×10^{-4} 2) 1.10×10^{-11} 3) 1.66×10^{-6} 4) 1.40×10^{-4} 5) 3.32×10^{-6}

2. What is the maximum number of grams of $Cu(IO_3)_2$ ($K_{sp} = 1.44 \times 10^{-7}$, MM = 413.) that will dissolve in an aqueous solution whose volume is 205. mL?
   1) 0.279 2) 321 3) 0.0321 4) 0.388 5) 2.79×10^{-3}

3. Given that 8.30×10^{-3} g of $Ag_2Cr_2O_7$ (MM = 438.) dissolve in 100. mL of water, then what is its solubility product? [Assume that the total volume is 100. mL]
   1) 3.59×10^{-8} 2) 2.73×10^{-11} 3) 6.82×10^{-12} 4) 1.90×10^{-4} 5) 7.18×10^{-8}

4. Calculate the pH of a saturated aqueous solution of $Co(OH)_2$ ($K_{sp} = 2.5 \times 10^{-16}$).
   1) 8.60 2) 9.10 3) 8.90 4) 9.40 5) 9.20

5. Which of the following will be the most water soluble?
   1) $AgBrO_3$ ($K_{sp} = 9.3 \times 10^{-10}$) 2) $BaSO_4$ ($K_{sp} = 1.1 \times 10^{-10}$) 3) AgBr ($K_{sp} = 5.0 \times 10^{-13}$)
   4) $La(IO_3)_3$ ($K_{sp} = 6.4 \times 10^{-12}$) 5) Ag_2CO_3 ($K_{sp} = 8.1 \times 10^{-12}$)

6. In which of the following will $Mg(OH)_2$ ($K_{sp} = 1.5 \times 10^{-11}$) be the least soluble in?
   1) pure water 2) 0.015 M $Ba(OH)_2$ 3) 0.015 M $MgCl_2$
   4) 0.020 M $MgBr_2$ 5) In two of the above choices.

7. What is the largest $[Ca^{2+}]$ (in M) that will not cause precipitation of CaF_2 ($K_{sp} = 3.6 \times 10^{-11}$) in a solution that is 4.0×10^{-4} M NaF?
   1) 2.2×10^{-4} 2) 1.1×10^{-7} 3) 5.6×10^{-5} 4) 9.0×10^{-8} 5) 4.5×10^{-3}

8. In which of the following is both the outcome and rationale correctly identified when the following concentrations of $[Ba^{2+}]$ and $[F^-]$ are mixed? K_{sp} (BaF_2) = 1.0×10^{-6}

	$[Ba^{2+}]$	$[F^-]$	Outcome	Rationale
1)	0.0250	0.0100	no precipitation occurs	$Q_{sp} > K_{sp}$
2)	0.0250	0.00633	solution is just saturated	$Q_{sp} = K_{sp}$
3)	0.0250	0.00525	solution is unsaturated	$Q_{sp} < K_{sp}$

   4) Two of the above outcomes and explanations are correct.
   5) None of the above outcomes are correct.

9. Which of the following is expected to be more soluble in an acidic solution than in pure water?
   1) $PbCl_2$ 2) $Cu(OH)_2$ 3) $CuSO_3$
   4) Two of the above choices. 5) All of the above choices.

10. At what pH will $Mg(OH)_2$ ($K_{sp} = 1.5 \times 10^{-11}$) be ready to start to precipitate in a 1.0×10^{-3} M $Mg(NO_3)_2$ solution?
   1) 6.18 2) 10.09 3) 3.91 4) 7.82 5) 9.00

11. What is the maximum number of moles of $PbSO_4$ ($K_{sp} = 1.8 \times 10^{-8}$) that will dissolve in 1.0 L of 0.0200 M K_2SO_4?
   1) 3.6×10^{-10} 2) 2.2×10^{4} 3) 4.5×10^{-5} 4) 9.0×10^{-7} 5) 2.8×10^{9}

12. What is the molar solubility of CaF_2 ($K_{sp} = 3.6 \times 10^{-11}$) in a solution that is 2.0×10^{-2} M NaF?
   1) 9.0×10^{-8} 2) 7.2×10^{-13} 3) 4.2×10^{-5} 4) 3.6×10^{-11} 5) 1.8×10^{-9}

MODULE 10 - ANSWERS

1.

Compound	MM	Solubility (g/L)	Molar Solubility (mol/L)	K_{sp} Solubility Product
$AgBrO_3$	235.8	0.0072	3.1×10^{-5}	9.6×10^{-10}
$Cu(IO_3)_2$	413.3	1.3	3.1×10^{-3}	1.2×10^{-7}
$Co_3(AsO_4)_2$	454.5	0.00042	9.3×10^{-7}	7.5×10^{-29}
PbF_2	245.2	0.46	1.9×10^{-3}	2.7×10^{-8}

2. a) 4.8×10^{-5} M b) 3.3×10^{-3} g

3. 2.4×10^{-9} mol

4. 1.8×10^{-11}

5. no, Q_{sp} (6.5×10^{-5}) < K_{sp} (8.6×10^{-5})

6. a) CoS b) Ag_3PO_4

7. a) 4.8×10^{-5} M b) 1.5×10^{-8} M

8. a) 1.6×10^{-4} M b) 6.7×10^{-8} M c) 1.6×10^{-5} M

9. a) 1.3×10^{-3} M b) 2.2×10^{-7} M

10. 3.1×10^{-4} g/L

11. 1.1×10^{-6} g/L

12. 0.0018 mol

13. yes, Q_{sp} (8.5×10^{-7}) > K_{sp} (1.7×10^{-8})

14. yes, Q_{sp} (2.5×10^{-8}) > K_{sp} (1.1×10^{-10})

15. $PbCO_3$ and PbF_2

16. a) According to the solubility rules, no ppt is expected because both products formed (i.e., $KC_2H_3O_2$ + $AgNO_3$) are water soluble.

 b) The products of this reaction are KNO_3 + AgCl. KNO_3 will not ppt in accordance with the solubility rules. According to the solubility rules, all Cl^- are soluble with the expection of Ag^+, Pb^{2+}, and Hg_2^{2+}, therefore, there is a possibility that AgCl will precipitate if Qsp > Ksp. However, since Qsp (2.5×10^{-12}) < Ksp (1.8×10^{-10}), AgCl will not precipitate at the Ag^+ and Cl^- concentrations which were given in this problem.

ANSWERS TO MULTIPLE CHOICE PRACTICE EXAM

1	2	3	4	5	6	7	8	9	10	11	12
4	1	2	3	4	2	1	4	4	2	4	1

MODULE 11. *Electrochemistry*

I. Introduction

Electrochemistry is a topic in chemistry that deals with the interconversion of electrical energy and chemical energy. All electrochemical reactions involve the transfer of electrons from one substance to another via redox reactions.

Reduction is defined as the gain of electrons. For example, $Cu^{2+} + 2\,e^- \rightarrow Cu$

Oxidation is defined as the loss of electrons. For example, $Zn \rightarrow Zn^{2+} + 2e^-$

There can be no oxidation without an accompanying reduction or vice-versa. Often times spectator ions (e.g., Na^+, K^+, Cl^- NO_3^-) are not shown for redox reactions. In order to determine which specie in a redox reaction has been oxidized and which has been reduced, one must first determine the change in oxidation number that is occurring. For example,

$$Cu^{2+} + Zn \rightarrow Cu + Zn^{2+}$$

Copper(II) has been reduced (oxidation number has been reduced from +2 to 0, i.e., it has gained $2e^-$). The reagent that gets reduced is known as the ***oxidizing agent (oxidant)***.

Zinc metal has been oxidized (oxidation number has increased from 0 to +2, i.e., it has lost $2e^-$). The reagent that gets oxidized is known as the ***reducing agent (reductant)***.

The electrochemical reactions which will be studied in this module are performed in a reacting system that is contained in a cell or cells. There are two types of electrochemical cells:

a) ***Electrolytic Cell*** - a cell that uses electrical energy to cause a nonspontaneous ($\Delta G° > 0$) reaction to occur via a process called *electrolysis*.

b) ***Voltaic (Galvanic) Cell*** - a cell that uses chemical energy from a spontaneous ($\Delta G° < 0$) reaction to produce electrical energy.

The electric current that is either generated (in voltaic cells) or is necessary (in electrolytic cells) enters or exits via electrodes. ***Electrodes*** are surfaces upon which reduction or oxidation half-reactions occur. Electrodes may or may not participate in the reaction. Those that do not participate are called ***inert electrodes***. The more common inert electrodes are made up of platinum (Pt) or graphite (i.e., $C_{(s)}$). *Regardless of the kind of cell, the electrodes are identified as either:*

a) ***Anode*** - the electrode on which oxidation (i.e., loss of e^-) takes place.

b) ***Cathode*** - the electrode on which reduction (i.e., gain of e^-) takes place.

Also, regardless of the cell, electrons always get transferred from the anode to the cathode.

Other aspects of electrochemistry involve electricity. The more salient points of electricity involve the concepts of current and voltage.

The amount of electric charge (e^-) flowing past a specified circuit point per unit time is defined as current (i). The unit used to measure current is the *ampere* (*A or amp*). An ampere is defined as:

$$A = \frac{C}{sec} = \frac{6.24 \times 10^{18} \text{ electrons}}{sec} \qquad 1 \text{ Coulomb} = 6.24 \times 10^{18} \text{ electrons}$$

The quantity of electricity carried by 1 mol of electrons is called a *faraday* (*F*).

$$1 \text{ mol electrons} = 6.02 \times 10^{23} \text{ electrons} = 1\text{ F} = 96{,}500\text{ C}$$

An electric charge moves from a point of high electrical potential to a point of low electrical potential.

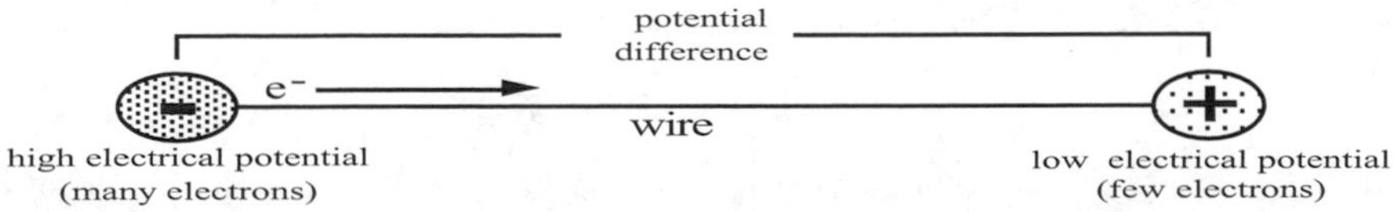

A potential difference is the difference in electrical potential between two points. As a result of a difference in potential, electron (current) flow occurs from the region of high electrical potential to the region of low electrical potential. The unit used to measure a difference in potential is called a *volt* (*V*). A volt is defined as:

$$V = \frac{\text{Joule (J)}}{\text{coulomb (C)}}$$

Current and voltage are related to each other in the following manner:

$$V = i R$$ [where R is the resistance (units - ohms)]

As can be seen from the above equation, $V \propto i$.

II. Electrolytic Cells

A nonspontaneous reaction is forced to occur in an electrolytic cell by the application of electrical current supplied by a battery. A *battery* is an electrochemical cell, or often, several electrochemical cells connected in series, that can be used as a source of electric current at a constant voltage. *Electrolysis* is the process in which electrical energy is used to cause a nonspontaneous chemical reaction to occur. The electrodes that are employed are usually inert electrodes (i.e., they do not participate in the reaction).

By convention, for electrolytic cells, the ***cathode*** (- electrode) is on the left and the ***anode*** (+ electrode) is on the right. A direct current (dc) battery provides the electrical energy that forces the nonspontaneous reaction to occur. Electrons are consumed in the cathode (reduction) half-reaction and produced in the anode (oxidation) half-reaction. *The electrons travel from the anode to the cathode.*

There are two types of reactions that occur in an electrolytic cell: those of a molten salt and those of a salt in aqueous solution.

A. Electrolysis of Molten Salts (With Particular Emphasis on Binary Salts)

Salts in the solid state do not conduct electricity well. However, when molten (melted), salts are excellent conductors because their ions are free to move. Molten salt electrolysis requires very high temperatures (250 - 2000°C).

The stylized cell to the right gives an example of the electrolysis of molten NaCl. Molten NaCl looks just like water. When Na^+ is reduced at the cathode, Na is produced. The Na remains a liquid because the temperature is above its melting point. The silvery looking metal floats to the top because it is less dense than molten NaCl. At the anode Cl^- is getting oxidized to Cl_2, which is a pale green gas.

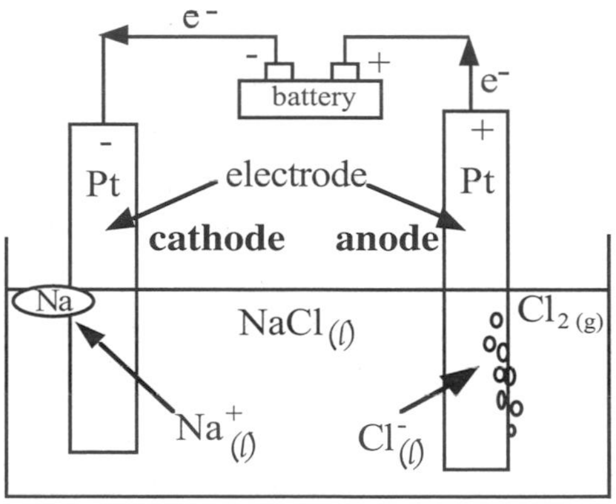

$Na^+_{(l)} + e^- \rightarrow Na_{(l)}$ reduction half-reaction

$Cl^-_{(l)} \rightarrow \frac{1}{2} Cl_{2(g)} + e^-$ oxidation half-reaction

Net Reaction: $\underbrace{Na^+ + Cl^-}_{NaCl_{(l)}} \rightarrow Na_{(l)} + \frac{1}{2} Cl_{2(g)}$

Since an explosive reaction between Na and Cl_2 to produce NaCl can occur, a specialized electrolytic cell (called the *Downs cell*) for the electrolysis of molten NaCl has been developed.

B. Electrolysis of Aqueous Salts

Aqueous salt solutions are excellent conductors of electricity even at room temperature. Aqueous salt solutions contain water.

• *In an aqueous salt solution, there are two possibilities for reduction at the cathode:*

a) $M^{n+} + n\,e^- \rightarrow M$ (All metal ions get reduced except: IA^+, IIA^{2+}, or Al^{3+})

b) $2\,H_2O + 2\,e^- \rightarrow H_2 + 2\,OH^-$ (If metal ion is IA^+, IIA^{2+}, or Al^{3+}, then water gets reduced)

- *In an aqueous salt solution, there are two possibilities for oxidation at the anode:*

a) $X^- \rightarrow \frac{1}{2} X_2 + e^-$ (Of the common anions only Cl^-, Br^-, or I^- get oxidized)

b) $H_2O \rightarrow 2 H^+ + \frac{1}{2} O_2 + 2 e^-$ (If anion is <u>not</u> Cl^-, Br^-, or I^-, then water gets oxidized)

Later on in this module (pg 11-8) oxidation and reduction/oxidation potentials will be discussed, and it is there that you will quantitatively see why water either gets reduced or oxidized preferentially over the other species present in the aqueous solution.

Consider the following electrolytic cell that contains aqueous NaCl

Since the metal ion in solution is Na^+ (which is in IA), it will <u>not</u> get reduced at the cathode; instead, water gets reduced at the cathode.

$$2 H_2O + 2 e^- \rightarrow H_2 + 2 OH^-$$

Hydrogen gas will be produced at the cathode. The pH near the cathode will be basic because OH^- is being produced as well.

Since the anion in solution is Cl^-, it will get oxidized at the anode instead of water.

$$Cl^- \rightarrow \frac{1}{2} Cl_2 + e^-$$

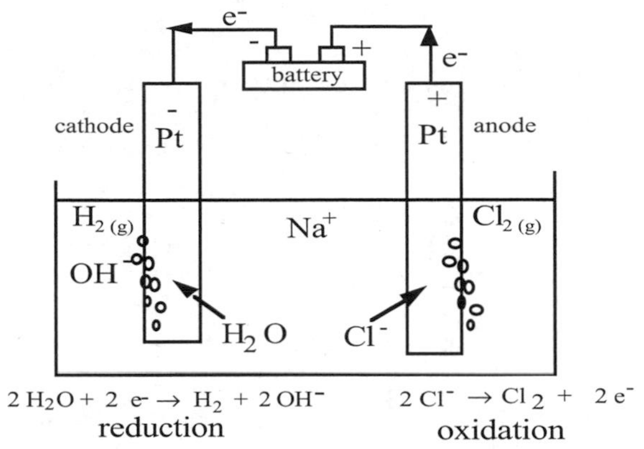

The electrons lost by the substance getting oxidized (reductant) must equal the electrons gained by the substance getting reduced (oxidant).

Thus, for the electrolysis of aqueous NaCl, the balanced redox reaction is:

$$2 H_2O + 2 e^- \rightarrow H_2 + 2 OH^- \quad \text{(Cathode - reduction half-reaction)}$$

$$2 \times (Cl^- \rightarrow \tfrac{1}{2} Cl_2 + e^-) \quad \text{(Anode - oxidation half-reaction)}$$

$$2 H_2O + 2 Cl^- \rightarrow H_2 + 2 OH^- + Cl_2 \quad \text{(Balanced Redox Reaction)}$$

Consider the following electrolytic cell that contains aqueous $CuSO_4$.

Since the metal ion in solution is Cu^{2+}, it will get reduced at the cathode instead of water.

$$Cu^{2+} + 2 e^- \rightarrow Cu$$

Metallic copper will plate onto the cathode.

Since the anion in solution is SO_4^{2-}, it will <u>not</u> get oxidized at the anode; instead, water gets oxidized at the anode. Oxygen gas will be produced at the anode. The pH near the anode will be acidic because H^+ is being produced as well.

$$H_2O \rightarrow \frac{1}{2} O_2 + 2 H^+ + 2 e^-$$

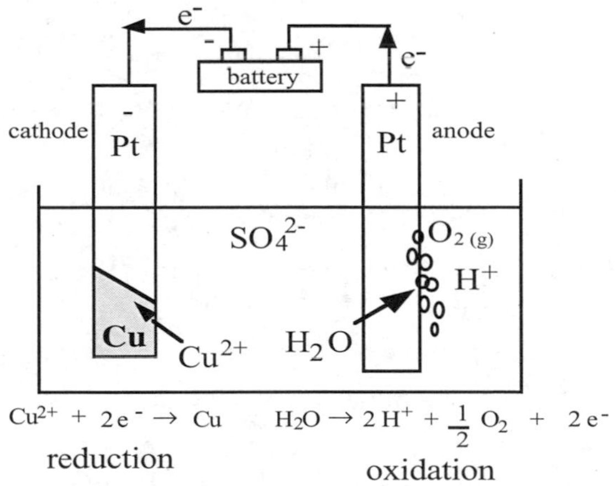

The electrons lost by the substance getting oxidized (reductant) must equal the electrons gained by the substance getting reduced (oxidant).

In this case, since the number of electrons is the same, all we need to do is add up the two half reactions. Thus, for the electrolysis of aqueous $CuSO_4$, the balanced redox reaction is:

$$Cu^{2+} + 2 e^- \rightarrow Cu \quad \text{(Cathode - reduction half-reaction)}$$

$$H_2O \rightarrow \tfrac{1}{2} O_2 + 2 H^+ + 2 e^- \quad \text{(Anode - oxidation half-reaction)}$$

$$Cu^{2+} + H_2O \rightarrow Cu + \tfrac{1}{2} O_2 + 2 H^+ \quad \text{(Balanced Redox Reaction)}$$

Example Problems

1. Answer the following questions pertaining to the electrolysis of aqueous LiF.
   a) What happens at the cathode?
      Since Li^+ is a IA metal ion, it will not get reduced; instead, water gets reduced.
      $2\ H_2O\ +\ 2\ e^-\ \rightarrow\ H_2\ +\ 2\ OH^-$
   b) What happens at the anode?
      Since F^- is not Cl^-, Br^-, or I^-, it will not get oxidized; instead, water gets oxidized.
      $H_2O \rightarrow\ 2\ H^+ + \frac{1}{2}\ O_2 +\ 2\ e^-$
   c) What is the net reaction?

$2\ H_2O\ +\ 2\ e^-\ \rightarrow\ H_2\ +\ 2\ OH^-$	(Cathode - reduction half-reaction)
$H_2O \rightarrow \frac{1}{2}\ O_2 + 2\ H^+\ +\ 2\ e^-$	(Anode - oxidation half-reaction)
$3\ H_2O\ \rightarrow\ H_2\ +\ \frac{1}{2}\ O_2\ +\ 2\ H^+\ +\ 2\ OH^-$	$(2\ H^+\ +\ 2\ OH^-\ =\ 2\ H_2O)$

The net reaction becomes: $H_2O\ \rightarrow H_2\ +\ \frac{1}{2}\ O_2$

2. Answer the following questions pertaining to the electrolysis of molten LiF.
   a) What happens at the cathode?
      Li^+ gets reduced --- $Li^+ +\ e^-\ \rightarrow\ Li$
   b) What happens at the anode?
      F^- gets oxidized --- $F^-\ \rightarrow\ \frac{1}{2}\ F_2\ +\ e^-$
   c) What is the net reaction?

$Li^+ +\ e^-\ \rightarrow\ Li$	(Cathode - reduction half-reaction)
$F^-\ \rightarrow\ \frac{1}{2}\ F_2\ +\ e^-$	(Anode - oxidation half-reaction)
$Li^+ +\ F^-\ \rightarrow\ \frac{1}{2}\ F_2\ +\ Li$	

C. Calculations Involving Electrolytic Reactions (Faraday's Law)

Michael Faraday's studies of electrolysis led him to conclude that the amount of a substance that undergoes oxidation or reduction at each electrode during electrolysis is directly proportional to the amount of electricity that passes through the cell.

Consider the following reduction half-reaction:

$$Cr^{3+}\ +\ 3\ e^-\ \rightarrow\ Cr$$

The following equalities can be drawn from the above reaction:

$$1\ \text{mol}\ Cr^{3+} = 1\ \text{mol Cr}\ = 3\ \text{mol}\ e^-\ =\ 3\ \text{F}$$

$$\text{where, } 1\ \text{F}\ =\ 1\ \text{mol}\ e^-\ =\ 6.02 \times 10^{23}\ e^-\ =\ 96{,}500\ \text{C}$$

The amount of electricity (moles of electrons) that passes through a cell can be obtained as follows:

$$\text{mol}\ e^-\ =\ t\ (s)\ \times\ \text{current}\left(\frac{C}{s}\right)\ \times\ \left(\frac{1\ \text{mol}\ e^-}{96{,}500\ C}\right)$$

$$\text{where, current}\ \rightarrow\ \frac{C}{s}\ =\ A\ =\ \text{amp}$$

There are several common problem types that are performed. Usually, these problems require the use of balanced redox half-reactions.

Example 1: *If the electrolysis of 450. mL of aqueous copper(II) sulfate was performed with the application of 2.50 A of current for 60 minutes, then answer the following questions.*

Before proceeding, we need to have balanced redox half-reactions available for the given reactants.

$Cu^{2+} + 2\ e^- \rightarrow Cu$ (Cathode - reduction half-reaction)

$H_2O \rightarrow \frac{1}{2}\ O_2 + 2\ H^+ + 2\ e^-$ (Anode - oxidation half-reaction)

Applied Current: 2.50 A = 2.50 C/s

Solving for Moles

How many mol of Cu (AW = 63.5) were platted out?

$$?\ \text{mol Cu} = 60\ \text{min}\left(\frac{60\ \text{s}}{1\ \text{min}}\right)\left(\frac{2.50\ \text{C}}{1\ \text{s}}\right)\left(\frac{1\ \text{mol e}^-}{96{,}500\ \text{C}}\right)\left(\frac{1\ \text{mol Cu}}{2\ \text{mol e}^-}\right) = 0.0466\ \text{mol Cu}$$

Solving for Grams

How many grams of Cu (AW = 63.5) were platted out?

$$?\ \text{g Cu} = 60\ \text{min}\left(\frac{60\ \text{s}}{1\ \text{min}}\right)\left(\frac{2.50\ \text{C}}{1\ \text{s}}\right)\left(\frac{1\ \text{mol e}^-}{96{,}500\ \text{C}}\right)\left(\frac{1\ \text{mol Cu}}{2\ \text{mol e}^-}\right)\left(\frac{63.5\ \text{g Cu}}{1\ \text{mol Cu}}\right) = 2.96\ \text{g Cu}$$

Solving for pH

What is the final pH of the solution?

First find moles of H^+ that were produced as a result of of the electrolysis of water at the anode.

$$?\ \text{mol H}^+ = 60\ \text{min}\left(\frac{60\ \text{s}}{1\ \text{min}}\right)\left(\frac{2.50\ \text{C}}{1\ \text{s}}\right)\left(\frac{1\ \text{mol e}^-}{96{,}500\ \text{C}}\right)\left(\frac{2\ \text{mol H}^+}{2\ \text{mol e}^-}\right) = 0.0933\ \text{mol H}^+$$

$$\text{pH} = -\log\ [\text{H}^+] = -\log\left(\frac{0.0933\ \text{mol H}^+}{450 \times 10^{-3}\ \text{L soln}}\right) = 0.68$$

Solving for Volume of Gas Produced at STP

How many liters of oxygen would be produced at STP (at STP - 1 mol gas = 22.4 L)?

$$?\ \text{L}_{\text{STP}}\ \text{O}_2 = 60\ \text{min}\left(\frac{60\ \text{s}}{1\ \text{min}}\right)\left(\frac{2.50\ \text{C}}{1\ \text{s}}\right)\left(\frac{1\ \text{mol e}^-}{96{,}500\ \text{C}}\right)\left(\frac{0.5\ \text{mol O}_2}{2\ \text{mol e}^-}\right)\left(\frac{22.4\ \text{L}_{\text{STP}}}{1\ \text{mol O}_2}\right) = 0.522\ \text{L}$$

Example 2: *A current of 476 mA was applied to LiBr $_{(aq)}$. If 275 mL of dried gas were collected at the cathode at STP, then for how many minutes was the current applied?*

Before proceeding, we need to have balanced redox half-reactions available for the given reactants.

$2\ H_2O + 2\ e^- \rightarrow H_2 + 2\ OH^-$ (Cathode - reduction half-reaction)

$Br^- \rightarrow \frac{1}{2}\ Br_2 + e^-$ (Anode - oxidation half-reaction)

Applied Current: 476 mA = 476×10^{-3} A = 476×10^{-3} C/s

Solving for Time

$$?\ \text{min} = 275\ \text{mL H}_2\left(\frac{1\ \text{mol H}_2}{22{,}400\ \text{mL}_{\text{STP}}}\right)\left(\frac{2\ \text{mol e}^-}{1\ \text{mol H}_2}\right)\left(\frac{96{,}500\ \text{C}}{1\ \text{mol e}^-}\right)\left(\frac{1\ \text{s}}{476 \times 10^{-3}\ \text{C}}\right)\left(\frac{1\ \text{min}}{60\ \text{s}}\right) = 83.0\ \text{min}$$

hydrogen gas is produced during electrolysis

Example 3: ***[OPTIONAL]*** *An aqueous solution of a platinum salt underwent electrolysis with the application of 2.50 A of current for 4 hours. As a result, 18.2 g of metallic platnium were plated out.*

Since the reactants were really not given, we do not have a balanced redox half-reactions available.

Solving for the Oxidation State

What is the oxidation state of the platinum (AW = 195.1)?

First we will solve for the number of moles electrons passing through the cell.

$$? \text{ mol e}^- = 4 \text{ hr}\left(\frac{60 \text{ min}}{1 \text{ hr}}\right)\left(\frac{60 \text{ s}}{1 \text{ min}}\right)\left(\frac{2.50 \text{ C}}{1 \text{ s}}\right)\left(\frac{1 \text{ mol e}^-}{96{,}500 \text{ C}}\right) = 0.373 \text{ mol e}^-$$

Then from the g of Pt that were plated out, we can find mol Pt = mol Pt^{n+}

$$? \text{ mol Pt} = 18.2 \text{ g Pt}\left(\frac{1 \text{ mol Pt}}{195.1 \text{ g Pt}}\right) = 0.0933 \text{ mol Pt}$$

The oxidation state is:

$$\frac{\text{mol e}^-}{\text{mol Pt}} = \frac{0.373 \text{ mol e}^-}{0.0933 \text{ mol Pt}} = 4 \qquad (Pt^{4+} + 4\,e^- \rightarrow Pt)$$

III. **Voltaic (Galvanic) Cells**

A spontaneous redox reaction involves the transfer of electrons from the specie being oxidized (i.e., losing e^-) at the anode to the specie being reduced (i.e., gaining e^-) at the cathode. A *voltaic* (or *galvanic*) *cell* is a device that is used to force electrons through an external circuit rather than the electrons being transferred directly from the reducing to the oxidizing agent. The design of the voltaic cell prevents the species being reduced and oxidized from being in direct physical contact (see the figure to your right).

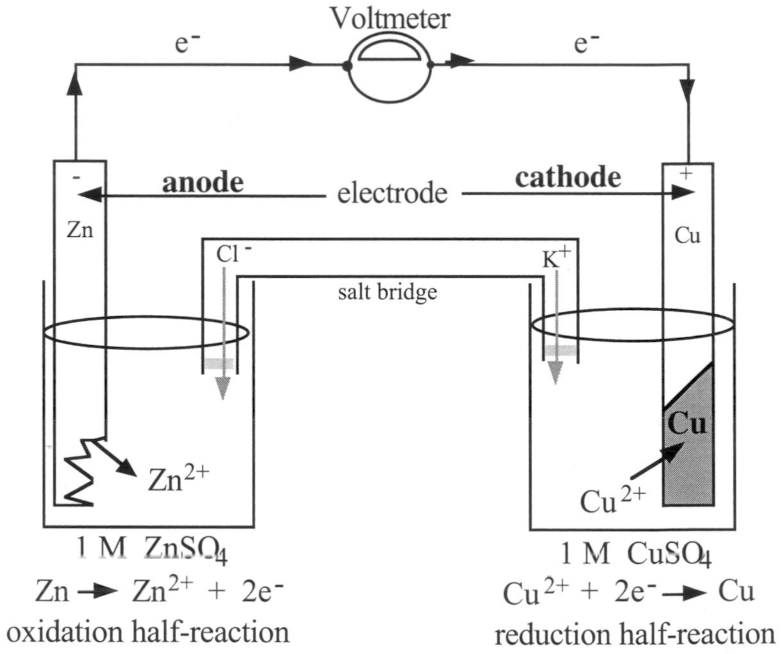

Net Reaction: $Zn + Cu^{2+} \rightarrow Zn^{2+} + Cu$

Cell Notation: $Zn \mid Zn^{2+}\,(1\ M) \parallel Cu^{2+}\,(1\ M) \mid Cu$

The following aspects of a voltaic cell should be understood:

- An **electrode**, is placed in each cell compartment to provide a means for electrons to be transferred in the external circuit.
- By convention, the cell compartment on the left contains the ***anode*** (- electrode) and the chemicals involved in the *oxidation half reaction.*

  NOTE: In the above voltaic cell, the Zn electrode participates in the reaction. The Zn electrode loses two electrons that go through the circuit. When Zn loses two electrons, it gets converted to Zn^{2+}. As a result of this reaction, the Zn electrode starts to lose weight and the concentration of Zn^{2+} in the solution increases.

- By convention, the cell compartment on the right contains the ***cathode*** (+ electrode), as well as, the chemicals involved in the *reduction half reaction.*

NOTE: In the Zn | Zn^{2+} || Cu^{2+} | Cu voltaic cell, the Cu electrode does not participate in the reaction. This electrode could have been composed of any inert conducting material. The Cu electrode transfers the two electrons that come through the circuit from the Zn, to the Cu^{2+} in the solution. When Cu^{2+} gains two electrons, it gets converted to Cu. The Cu produced plates onto the Cu electrode. As a result of this reaction, the Cu electrode starts to gain weight, while the concentration of the Cu^{2+} in solution starts to decrease.

- To complete the circuit, the solutions are connected by a conducting medium, known as a **salt bridge**. A KCl solution is normally employed in the salt bridge. A salt bridge serves: to prevent mixing of the electrode solutions while allowing electrical contact between them and to maintain the electrical neutrality in each cell by allowing ion flow into and out of the salt bridge. Cl^- enters the anode half-cell, while K^+ enters the cathode half-cell. Without a salt bridge, the reaction would cease.
- Electrons flow through an external circuit from the anode to the cathode via a wire that connects them with a force (called **electromotive force - emf**) that varies depending on the nature of the reacting species. The emf generated by a system is represented with the symbol $\mathcal{E}$. Later on, we will see that this emf also varies with the concentration of the species and the temperature at which the cell is operated. The emf (voltage or potential) that is produced from the spontaneous redox reaction is measured with a voltmeter (potentiometer) in the unit of volts (V). As the reaction proceeds, the cell voltage decreases. When the cell voltage reaches zero, the reaction has reached equilibrium.
- An abbreviated version of a voltaic cell, called a **cell notation**, is commonly employed.

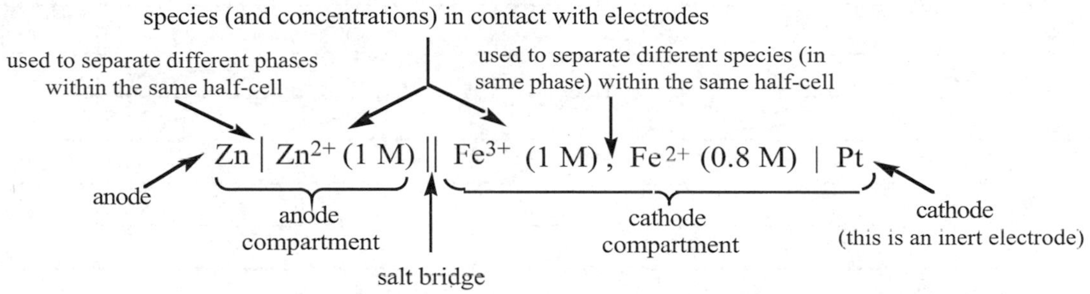

- **Standard Conditions** (°) that cells are run are the following ***unless otherwise noted***.
  For aqueous solutions, the concentration is 1 M
  For gases, the pressure is 1 bar ≈ 1 atm
  The temperature is 25°C

A. Standard Electrode Potentials

It is impossible to measure the potential of a single electrode; but if we arbitrarily set the potential value of a particular electrode at zero, we can use it to determine the relative potential of other electrodes. The **standard hydrogen electrode (SHE)** serves such a purpose. Thus, the standard potential for either the SHE serving as the anode or the cathode is equal to exactly zero.

SHE as Anode

$H_2 \rightarrow 2\,H^+ + 2\,e^-$ $\mathcal{E}° = 0$ V

SHE as Cathode

$2\,H^+ + 2\,e^- \rightarrow H_2$ $\mathcal{E}° = 0$ V

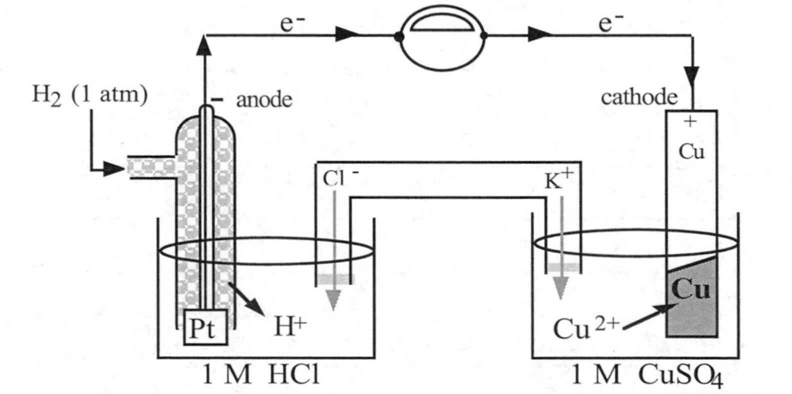

$H_2 \rightarrow 2\,H^+ + 2\,e^-$ oxidation half-reaction

$Cu^{2+} + 2\,e^- \rightarrow Cu$ reduction half-reaction

Net Reaction: $H_2 + Cu^{2+} \rightarrow 2\,H^+ + Cu$ $\mathcal{E}° = 0.337$ V

Cell Notation: Pt | H_2 (1 atm) | H^+ (1 M) || Cu^{2+} (1 M) | Cu

In the above voltaic cell, the SHE functions as the anode in the left half-cell. The standard electrode potential of the copper half-cell is 0.337 V as it functions as the cathode in a Cu-SHE cell.

$H_2 \rightarrow 2\,H^+ + 2\,e^-$	0.000 V	(Anode)
$Cu^{2+} + 2\,e^- \rightarrow Cu$	0.337 V	(Cathode)
$H_2 + Cu^{2+} \rightarrow 2\,H^+ + Cu$	0.337 V	

By measuring the potential of other standard electrodes versus the SHE we can develop standard electrode potentials for other substances. By convention, the standard potential of electrodes are tabulated as *standard reduction half reactions* and are given in Table 1.

Table 1. Standard Reduction Potentials

Reduction Half-Reaction	$\mathcal{E}°$ (volts)
$Li^+ + e^- \rightarrow Li$	-3.045
$K^+ + e^- \rightarrow K$	-2.925
$Ca^{2+} + 2\,e^- \rightarrow Ca$	-2.87
$Na^+ + e^- \rightarrow Na$	-2.714
$Mg^{2+} + 2\,e^- \rightarrow Mg$	-2.37
$Al^{3+} + 3\,e^- \rightarrow Al$	-1.66
$2\,H_2O + 2\,e^- \rightarrow H_2 + 2\,OH^-$	-0.80
$Zn^{2+} + 2\,e^- \rightarrow Zn$	-0.7628
$Cr^{3+} + 3\,e^- \rightarrow Cr$	-0.74
$Fe^{2+} + 2\,e^- \rightarrow Fe$	-0.44
$Ni^{2+} + 2\,e^- \rightarrow Ni$	-0.25
$Sn^{2+} + 2\,e^- \rightarrow Sn$	-0.14
$Pb^{2+} + 2\,e^- \rightarrow Pb$	-0.126
$2\,H^+ + 2\,e^- \rightarrow H_2$ (SHE)	**0.000**
$HgCl_{2\,(s)} + 2\,e^- \rightarrow 2\,Hg_{(s)} + 2\,Cl^-$ **(SCE = Saturated Calomel Electrode)**	0.241
$Cu^{2+} + 2\,e^- \rightarrow Cu$	0.337
$I_2 + 2\,e^- \rightarrow 2\,I^-$	0.535
$Fe^{3+} + e^- \rightarrow Fe^{2+}$	0.77
$Hg^{2+} + 2\,e^- \rightarrow Hg$	0.789
$Ag^+ + e^- \rightarrow Ag$	0.7994
$Br_2 + 2\,e^- \rightarrow 2\,Br^-$	1.08
$2\,H^+ + \frac{1}{2}\,O_2 + 2\,e^- \rightarrow H_2O$	1.23
$Cl_2 + 2\,e^- \rightarrow 2\,Cl^-$	1.360
$Au^{3+} + 3\,e^- \rightarrow Au$	1.50
$MnO_4^- + 8\,H^+ + 5\,e^- \rightarrow Mn^{2+} + 4\,H_2O$	1.51
$F_2 + 2\,e^- \rightarrow 2\,F^-$	2.87

Statements that can be made regarding standard electrode potentials in comparison to the SHE:

Reactions with **Positive** Reduction Potentials

Reduction occurs more readily than the reduction of $2\,H^+ \rightarrow H_2$

The SHE will be the anode.

Reactions with **Negative** Reduction Potentials

Reduction does not readily occur in comparison to the reduction of $2\,H^+ \rightarrow H_2$

The SHE will be the cathode.

When using standard reduction potentials of half-reactions to determine the standard potential of a half reaction or a voltaic cell operated under standard conditions, several important facts must be remembered:

1. $\mathcal{E}°$ changes sign when the reaction is reversed.

   $F_2 + 2\,e^- \rightarrow 2\,F^-$ $\mathcal{E}° = 2.87$ V

   $2\,F^- \rightarrow F_2 + 2\,e^-$ $\mathcal{E}° = -2.87$ V

2. Changing the stoichiometric coefficients of a half-reaction does not affect the value of $\mathcal{E}°$ because an electrode potential is an *intensive property.*

   $F_2 + 2\,e^- \rightarrow 2\,F^-$ $\mathcal{E}° = 2.87$ V

   $2\,F_2 + 4\,e^- \rightarrow 4\,F^-$ $\mathcal{E}° = 2.87$ V

3. The more positive $\mathcal{E}°$ is for a half-reaction, the greater the tendency for that reaction to occur as written.

   $F_2 + 2\,e^- \rightarrow 2\,F^-$ $\mathcal{E}° = 2.87$ V

   $Li^+ + e^- \rightarrow Li$ $\mathcal{E}° = -3.045$ V

   The reduction of F_2 occurs more readily than the reduction of Li^+. Thus, F_2 is a better oxidizing agent than Li^+.

   Conversely, the oxidation (i.e., the reverse reaction) of Li occurs more readily than the oxidation of F^-. Thus, Li is a better reducing agent than F^-.

4. A voltaic cell exhibits a positive $\mathcal{E}°$; thus, for any spontaneous redox process the sum of the oxidation and reduction half-reaction potentials must always be a positive number. Therefore, *always leave the more positive reduction half-reaction as is and reverse the other half-reaction.*

   Given the following two reduction half-reactions.

   $Cu^{2+} + 2\,e^- \rightarrow Cu$ $\mathcal{E}° = 0.337$ V

   $Cr^{3+} + 3\,e^- \rightarrow Cr$ $\mathcal{E}° = -0.74$ V

   The more positive Cu^{2+} half reaction is left as is and the Cr^{3+} half-reaction must be reversed. Also, the coefficients of the Cu^{2+} half-reaction need to be multiplied by 3 and that of the Cr^{3+} half reaction must be multiplied by 2 so that the electrons cancel out.

	$\mathcal{E}°$ (V)
$3\,Cu^{2+} + 6\,e^- \rightarrow Cu$	0.337
$2\,Cr \rightarrow 2\,Cr^{3+} + 6\,e^-$	0.74
$3\,Cu^{2+} + 2\,Cr \rightarrow 3\,Cu + 2\,Cr^{3+}$	1.08

   For the above voltaic cell:

   Cr is the anode. As the reaction proceeds the Cr anode starts to lose weight as it gets converted into Cr^{3+}.

   Cu (or some inert electrode) is the cathode. As Cu^{2+} gets converted into Cu, the Cu plates onto the cathode; as a result, the cathode starts to gain weight.

   Standard Cell Notation: $Cr \mid Cr^{3+}\,(1\,M) \parallel Cu^{2+}\,(1\,M) \mid Cu$

Example Problems

1. Would current flow occur spontaneously in the following cell? $Ag \mid Ag^+\,(1\,M) \parallel Cu^{2+}\,(1\,M) \mid Cu$

   Ag is the anode with the following half-reaction: $2\,Ag \rightarrow 2\,Ag^+ + 2\,e^-$ $\mathcal{E}° = -0.7994$ V

   Cu is the cathode with the following half-reaction: $Cu^{2+} + 2\,e^- \rightarrow Cu$ $\mathcal{E}° = 0.337$ V

   Since $\mathcal{E}°$ for the reaction is negative (-0.462 V), current will not flow spontaneously in the cell.

2. Use the following standard reduction potentials,

	$\mathcal{E}°$
$Fe^{2+} + 2\,e^- \rightarrow Fe$	-0.44 V
$Ni^{2+} + 2\,e^- \rightarrow Ni$	-0.25 V
$Sn^{2+} + 2\,e^- \rightarrow Sn$	-0.14 V
$Pb^{2+} + 2\,e^- \rightarrow Pb$	-0.126 V

to answer the following questions.

a) What is the most easily reduced?

Pb^{2+}, it has the most positive standard reduction potential.

b) What is the most easily oxidized?

Fe, it has the most positive standard oxidation potential (i.e., reverse of the reduction reaction).

c) What is the best oxidizing agent?

The reagent that is most easily reduced is the best oxidizing agent. Since Pb^{2+} has the most positive standard reduction potential, it is the best oxidizing agent on the list.

d) What is the best reducing agent?

The reagent that is most easily oxidized is the best reducing agent. Since Fe has the most positive standard oxidation potential, it is the best reducing agent on the list.

e) Give the standard cell notation for the voltaic cell that would produce the greatest emf.

The cell with the greatest emf would need to be constructed from the substance that is oxidized the most readily (this would make up the anode half-cell) and the substance that is reduced the most readily (this would make up the cathode half-cell).

$Fe \mid Fe^{2+}\,(1\ M) \parallel Pb^{2+}\,(1\ M) \mid Pb$ $\mathcal{E}° = 0.314\ V$

f) Select a suitable reagent (metal or metal ion) capable of reducing Sn^{2+} to Sn.

Ni or Fe. The oxidation reaction of either Ni or Fe would produce a positive emf when coupled with the reduction of Sn^{2+} to Sn.

g) Select a suitable reagent (metal or metal ion) capable of oxidizing Pb to Pb^{2+}.

There is no such reagent on the list. The reduction reaction of none of the species would produce a positive emf when coupled with the oxidation of Pb to Pb^{2+}.

B. Obtaining ΔG and K from Electrode Potentials

The relationship between cell emf and the Standard Gibbs Free Energy Change for any redox process is given by:

$$\Delta G° = -\,n\,F\,\mathcal{E}° \qquad \text{(eq. 1)}$$

where, n = moles of e^- transferred $F = 96{,}500\ \frac{J}{mol\ e^- \cdot V} = 23.1\ \frac{kcal}{mol\ e^- \cdot V}$

You may recall the relationship that exists between ΔG° and K (equilibrium constant):

$$\Delta G° = -\,RT \ln K = -\,2.303\,RT \log K \qquad \text{(eq. 2)}$$

Remembering that pure liquids (e.g., Br_2 and Hg) and solids (e.g., Cu and Li) do not enter into an equilibrium expression, the equilibrium constant for the following redox reaction is:

$Cu^{2+} + Li \rightarrow Cu + 2\,Li^+$ $K = \frac{[Li^+]^2}{[Cu^{2+}]}$

Combining eq. 1 and eq. 2, setting the temperature to 25°C (298 K) in log form of eq. 2, substituting for the constants R (8.314 J/mol • K) in eq. 2 and F (96,500 J/mol e⁻ • V) in eq. 1, and subsequent rearrangement yields,

$$\mathcal{E}^\circ = \frac{0.0592}{n} \log K \qquad \text{(eq. 3)}$$

Thus, if any one of the three quantities ΔG°, K, or $\mathcal{E}^\circ$, is known, the other two can be calculated using eq. 1, 2, and/or 3.

For all redox reactions under *standard conditions*:

ΔG°	K	$\mathcal{E}^\circ$	Reaction Under Standard-State Conditions
Negative	> 1	Positive	Spontaneous
0	1	0	At Equilibrium
Positive	< 1	Negative	Nonspontaneous

For reactions conducted at 25°C and concentrations <u>other than</u> 1 M for aqueous solutions or 1 bar ≈ 1 atm for gases, the ***Nernst Equation*** is used:

$$\mathcal{E} = \mathcal{E}^\circ - \frac{0.0592}{n} \log Q \qquad \text{(eq. 4)}$$

where, n = moles of e⁻ transferred Q = reaction quotient

If the reaction is at equilibrium, then Q = K (equilibrium constant) and $\mathcal{E} = 0$

By using the Nernst equation one can calculate the maximum potential before any current flow has occurred. As the electrons / current flows from the anode to the cathode, the cell discharges and as a result, $\mathcal{E}$ will change. As a matter of fact, as the cell discharges it will reach equilibrium - then, Q = K and $\mathcal{E}$ = 0. A "dead" battery is one in which the redox reaction occurring in the cell has reached equilibrium. At equilibrium there is no longer a chemical driving force for electrons to flow (i.e., the components in each half cell have the same free energy - ΔG = 0) and the cell no longer has the ability to do any work.

<u>Example Problems</u>

1. Consider the following cell notation: Ca | Ca^{2+} (x M) || Ag^{+} (y M) | Ag

   a) Write a balanced redox reaction and calculate the standard cell potential (in V) using Table 1 (Standard Reduction Potentials) given above.

   Under standard conditions [Ca^{2+}] = 1.0 M and [Ag^{+}] = 1.0 M (i.e., x = 1.0 and y = 1.0)

	$\mathcal{E}^\circ$ (V)	
$Ca \rightarrow Ca^{2+} + 2\,e^-$	2.87	(Anode - oxidation)
$2\,Ag^+ + 2\,e^- \rightarrow 2\,Ag$	0.7994	(Cathode - reduction)
$Ca + 2\,Ag^+ \rightarrow Ca^{2+} + 2\,Ag$	3.67	

   b) Using the standard cell potential obtained above, calculate ΔG° (in J).

   $\Delta G^\circ = -\,n\,F\,\mathcal{E}^\circ$

   $\Delta G^\circ = -\,2\text{ mol e}^- \cdot 96{,}500\,\frac{\text{J}}{\text{mol e}^- \cdot \text{V}} \cdot 3.67\text{ V} = -\,7.08 \times 10^5\text{ J}$

c) Using the standard cell potential obtained above, calculate the equilibrium constant .

$$\mathcal{E}^\circ = \frac{0.0592}{n} \log K \quad \rightarrow \quad 3.67\ V = \frac{0.0592}{2} \log K$$

$\log K = 124$

$K = 10^{124}$

d) If $[Ca^{2+}] = 0.598$ M and that for $[Ag^+] = 0.0781$ M at 25°C, then calculate the cell potential (in V) using Table 1 (Standard Reduction Potentials) given above.

In this particular case we need to use the Nernst Equation:

$$\mathcal{E} = \mathcal{E}^\circ - \frac{0.0592}{n} \log Q$$

$$\mathcal{E} = \mathcal{E}^\circ - \frac{0.0592}{n} \log \frac{[Ca^{2+}]}{[Ag^+]^2}$$

$$\mathcal{E} = 3.67 - \frac{0.0592}{2} \log \frac{[0.598]}{[0.0781]^2}$$

$$\mathcal{E} = 3.67 - 0.059 = 3.61\ V$$

2. Consider the following cell notation: $Zn \mid Zn^{2+}\ (5.0\ M) \parallel H^+\ (?\ M) \mid H_2\ (0.46\ atm) \mid Pt$. If the potential for this cell is 0.67 V, then:

a) Write a balanced redox reaction and calculate the standard cell potential (in V) using Table 1 (Standard Reduction Potentials) given above.

	$\mathcal{E}^\circ$ (V)	
$Zn \rightarrow Zn^{2+} + 2\ e^-$	0.7628	(Anode - oxidation)
$2\ H^+ + 2\ e^- \rightarrow H_2$	0.00	(Cathode - reduction)
$Zn + 2\ H^+ \rightarrow Zn^{2+} + H_2$	0.76	

b) What is the reaction quotient for this reaction?

$$\mathcal{E} = \mathcal{E}^\circ - \frac{0.0592}{n} \log Q$$

$$0.67 = 0.76 - \frac{0.0592}{2} \log Q$$

$$0.67 = 0.76 - 0.0296 \log Q$$

$$\log Q = \frac{0.67 - 0.76}{-0.0296} = 3.04$$

$$Q = 10^{3.04} = 1.10 \times 10^3$$

c) What is $[H^+]$?

From the reaction quotient calculated above, we can solve for $[H^+]$.

$$Q = \frac{[Zn^{2+}]\ P_{H_2}}{[H^+]^2} \quad \rightarrow \quad 1.10 \times 10^3 = \frac{(5.0)\ (0.46)}{[H^+]^2}$$

$$[H^+] = \sqrt{\frac{5.0 \times 0.46}{1.10 \times 10^3}} = 0.0457\ M$$

C. Concentration Cells

As we have seen, different concentrations of ions in half-cells give different cell potentials. A concentration cell is a voltaic cell in which both half-cells are composed of the same species but their concentrations are different. Current will flow spontaneously from the anode half-cell containing the less concentrated solution to the cathode half-cell containing the more concentrated solution. Why is this the case? Chemical systems can be said to be egalitarian and as such will try to achieve equality. As the electrons get transferred from the anode to the cathode, the $[Cu^{2+}]$ in the anode half-cell increases while the $[Cu^{2+}]$ in the cathode half-cell decreases. This process continues until the two concentrations are equal. When the two concentrations are equal, $\mathcal{E}$ for the cell will equal zero and equilibrium will have been established.

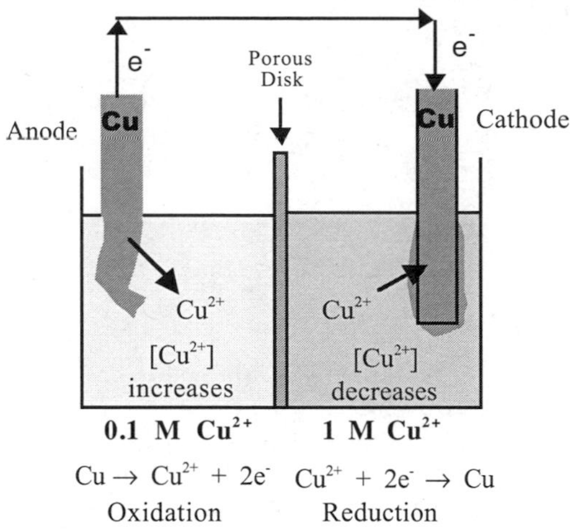

D. Voltaic Cells in Action (ENRICHMENT)

A battery is a voltaic cell or a group of voltaic cells that produces electricity as a redox reaction takes place. As the reaction takes place the reagents are consumed and further reaction stops when the limiting reagent has all been consumed.

A familiar type of voltaic cell is the primary cell called a dry cell that was patented by G. Leclanché in 1866. A primary cell can't be recharged. A typical dry cell is shown to your right, with a cut-away section so that the interior of the battery can be seen.

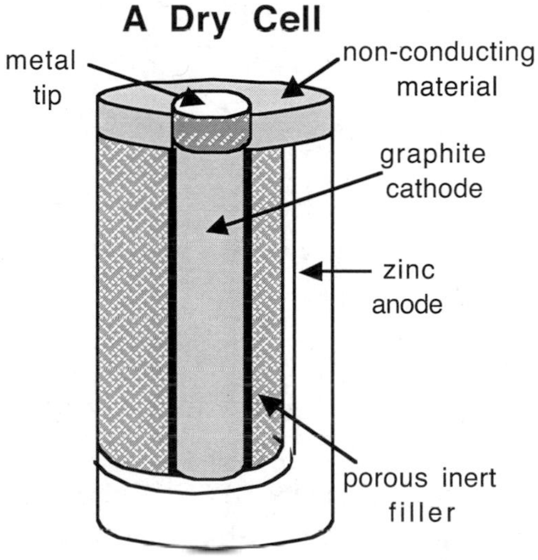

The top of the battery is sealed off with a non-conducting material.

The cathode consists of a graphite rod tipped with a metal contact which serves as the battery's positive pole. The battery is filled with a mixture of MnO_2, NH_4Cl, $ZnCl_2$ and a porous inert filler. The graphite rod serves as the cathode. The half-reactions occurring at the cathode are rather complex, but can be approximated as follows:

$$2\,NH_4^+ + 2\,MnO_2 + 2\,e^- \rightarrow 2\,NH_3 + Mn_2O_3 + H_2O \quad \text{(reduction, cathode)}$$

The anode is a cylindrical zinc casing. The bottom of the battery is usually exposed and serves as the negative pole.

$$Zn \rightarrow Zn^{2+} + 2\,e^- \quad \text{(oxidation, anode)}$$

The above mixture is separated from the zinc walls of the battery by a porous material that is soaked in a a solution of the above mentioned salts. The cell starts to operate as the electrodes are connected externally and the Zn anode starts transferring its electrons.

The dry cell generates a potential difference of ~ 1.5 V.

EXERCISES

General Concepts

1. Define the following: a) anode b) cathode c) electrolytic cell d) voltaic (galvanic) cell
2. By convention, in an electrolytic cell the cathode or anode is on the left and it is the positive or negative electrode.
3. By convention, in a voltaic cell the cathode or anode is on the left and it is the positive or negative electrode.

Electrolytic Cells

4. Write equations for the reduction, oxidation, and net reaction which occurs in the electrolysis of each of the following:
   a) $Mn(NO_3)_2$ (aq) b) LiBr (l) c) AlF_3 (aq) d) Molten AuI_3
5. Consider the electrolytic cell diagrammed just below.
   a) Which is the cathode?
   b) Which is the anode?
   c) Write an equation for the oxidation, reduction, and net reaction.
   d) Which electrode is the negative electrode?
   e) Which electrode is the positive electrode?
   f) Is there an electrode which gains mass as a result of the platting out of a metal onto it? If so, which electrode is it?
   g) Is the pH near one of the electrodes increasing? If so, which electrode is it?

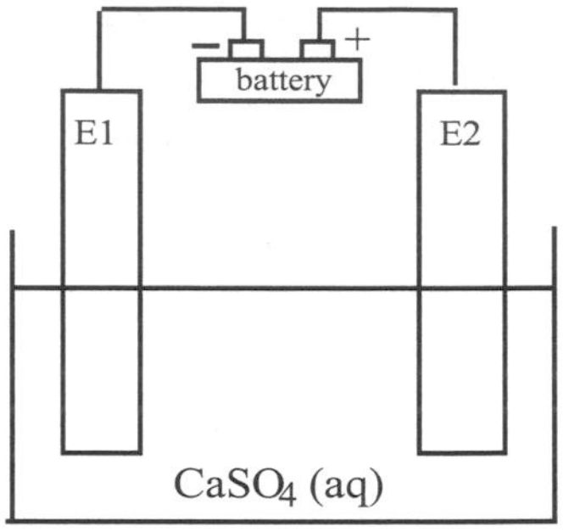

6. A current of 2.21 A is passed through an aqueous solution of $Cd(NO_3)_2$ for 10.4 min. How many grams of Cd (AW = 112.4) will be produced?
7. How much electrical charge (in C) must be passed through an electrolytic cell containing $AgNO_3$ (aq) in order to electroplate 0.775 mg of silver (AW = 107.9) onto a spoon? [Note: Steps involved in solving problem: mg Ag → g Ag → mol Ag → mol e^- → C]
8. How many grams of Cu (AW = 63.5) can be plated out in 30 minutes when an aqueous solution of $Cu(NO_3)_2$ is electrolyzed using a current of 3000 mA?
9. In the electrolysis of $NiSO_4$ (aq),
   a) What is produced at the cathode and at the anode?
   b) How many minutes will it take to plate out 5.09 g of Ni (AW = 58.7) at a current of 1.0 A?
   c) How many liters of O_2 at STP are liberated when a current of 1.0 A is applied for 279 min?
   d) What current (in mA) must be applied in order to obtain 0.0867 mol of Ni in 279 min?
10. How many hours must a current of 0.467 A be applied to a solution of $CdSO_4$ in order to obtain 536 mL of dry O_2 gas at STP?
11. What is the final pH of an aqueous solution of $Zn(NO_3)_2$ after a current of 689 mA has been applied to 350 mL of it for 18 minutes?
12. The electrolysis of 300 mL of an aqueous NaCl solution for 1.5 hours using a current of 0.500 A was conducted. What is the final pH of the solution after electrolysis?
13. The molar mass of an unknown metal can be determined via an electrolysis experiment. An unknown metal ion (M) plates out onto the cathode as a current of 2.00 A is applied for 36.0 min to an aqueous solution of MCl_2. If 1.463 g of the metal were platted out, then what is the metal's identity? [Note: Steps involved in solving problem: min → sec → C → mol e^- → mol M; once mol M are obtained, divide the given g M by the calculated mol M (i.e., g M/ mol M) - this will give you the molar mass of the metal, then look for the metal that has this MM in the periodic table.]
14. An aqueous solution of an unknown chromium salt was electrolyzed with a current of 3.00 A for 60 minutes. This produced 1.94 g of Cr (MM = 52.0) metal at the cathode. Given this information, what is the oxidation number of the chromium salt? **[OPTIONAL]**

Voltaic Cells

15. With the aid of the information given in Table 1 (pg 11-8), will the reaction:

$$Fe^{2+} + 2\,Ag \rightarrow Fe + 2\,Ag^{+}$$

be spontaneous under standard conditions? EXPLAIN.

16. A cell is constructed by immersing a strip of silver in 1.0 M $AgNO_3$ in one cell compartment and a strip of lead in 1.0 M $Pb(NO_3)_2$ in another cell compartment. A wire and a salt bridge are included to complete the cell. With the aid of the information given in Table 1 (pg 11-8), what is this cell's potential?

17. Consider the voltaic cell diagrammed below, as well as, the information given in Table 1 (pg 11-8).

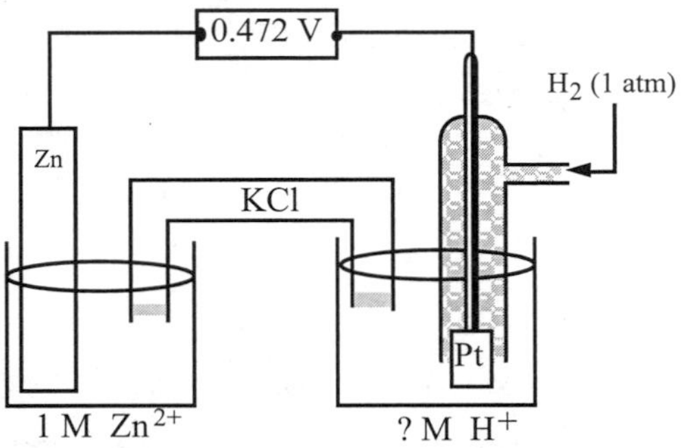

a) What is the anode?
b) What is the cathode?
c) Write an equation and electrode potential for the oxidation, reduction, and net reaction for the voltaic cell under **standard** conditions.
d) What is the reaction quotient (Q) for the reaction occuring in the voltaic cell?
e) What is the $[H^+]$ in the cathode half-cell of the voltaic cell?
f) Write the cell notation for the voltaic cell.
g) Which electrode is classified as the negative electrode?
h) What is $\Delta G°$ (in **kcal**)?
i) Towards which cell (left or right) will the Cl^- ion from the salt bridge migrate?
j) Which electrode, if any, will start to decrease in weight as the reaction progresses?

18. Consider the following cell notation: $Sn \mid Sn^{2+}\,(x\,M) \parallel Ag^{+}\,(y\,M) \mid Ag$

a) Write equations and electrode potentials for the cathode, anode, and net reaction for the reaction under standard conditions using Table 1 (pg 11-8).
b) What is getting reduced?
c) What is getting oxidized?
d) Relative to the SHE would the $Sn^{2+} + 2\,e^- \rightarrow Sn$ half reaction act as the cathode or anode half-cell?
e) Which of the species in the reaction is the least readily reduced?
f) Which of the species in the reaction is the least readily oxidized?
g) What is $\Delta G°$ (in **kJ**) for the reaction under standard conditions?
h) What is the equilibrium constant for the reaction under standard conditions?
i) If the $[Sn^{2+}] = 0.25$ M and that of $[Ag^+] = 1.57$ M, then what is cell potential (in volts)?

19. For the cell $Zn \mid Zn^{2+}\,(1\,M) \parallel In^{3+}\,(1\,M) \mid In$, $\mathcal{E}° = 0.42$ V. Given this information and the standard reduction for Zn^{2+} (-0.76 V), calculate the standard reduction potential for the cathode half reaction?

20. Consider the following voltaic cell: $Ag \mid Ag^{+}\,(?\,M) \parallel Fe^{3+}\,(?\,M), Fe^{2+}\,(?\,M) \mid Pt$

a) Using Table 1 (pg 11-8), what is the standard cell potential (in V) for the cell?
b) Will the current flow in the above cell under standard conditions be spontaneous?
c) What is the cell potential (in V) if $[Ag^+] = 0.10$ M, $[Fe^{3+}] = 0.80$ M, and $[Fe^{2+}] = 0.020$ M?
d) Will the current flow under the conditions in "c" (previous problem) be spontaneous?

21. The measured potential for the following cell is 1.02 V.

$$Pt \mid H_2\,(1\,atm) \mid H^{+}\,(?\,M) \parallel Ag^{+}\,(1.0\,M) \mid Ag$$

Given that the standard cell potential is 0.80 V, then calculate the solution's: a) $[H^+]$ and b) pH

22. Use the following data to answer the following questions.

$Ag^{+} + e^{-} \rightarrow Ag$ $\qquad \mathcal{E}° = 0.80$ V

$Al^{3+} + 3e^{-} \rightarrow Al$ $\qquad \mathcal{E}° = -1.66$ V

a) What is the standard cell potential (in V) for a voltaic cell that involves the above half-reactions?

b) What is cell voltage at equilibrium?

c) What is the equilibrium constant for the reaction for a voltaic cell that involves the above half-reactions?

d) What is the cell potential (in V) if $[Ag^{+}] = 0.50$ M and $[Al^{3+}] = 1.0$ M for a voltaic cell that involves the above half-reactions?

23. The standard reduction potential for - $Zn^{2+} + 2e^{-} \rightarrow Zn$ - is -0.7628 V. If $[Zn^{2+}] = 1.0 \times 10^{-6}$ M, then calculate this half-reaction's reduction potential (in V)?

24. Consider the voltaic cell conventionally diagrammed below, as well as, the following standard half reduction potentials.

$Pb^{2+} + 2e^{-} \rightarrow Pb$ $\qquad \mathcal{E}° = -0.126$ V

$MnO_4^{-} + 8H^{+} + 5e^{-} \rightarrow Mn^{2+} + 4H_2O$ $\qquad \mathcal{E}° = 1.51$ V

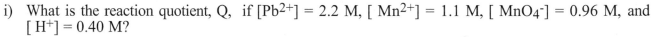

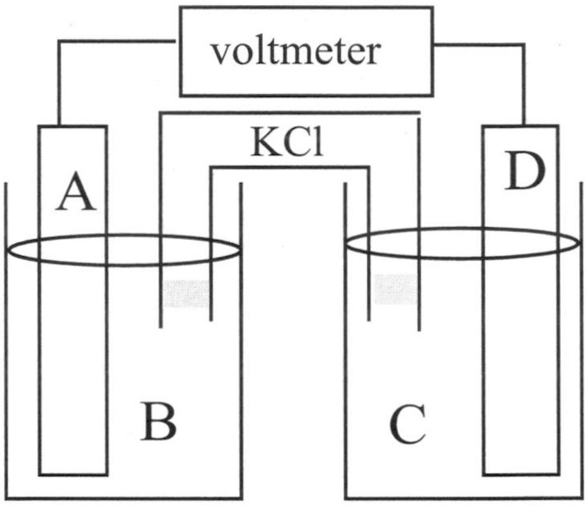

a) What is the identity of **A**?

b) What is the identity of **D**?

c) What is the standard cell notation?

d) What is the net reaction and standard cell potential (in V) for the voltaic cell under **standard** conditions?

e) What is $\Delta G°$ (in **J**)?

f) Calculate the equilibrium constant for the cell under standard conditions.

g) What is in the cell compartment that contains the anode?

h) What is in the cell compartment that contains the cathode?

i) What is the reaction quotient, Q, if $[Pb^{2+}] = 2.2$ M, $[Mn^{2+}] = 1.1$ M, $[MnO_4^{-}] = 0.96$ M, and $[H^{+}] = 0.40$ M?

j) What is the cell potential (in V) if $[Pb^{2+}] = 2.2$ M, $[Mn^{2+}] = 1.1$ M, $[MnO_4^{-}] = 0.96$ M, and $[H^{+}] = 0.40$ M?

25. Calculate the cell potential (in V) for the following concentration cell:

$$Cu \mid Cu^{2+}\ (0.500\ M) \parallel Cu^{2+}\ (1.00\ M) \mid Cu$$

26. While referring to Table 1 (pg 11-8), select a suitable reagent (metal or metal ion) that is capable of accomplishing the following: **[OPTIONAL]**

a) An oxidizing agent capable of oxidizing Ni to Ni^{2+} but not H_2 to H^{+}.

b) A reducing agent capable of reducing Cu^{2+} to Cu but not Pb^{2+} to Pb.

MULTIPLE CHOICE PRACTICE EXAM FOR MODULE 11

1. Which of the following statements is (are) correct about electrolytic cells?
   1) An electrolytic cell uses chemical energy to cause a spontaneous reaction to occur.
   2) The cathode is the positive electrode in an electrolytic cell.
   3) In an electrolytic cell the electrons travel from the cathode to the anode.
   4) Two of the above choices are correct.
   5) None of the above choices are correct.

2. Which of the following statements is/are true about the electrolysis of aqueous $MgBr_2$?
   1) The pH of the solution near the cathode will increase as the electrolysis reaction proceeds.
   2) Mg will plate out at the cathode.
   3) Mg^{2+} is getting reduced at anode.
   4) Br^- is getting reduced at the cathode.
   5) None of the above statements is correct.

3. The half-reaction that occurs at the anode in the electrolysis of molten NaBr is:
   1) $2\ H_2O + 2\ e^- \rightarrow H_2 + 2\ OH^-$
   2) $H_2O \rightarrow 2\ H^+ + \frac{1}{2}\ O_2 + 2\ e^-$
   3) $Br^- \rightarrow \frac{1}{2}\ Br_2 + e^-$
   4) $Na^+ + e^- \rightarrow Na$
   5) $Na \rightarrow Na^+ + e^-$

4. Which of the following is <u>not</u> a likely product that would be obtained from the electrolysis of aqueous $BaCl_2$?
   1) H_2 2) Ba 3) Cl_2
   4) Two of the above choices are correct. 5) All of the above choices are correct.

5. Which of the following statements is (are) true about the electrolysis of aqueous $CuSO_4$?
   1) Cu plates onto the anode.
   2) The pH around the anode increases.
   3) O_2 is produced at the positive electrode.
   4) Two of the above choices are correct.
   5) None of the above choices are correct.

6. Which of the following is (are) **<u>false</u>** about the electrolytic cell to the right?
   1) The mass of the electrode labeled E1 will increase as metallic Zn plates onto it.
   2) E1 is the anode.
   3) As the bromide ion gets oxidized at the surface of the electrode labeled E2, it gets converted into molecular bromine.
   4) Electrons travel from the electrode labeled E2 to E1.
   5) More than one of the above statements is false.

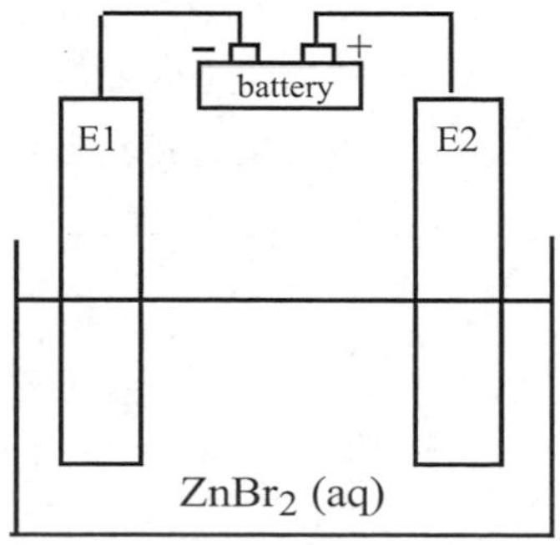

7. How many grams of metallic copper (AW = 63.5) can be obtained when a 2.00 A current is applied for 10 min to an aqueous $CuSO_4$ solution?
   1) 0.10 2) 0.18 3) 0.58 4) 0.79 5) 0.39

8. How many liters of chlorine gas could theoretically be obtained at STP during the electrolysis of molten NaCl if a current of 350 mA is applied for 100 min?

1) 0.244 2) 0.487 3) 0.122 4) 487 5) 244

9. What will the final pH be when a current of 0.689 amps is applied to 350 mL of $Zn(NO_3)_2$ $_{(aq)}$ for 18 min?

1) 0.02 2) 1.66 3) 3.63 4) 1.96 5) 4.66

10. If a current of 6.00 A was passed during the electrolysis of aqueous $Al(NO_3)_3$ for 2.00 hr, then how many Faradays (F) passed through the electrolytic cell?

1) 0.448 2) 0.896 3) 0.224 4) 4.32×10^4 5) 8.00

11. Which of the following statements is (are) true about a voltaic cell with the following cell notation?

$$Cu \mid Cu^{2+}\ (1.0\ M) \parallel Au^{3+}\ (1.0\ M) \mid Au$$

1) Gold(III) ions move toward the cathode to produce metallic gold.
2) Oxidation of Cu^{2+} occurs at the anode.
3) The copper anode is the positive electrode.
4) Two of the above choices are correct.
5) None of the above choices are correct.

12. Which of the following statements is (are) true about a voltaic cell with the following cell notation?

$$Pt \mid H_2\ (1.0\ atm) \mid HCl\ (1.0\ M) \parallel Cu^{2+}\ (1.0\ M) \mid Cu$$

1) The positive ion from the salt bridge enters the anode compartment.
2) The SHE acts as the positive electrode.
3) Electrons from the SHE anode flow to the cathode to reduce metallic copper into Cu^{2+}.
4) Two of the above choices are correct.
5) None of the above choices are correct.

Use the following data to answer questions 13 - 16

	ℰ° (volts)
$\mathbf{Mn^{2+} + 2\ e^- \rightarrow Mn}$	**-1.03**
$\mathbf{Fe^{3+} + 3\ e^- \rightarrow Fe}$	**-0.04**

13. Which of the following statements is (are) true?

1) The SHE would act as the cathode in a reaction with a Mn anode.
2) Mn^{2+} will react spontaneously with Fe.
3) Mn will reduce Fe to Fe^{3+}.
4) Fe will act as the anode in a voltaic cell involving the above half reactions.
5) More than one of the above statements are true.

14. What is the standard cell reaction and potential for a voltaic cell that involve the above half reactions?

1) $3\ Fe^{3+} + 2\ Mn \rightarrow 3\ Fe + 2\ Mn^{2+}$ ℰ° = 3.382 V
2) $2\ Mn^{2+} + 3\ Fe^{3+} \rightarrow 2\ Fe + 3\ Mn$ ℰ° = -1.07 V
3) $2\ Fe^{3+} + 3\ Mn \rightarrow 2\ Fe + 3\ Mn^{2+}$ ℰ° = 3.01 V
4) $2\ Mn^{2+} + 3\ Fe \rightarrow 2\ Fe^{3+} + 3\ Mn$ ℰ° = 1.07 V
5) $2\ Fe^{3+} + 3\ Mn \rightarrow 2\ Fe + 3\ Mn^{2+}$ ℰ° = 0.99 V

15. What is ΔG° (in kcal) for a voltaic cell that involve the above half reactions?

1) -137 2) 45.7 3) 114 4) 5.73×10^5 5) 23.1

16. What is the equilibrium constant (at 25°C) for a voltaic cell that involve the above half reactions?

1) 100 2) 10^{84} 3) 10^{100} 4) 2.00 5) 10^{2754}

Use the following standard reduction potentials to answer questions 17 - 23

	ε° (volts)
$Ni^{2+} + 2e^- \rightarrow Ni$	**-0.25**
$Sn^{2+} + 2e^- \rightarrow Sn$	**-0.14**
$2H^+ + 2e^- \rightarrow H_2$	**0.00**
$Cu^{2+} + 2e^- \rightarrow Cu$	**0.337**
$Fe^{3+} + e^- \rightarrow Fe^{2+}$	**0.77**

17. Which of the following would be the best reducing agent?

1) Ni^{2+} 2) Fe^{3+} 3) H_2 4) Sn 5) Cu

18. Give the standard cell notation and voltage for the voltaic cell that would produce the greatest electromotive force.

1) Pt | Fe^{3+} (1 M), Fe^{2+} (1 M) || Cu^{2+} (1 M) | Cu ε° = 1.11 V
2) Ni | Ni^{2+} (1 M) || Fe^{3+} (1 M), Fe^{2+} (1 M) | Pt ε° = 1.02 V
3) Pt | Fe^{3+} (1 M), Fe^{2+} (1 M) || Ni^{2+} (1 M) | Ni ε° = 1.02V
4) Ni | Ni^{2+} (1 M) || Fe^{3+} (1 M), Fe^{2+} (1 M) | Pt ε° = 0.52 V
5) Cu | Cu^{2+} (1 M) || Fe^{3+} (1 M), Fe^{2+} (1 M) | Pt ε° = 1.11 V

19. Which of the following reactions *as written*, could be used to construct a voltaic cell under standard conditions?

1) $Ni^{2+} + Sn \rightarrow Ni + Sn^{2+}$
2) $2H^+ + 2Fe^{3+} \rightarrow H_2 + 2Fe^{2+}$
3) $2H^+ + Cu \rightarrow H_2 + Cu^{2+}$
4) $Cu^{2+} + Sn \rightarrow Cu + Sn^{2+}$
5) Two of the above choices.

20. Which of the following is (are) true about the voltaic cell to the right?

1) Sn is the negative electrode.
2) Oxidation occurs at the Cu electrode.
3) Electrons travel from the Sn cathode to the Cu anode.
4) The Cu electrode starts to lose weight as the reaction progresses.
5) None of the above choices.

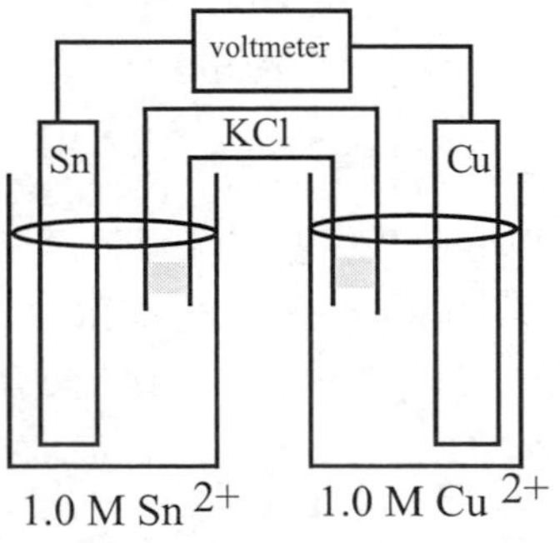

21. Which of the following is (are) true about the voltaic cell diagrammed in the previous page?
    1) K^+ moves into the Sn half-cell as the reaction progresses.
    2) The mass of the Sn in the Sn half-cell is increasing as the reaction progresses.
    3) The concentration of Cu^{2+} in the Cu half-cell increases as the reaction progresses.
    4) Two of the above statements are correct.
    5) None of the above statements are correct.

22. Which of the following is the correct reaction and standard cell voltage for the above voltaic cell diagram?
    1) $Cu + Sn \rightarrow Cu^{2+} + Sn^{2+}$ $\mathcal{E}° = 0.477$ V
    2) $Cu + Sn^{2+} \rightarrow Cu^{2+} + Sn$ $\mathcal{E}° = 0.477$ V
    3) $Cu^{2+} + Sn \rightarrow Cu + Sn^{2+}$ $\mathcal{E}° = 0.477$ V
    4) $Cu^{2+} + Sn \rightarrow Cu + Sn^{2+}$ $\mathcal{E}° = 0.197$ V
    5) $Cu + Sn^{2+} \rightarrow Cu^{2+} + Sn$ $\mathcal{E}° = 0.197$ V

23. Consider the following standard cell notation

$$Ni \mid Ni^{2+} (1.0\ M) \parallel H^+ (?\ M) \mid H_2 (0.37\ atm) \mid Pt$$

If the cell potential is 0.18 V, then calculate the missing hydrogen ion concentration.

1) 2.3×10^3 2) 2.7 3) 1.6×10^{-4} 4) 0.25 5) 0.040

24. The standard electrode potential for the following cell, $Mn \mid Mn^{2+} (1.0\ M) \parallel Fe^{3+} (1.0\ M) \mid Fe$, is 0.99 V. Knowing that the standard reduction potential for the half-reaction: $Mn^{2+} + 2\ e^- \rightarrow Mn$ is -1.03 V, then what is the standard reduction potential (in V) for the $Fe^{3+} + 3\ e^- \rightarrow Fe$ half reaction.

1) -2.02 2) -0.10 3) 2.02 4) 0.04 5) -0.04

Consider the following information when answering questions 25 - 26.

One compartment of a voltaic cell is constructed by immersing a strip of silver in 1.0 M $AgNO_3$ and the other compartment is constructed by immersing a strip of lead in 1.0 M $Pb(NO_3)_2$. The circuit is completed by a wire and a salt bridge. As the cell operates the the lead strip loses mass.

25. Which of the following is (are) true about the voltaic cell?
    1) By convention, the item labeled D in the voltaic cell to the right is Ag and it is the positive electrode.
    2) The standard cell notation would be:

$$Pb \mid Pb^{2+} (1.0\ M) \parallel Ag^+ (1.0\ M) \mid Ag$$

    3) The reduction potential of Ag^+ is more positive than that of Pb^{2+}.
    4) Two of the above choices.
    5) All of the above choices.

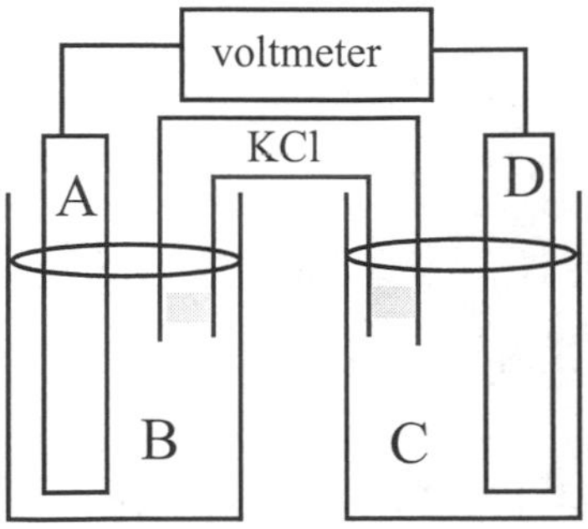

26. Which of the following is (are) true about the voltaic cell?
    1) The net reaction that is occurring is: $Pb + 2\ Ag^+ \rightarrow Pb^{2+} + 2\ Ag$
    2) Ag^+ is being oxidized to Ag in the compartment to the right in the above voltaic cell.
    3) The chloride ions in the salt bridge enter the compartment containing the silver cathode.
    4) Two of the above choices.
    5) None of the above choices.

27. The galvanic cell, $Ni^{2+} + Zn \rightarrow Ni + Zn^{2+}$, has a standard cell potential of 0.51 V. What is the cell potential (in V) under the following conditions: $[Ni^{2+}] = 0.200$ M and $[Zn^{2+}] = 0.0300$ M?

1) 0.53 2) 0.51 3) 0.49 4) 0.55 5) 0.47

28. Consider the following reduction potentials.

Reduction Half-Reaction	$\varepsilon°$ (volts)
$Mg^{2+} + 2\,e^- \rightarrow Mg$	-2.37
$Cr_2O_7^{2-} + 14\,H^+ + 6\,e^- \rightarrow 2\,Cr^{3+} + 7\,H_2O$	1.33

Calculate the potential (in V) for the following voltaic cell.

$Mg \mid Mg^{2+}$ (0.49 M) $\parallel$ $Cr_2O_7^{2-}$ (2.6 M), Cr^{3+} (0.61 M), H^+ (0.040 M) $\mid$ Pt

1) 3.10 2) 3.52 3) 3.70 4) 2.90 5) 3.90

29. Calculate the cell potential (in V) for the following concentration cell:

$Cr \mid Cr^{3+}$ (0.0100 M) $\parallel$ Cr^{3+} (1.00 M) $\mid$ Cr

1) 0.059 2) 0.0395 3) 0.46 4) 0.020 5) 0.12

MODULE 11 - ANSWERS

1. a) Electrode where oxidation (loss of electrons) takes place.
   b) Electrode where reduction (gain of electrons) takes place.
   c) A cell that uses electrical energy to cause a nonspontaneous reaction to occur.
   d) A cell that uses chemical energy from a spontaneous reaction to produce electrical energy.
2. cathode, negative
3. anode, negative
4. a) $Mn^{2+} + 2\,e^- \rightarrow Mn$ (Cathode - reduction)
   $H_2O \rightarrow 2\,H^+ + \frac{1}{2}\,O_2 + 2\,e^-$ (Anode - oxidation)
   $Mn^{2+} + H_2O \rightarrow Mn + 2\,H^+ + \frac{1}{2}\,O_2$

   b) $Li^+ + e^- \rightarrow Li$ (Cathode - reduction)
   $Br^- \rightarrow \frac{1}{2}\,Br_2 + e^-$ (Anode - oxidation)
   $Li^+ + Br^- \rightarrow Li + \frac{1}{2}\,Br_2$

   c) $2\,H_2O + 2\,e^- \rightarrow H_2 + 2\,OH^-$ (Cathode - reduction)
   $H_2O \rightarrow 2\,H^+ + \frac{1}{2}\,O_2 + 2\,e^-$ (Anode - oxidation)
   $H_2O \rightarrow H_2 + \frac{1}{2}\,O_2$ $(2\,H^+ + 2\,OH^- = 2\,H_2O)$

   d) $Au^{3+} + 3\,e^- \rightarrow Au$ (Cathode - reduction)
   $3\,I^- \rightarrow \frac{3}{2}\,I_2 + 3\,e^-$ (Anode - oxidation)
   $Au^{3+} + 3\,I^- \rightarrow Au + \frac{3}{2}\,I_2$
5. a) E1 b) E2

   c) $2\,H_2O + 2\,e^- \rightarrow H_2 + 2\,OH^-$ (Cathode - reduction)
   $H_2O \rightarrow 2\,H^+ + \frac{1}{2}\,O_2 + 2\,e^-$ (Anode - oxidation)
   $H_2O \rightarrow H_2 + \frac{1}{2}\,O_2$ $(2\,H^+ + 2\,OH^- = 2\,H_2O)$

   d) E1 e) E2 f) No g) Yes, E1 (the cathode as OH^- is being produced there)
6. 0.803 g
7. 0.693 C
8. 1.78 g
9. a) cathode: Ni anode: H^+ and O_2 b) 279 min c) 0.971 L d) 1000 mA
10. 5.49 hr
11. 1.66
12. 12.97
13. Zn
14. +3
15. No, because $\mathcal{E}°$ is negative.
16. 0.93 V
17. a) Zn b) Pt

    c) $Zn \rightarrow Zn^{2+} + 2\,e^-$ $\mathcal{E}° = 0.763$ V (Anode - oxidation)
    $2\,H^+ + 2\,e^- \rightarrow H_2$ $\mathcal{E}° = 0.000$ V (Cathode - reduction)
    $Zn + 2\,H^+ \rightarrow Zn^{2+} + H_2$ $\mathcal{E}° = 0.763$ V (Net Reaction)

    d) 6.8×10^9 e) 1.2×10^{-5} M f) $Zn \mid Zn^{2+}\,(1\,M) \parallel H^+\,(1.2 \times 10^{-5}\,M) \mid H_2\,(1\,atm) \mid Pt$
    g) Zn (anode) h) -35.2 kcal i) left j) Zn

18. a) $Sn \rightarrow Sn^{2+} + 2\,e^-$ $\quad \mathcal{E}° = 0.14$ V (Anode - oxidation)

$2\,Ag^+ + 2\,e^- \rightarrow 2\,Ag$ $\quad \mathcal{E}° = 0.7994$ V (Cathode - reduction)

$Sn + 2\,Ag^+ \rightarrow Sn^{2+} + 2\,Ag$ $\quad \mathcal{E}° = 0.94$ V (Net Reaction)

b) Ag^+ c) Sn d) anode e) Sn^{2+} f) Ag g) -181 kJ h) 5.7×10^{31} i) 0.97 V

19. -0.34 V (The reaction in question is $In^{3+} + 3\,e^- \rightarrow In$)
20. a) -0.03 V b) no c) 0.124 V d) yes
21. a) 1.9×10^{-4} b) 3.72
22. a) 2.46 b) 0 V ($\mathcal{E}$ always equals 0 at equilibrium) c) 10^{125} d) 2.44 V
23. -0.94 V
24. a) Pb b) An inert electrode such as Pt or C (graphite)

c) Pb | Pb^{2+} (1.00 M) || MnO_4^- (1.00 M), H^+ (1.00 M), Mn^{2+} (1.00 M) | Pt

d) $5\,Pb + 2\,MnO_4^- + 16\,H^+ \rightarrow 5\,Pb^{2+} + 2\,Mn^{2+} + 8\,H_2O$ $\quad \mathcal{E}° = 1.64$ V

e) 1.58×10^6 J f) 10^{275}

g) By convention the cell compartment that contains the anode is on the left. Aside from the anode (Pb), it contains 1.0 M Pb^{2+} [i.e., $Pb(NO_3)_2$]

h) By convention the cell compartment that contains the cathode is on the right. Aside from the cathode (Pt or another inert electrode), it contains a 1.0 M solution of each of the following ions MnO_4^- [i.e., $KMnO_4$], H^+ [i.e., HCl], and Mn^{2+} [i.e., $Mn(NO_3)_2$].

i) 1.58×10^8 j) 1.59 V

25. 0.0089 V
26. a) Sn^{2+} or Pb^{2+} b) H_2

ANSWERS TO MULTIPLE CHOICE PRACTICE EXAM

1	2	3	4	5	6	7	8	9	10	11	12	13	14	15	16	17	18	19	20	21	22	23	24
5	1	3	2	3	2	5	1	2	1	1	5	1	5	1	3	4	2	4	1	5	3	5	5

25	26	27	28	29
5	1	1	2	2

MODULE 12. *Nuclear Chemistry*

I. Radioactivity or Radioactive Decay

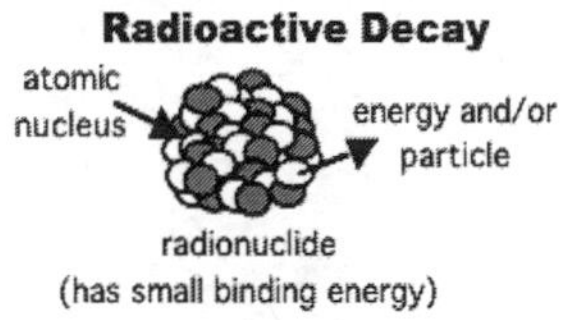

Radioactivity or radioactive decay is defined as the spontaneous release of energy and/or particles from the nucleus of an atom. The emitted energy and/or particles (i.e., *nucleons*) coming from the nucleus is referred to as *nuclear radiation.* Atoms that emit nuclear radiation are said to be radioactive are called *radioisotopes* or *radionuclides*.

Trefoil
Universal Symbol for Radioactivity

The vast number of *nuclides* (i.e., distinct kind of atom or nucleus characterized by a specific number of protons and neutrons) are stable. However, most elements do have at least a few isotopes that are radioactive. For example, carbon has several isotopes that are naturally occurring: carbon-12, carbon-13, and carbon-14. Carbon-14, which constitutes about a millionth of the carbon atoms in living things, is radioactive.

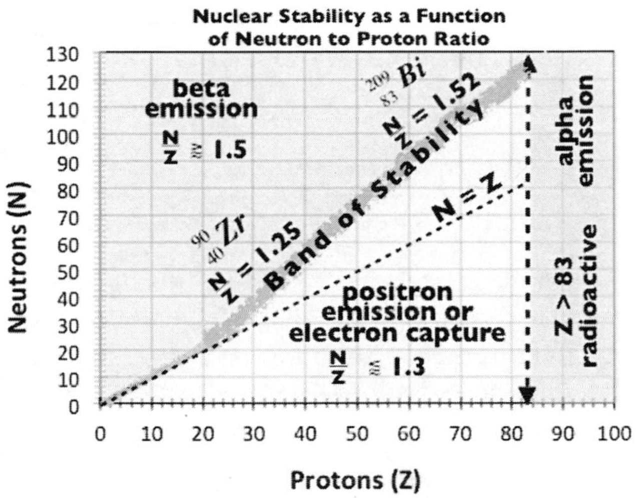

All elements having atomic numbers (Z) greater than 83 are radioactive. For the lighter nuclei (i.e., Z < 21), stable nuclei have approximately equal number of protons and neutrons (e.g., C-12 is stable whereas, C-14 is radioactive). For the heavier nuclides, a larger ratio of neutrons to protons (N/Z) is needed to counter the repulsive electrostatic force of so many protons being so close together. For nuclides with Z between 22 - 50 (e.g., Zr-90), this ratio is ~1.3 : 1, for nuclides with Z between 50 - 83 (e.g., Bi-209) this ratio is ~1.5 : 1.

The particles in the nucleus are held together by a very strong force. The energy associated with this strong force is called binding energy. The *binding energy* is basically the total energy required to separate nucleons (i.e., neutrons and protons). The band of stability in the above figure shows the neutron to proton (N/Z) ratio for stable nuclides.

The nature of radioactivity was discovered by *Henri Becquerel* in 1896. Quite by accident, Becquerel discovered that a uranium compound that he had been working on gave off "rays" that had never been detected before. About two years later *Marie* and *Pierre Curie* worked on a uranium ore known as pitchblende, which they suspected contained other radioactive elements. They discovered two new radioactive elements, polonium and radium. Becquerel and the Curies shared the Nobel Prize (in physics) for their work in radioactivity. Marie Curie became the first scientist to be awarded two Nobel prizes, one in physics and one in chemistry (for the discovery of radium and polonium). She died from prolonged exposure to radiation.

II. Kinds and Characteristics of Ionizing Radiation

There are several types of particles and/or rays that can emanate from a radioactive nucleus. The most common forms of nuclear radiation are named after the first three letters of the Greek alphabet: alpha (α) particles, beta (β) particles, and gamma (γ) rays.

The aforementioned types of nuclear radiation are called *ionizing radiation* because they possess enough energy to cause ionization. Ionizing radiation causes damage to human cells by ionizing the atoms in cells. Any potential radiation damage to the body begins with damage to atoms because organs in the body are made up of tissues, tissues are made up of cells, cells are made up of compounds, compounds are made up of elements, and elements are made up of atoms. Ionization causes a change in the chemical properties of atoms within the cell. This in turn causes undesirable chemical reactions to occur.

The table below gives you general information the four more common types of ionizing radiation.

Name	Symbol	Charge	Shielding	Distance Traveled
alpha	α or ${}^{4}_{2}\alpha$ or $\left[{}^{4}_{2}He^{2+}\right]$	+2	paper or clothing	2 – 4 cm
beta	β^- or ${}^{0}_{-1}\beta^-$ or $\left[{}^{0}_{-1}e^-\right]$	-1	heavy clothing	2 – 3 m
positron	β^+ or ${}^{0}_{+1}\beta^+$ or $\left[{}^{0}_{+1}e^+\right]$	+1	"	"
gamma	γ or ${}^{0}_{0}\gamma$	0	lead or concrete	500 m

penetrability increases

{**NOTE:** While alpha particles are the least penetrating, they are the most harmful if ingested or inhaled.}

Radiation Safety: *keep your distance, use adequate shielding, and minimize time of exposure.*

Approximately 82% of the ionizing radiation that we receive comes from natural sources, called *background radiation* [e.g., uranium in rocks, carbon in living organisms, radon gas, potassium in the human body, cosmic radiation from space] and ~18% comes from man-made sources [e.g., medical X-rays, nuclear fallout, consumer products - smoke detectors].

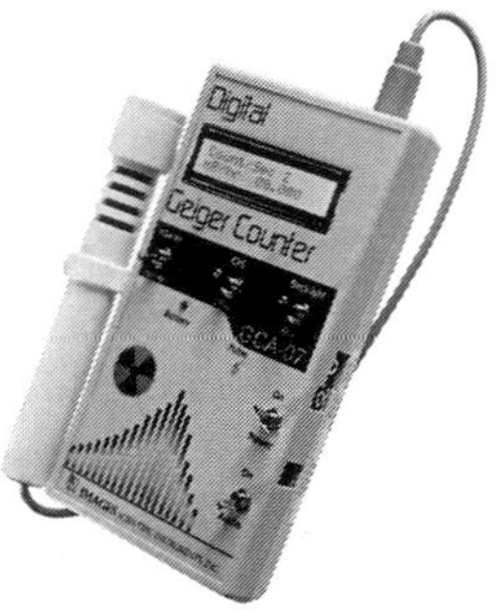

Special instruments (e.g., Geiger Counter) are needed to detect ionizing radiation coming from a radioactive source; we can't hear, feel, smell, or see nuclear radiation.

III. Nuclear Reactions: An Alchemist's Dream

One of the goals of *alchemy*, an ancient and mystical practice that preceded the science of chemistry, was to convert one element into another. Alchemists sought especially to convert an inexpensive metal such as lead into the precious metal gold strictly through the use of chemical reactions, which involve electron rearrangement. In order to accomplish the conversion of one element into another, the nucleus of the atom must be changed. When an element undergoes radioactive decay, a process known as transmutation usually occurs as well. *Transmutation* is the change of one element into another as a result of nuclear changes. Transmutation can occur naturally or by artificial means.

A nuclear reaction can be depicted by the use of the following generalized equation:

$$\textit{Parent} \rightarrow \textit{Daughter} + \textit{Radiation}$$

To balance nuclear reactions you need understand the symbolism behind an isotope symbol.

Mass Number (M) → 40
Symbol for Element → Ar
Atomic Number (Z) → 18

$${}^{40}_{18}Ar$$

Isotope Symbol for Argon-40

$M = \#p^+ + \#n$

$Z = \#p^+$

$M - Z = (\#p^+ + \#n) - \#p^+ = \#n$

The following are two examples of balanced nuclear equations - each involving a transmutation.

$$^{238}_{92}U \rightarrow {}^{234}_{90}Th + {}^{4}_{2}\alpha$$

parent daughter radiation

The above nuclear equation shows how U-238 is an alpha particle emitter (i.e., U-238 is radioactive) and how it gives birth to the daughter radionuclide, Th-234.

14 + 0 = **14**

$$^{14}_{6}C \rightarrow {}^{14}_{7}N + {}^{0}_{-1}\beta^-$$

7 + (-1) = **6**

The above nuclear equation shows how C-14 is a beta emitter and how it gives birth to the daughter N-14.

The following diagrams describe what is involved during the emission of an alpha particle, beta particle, gamma ray and positron from radionuclides. An example of an atom that stabilizes itself via an electron capture is also shown.

Alpha Emission

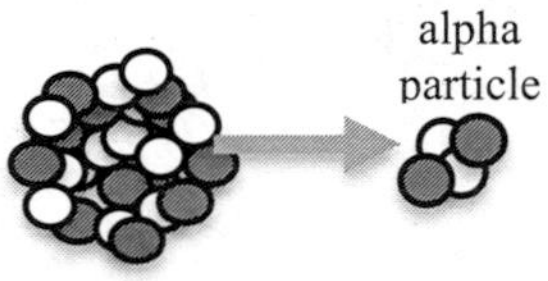

During alpha emission 2 protons and 2 neutrons (i.e., equivalent of a He nucleus) get ejected from the nucleus of the radionuclide.

$$^{240}_{94}\boldsymbol{Pu} \rightarrow {}^{236}_{92}\boldsymbol{U} + {}^{4}_{2}\alpha$$

Beta Emission

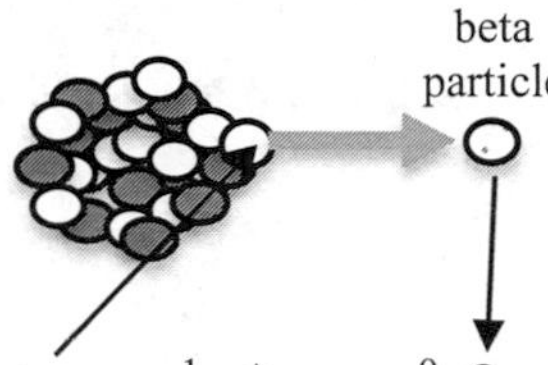

$$^{1}_{0}\boldsymbol{n} \rightarrow {}^{1}_{1}\boldsymbol{p}^+ + {}^{0}_{-1}\beta^-$$

During beta emission, a neutron gets converted into a proton and a beta particle (i.e., an electron). The proton stays in the nucleus and the beta particle gets ejected from the nucleus of the radionuclide.

$$^{208}_{81}\boldsymbol{Tl} \rightarrow {}^{208}_{80}\boldsymbol{Tl} + {}^{0}_{-1}\beta^-$$

Gamma Emission

A radionuclide that is just a gamma emitter is not undergoing transmutation and is releasing high energy gamma rays from its nucleus.

$$^{60m}_{27}Co \rightarrow {}^{60}_{27}Co + {}^{0}_{0}\gamma$$

m = metastable / unstable

Positron Emission

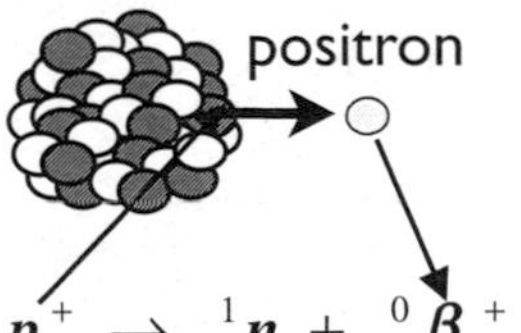

$$^{1}_{1}\boldsymbol{p}^+ \rightarrow {}^{1}_{0}\boldsymbol{n} + {}^{0}_{+1}\beta^+$$

During positron emission, a proton gets converted into a neutron and a positron particle (i.e., a "positive" electron). The neutron stays in the nucleus and the positron gets ejected from the nucleus of the radionuclide.

$$^{23}_{12}\boldsymbol{Mg} \rightarrow {}^{23}_{11}\boldsymbol{Na} + {}^{0}_{+1}\beta^+$$

Electron Capture

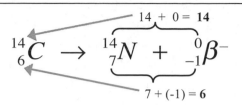

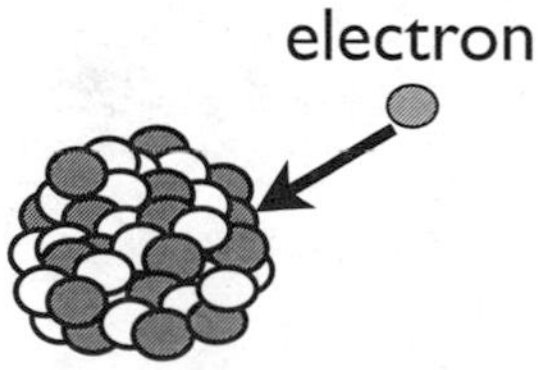

$$^{1}_{1}\boldsymbol{p}^+ + {}^{0}_{-1}\boldsymbol{e}^- \rightarrow {}^{1}_{0}\boldsymbol{n}$$

An electron close to the nucleus gets "captured" by the nucleus. The electron combines with the proton and gets converted into a neutron.

$$^{81}_{36}\boldsymbol{Kr} + {}^{0}_{-1}\boldsymbol{e}^- \rightarrow {}^{81}_{35}\boldsymbol{Br}$$

Alpha emission usually occurs with nuclides that have too many nucleons (i.e., those having Z > 83).

Beta emission occurs with those nucleons that are neutron rich.

Either positron emission or electron capture occurs with those nuclides that are neutron poor.

Nuclear reactions differ from ordinary chemical reactions in several ways:

1. A nuclear reaction involves a change in an atom's nucleus, usually producing a different element. A chemical reaction (e.g., $2\ H_2 + O_2 \rightarrow 2\ H_2O$) by contrast, involves only a change in distribution of the outer-shell electrons around the atom and never changes the nucleus or produces a different element.
2. Different isotopes of an element have essentially the same behavior in chemical reactions, but often have completely different behavior in nuclear reactions.
3. The rate of a nuclear reaction is unaffected by a change in temperature, pressure, or addition of a catalyst (i.e., substances that speed up chemical reactions). In contrast, chemical reactions are affected by temperature, pressure and catalysis.
4. The nuclear reaction of an atom is essentially the same, regardless of whether the atom is in a chemical compound or in an uncombined elemental form. In contrast, a chemical reaction of a particular element in a combined state is different from that in its uncombined state.
5. Energy changes in nuclear reactions are far greater than those accompanying a chemical reaction.

IV. Making an Educated Prediction About Nuclide Stability and Mode of Radioactive Decay

Nuclides having $Z > 83$ are all radioactive and *usually* tend to decay via alpha emission. For nuclides having $Z < 83$ radioactive decay can be predicted based on the Neutron (N) : Proton (Z).

- Nuclides having $Z < 21$ are stable if $N/Z \approx 1$
- Nuclides having $N/Z \gtrapprox 1.5$ (i.e., nuclides lying above the band of stability) tend to be unstable (i.e., radioactive) and *usually* decay via *beta emission* in an effort to stabilize themselves.
- Nuclides having $N/Z \lessapprox 1.3$ (i.e., nuclides lying below the band of stability) tend to be unstable and *usually* decay via *positron emission* or via *electron capture* in an effort to stabilize themselves.

Example Problems:

1. For each of the following predict whether or not each nuclide is expected to be stable or radioactive. If the nuclide is expected to be radioactive what method of decay is expected and then proceed to write a balanced nuclear equation.

   a) ${}^{40}_{20}Ca$ - This is expected to be stable because $Z < 21$ and $N/Z = 20/20 = 1$.

   b) ${}^{230}_{90}Th$ - This is radioactive because $Z > 83$. Elements with $Z>83$ usually tend to stabilize itself via alpha emission. The balanced nuclear equation would be as follows:

   $${}^{230}_{90}Th \rightarrow {}^{226}_{88}Ra + {}^{4}_{2}\alpha$$

   c) ${}^{105}_{47}Ag$ - Since $N/Z = 58/44 = 1.23 \lessapprox 1.3$, Ag-125 would tend to stabilize itself either by via positron emission or electron capture. The balanced nuclear equation for each would, positron emission and electron capture, respectively is:

   $${}^{105}_{47}Ag \rightarrow {}^{105}_{46}Pd + {}^{0}_{+1}\beta^{+} \quad || \quad {}^{105}_{47}Ag \ {}^{0}_{-1}\beta^{-} \rightarrow {}^{105}_{46}Pd$$

   d) ${}^{6}_{2}He$ - Since $N/Z = 4/2 = 2.0 \gtrapprox 1.5$ it would tend to stabilize itself via beta. The balanced nuclear equation would be as follows:

   $${}^{6}_{2}He \rightarrow {}^{6}_{3}Li + {}^{0}_{-1}\beta^{-}$$

V. Radioactive Decay Chains

The stability of the nucleus of a radioisotope may be achieved in a single decay, or a nucleus may decay through a series of states or steps before it reaches a truly stable "configuration". Each state or step will have its own unique characteristics, half-life (a discussion of half-life is given below) and type of radiation emitted as the move is made to the next state. Much scientific effort has been devoted to unraveling these decay chains, not only to achieve a basic understanding of nature, but also to design nuclear weapons and nuclear reactors. The unusually complicated decay of U-238, for example--the primary source of natural radioactivity on earth--proceeds as follows:

$$^{238}U \xrightarrow[\text{emission}]{\text{alpha}} {}^{234}Th \xrightarrow[\text{emission}]{\text{beta}} {}^{234}Pa \xrightarrow[\text{emission}]{\text{beta}} {}^{234}U \xrightarrow[\text{emission}]{\text{alpha}} {}^{230}Th \xrightarrow[\text{emission}]{\text{alpha}} {}^{226}Ra$$

$$\xrightarrow[\text{emission}]{\text{alpha}} {}^{222}Rn \xrightarrow[\text{emission}]{\text{alpha}} {}^{218}Po \xrightarrow[\text{emission}]{\text{alpha}} {}^{214}Pb \xrightarrow[\text{emission}]{\text{beta}} {}^{214}Bi \xrightarrow[\text{emission}]{\text{beta}} {}^{214}Po$$

$$\xrightarrow[\text{emission}]{\text{alpha}} {}^{210}Pb \xrightarrow[\text{emission}]{\text{beta}} {}^{210}Bi \xrightarrow[\text{emission}]{\text{beta}} {}^{210}Po \xrightarrow[\text{emission}]{\text{beta}} {}^{206}Pb \ (\text{stable})$$

VI. Nuclear Fission

Nuclear fission is the splitting of a nuclide into two smaller nuclides. Its discovery in 1938 led to vigorous research that helped develop weapons of mass destruction. Fission generally does not occur spontaneously. Elements having atomic numbers greater than 90 can be made to undergo fission.

Research quickly revealed that U-235 was a fissionable (or fissile) material. U-235 is found in less than 1% of naturally occurring uranium - U-238 being the most abundant isotope. When U-235 undergoes fission, 0.1% of its mass is converted into energy. Thus, if 1000 g of U-235 undergoes fission, 1 g of it (0.1% of 1000 g) would be converted into energy.

The amount of energy that is released when a single U-235 nucleus is split is not very great; however, investigations quickly revealed that the bombardment of U-235 with a neutron could begin a cascading reaction that could consume all the U-235 and release instantaneous energy in amounts never before achieved by humans. The release of neutrons from the first fission reaction become nuclear "bullets" capable of splitting other U-235 nuclei.

This continuous series of self-sustaining fission reactions is called a *nuclear chain reaction.*

The cleavage (or fission) of a U-235 nucleus can occur in many different ways and can produce many products. One such reaction is depicted below:

$$^{235}_{92}U + {}^{1}_{0}n \rightarrow {}^{140}_{56}Ba + {}^{93}_{36}Kr + 3\ {}^{1}_{0}n + ENERGY$$

The amount of U-235 needed to cause a nuclear explosion is called its critical mass. A *critical mass* is the minimum amount of fissionable material needed to sustain a nuclear chain reaction. A spontaneous chain reaction will occur only if ~33 lb or15 kg (i.e., this is the critical mass of U-235) of highly purified U-235 are quickly brought together in one place. U-235 is not alone in its ability to sustain a chain reaction. Pu-239, which occurs in nature only in trace amounts, can also generate a similar chain reaction to that of U-235. The fission of Pu-239 (critical mass is ~11 lb or 4 kg) is a bit more efficient and releases about 20% more energy than the fission of U-235.

VII. Nuclear Fusion

Nuclear fusion is the joining of two nuclides of smaller masses to form a single nuclide of larger mass. Nuclear fusion is a thermonuclear reaction that requires temperatures well over 10^6 °C. At such temperatures, the phase of matter known as plasma is formed. The temperature conditions for nuclear fusion exist in the sun and other stars. In a series of steps, hydrogen nuclei are fused into a helium nucleus and a tremendous amount of energy is released.

A combination of hydrogen-2 (called deuterium) and hydrogen-3 (called tritium) provided the power for the hydrogen bomb, which was a fusion bomb.

$$^{2}_{1}H + ^{3}_{1}H \rightarrow ^{4}_{2}He + ^{1}_{0}n + ENERGY$$

VIII. Energy - Mass Interconversion

The actual mass of a nucleus is always less than the sum of the masses of the free neutrons and protons that constitute it, the difference being the mass equivalent of the energy released when the nucleus is formed from its constituents (i.e., protons and neutrons). The difference in the mass of the nucleus vs. that of its individual constituents is known as the *mass defect.* Mass defect measures the total binding energy (and, hence, the stability) of an atomic nucleus.

The binding energy of nuclei is about a million times greater than the binding energy that holds atoms in a chemical bond together.

The conversion of mass into energy follows *Einstein's Equation*,

$E = mc^2$ where, E (in J), m (in kg), c (3×10^8 m/sec)

The conversion of a mere 0.001 kg (1 g) of mass into energy, according to Einstein's equation produces 9.0×10^{13} kg•m²/s² (9.0×10^{13} J) of energy. To put this number into perspective, this amount of energy would be enough to raise ~700,000 cars six miles into space.

The binding energy per nucleon as a function of mass number is shown in the plot below. Fe-56 has the largest binding energy indicating that this is the most stable nuclide in the universe. The shape of this curve suggest that there are two possibilities for converting significant amounts of mass into energy. Energy can be released if heavy nuclides (M > 56) can be split into smaller nuclide via fission. A second way in which energy can be released in a nuclear reaction is when lighter nuclides (Z < 56) are joined together via fusion.

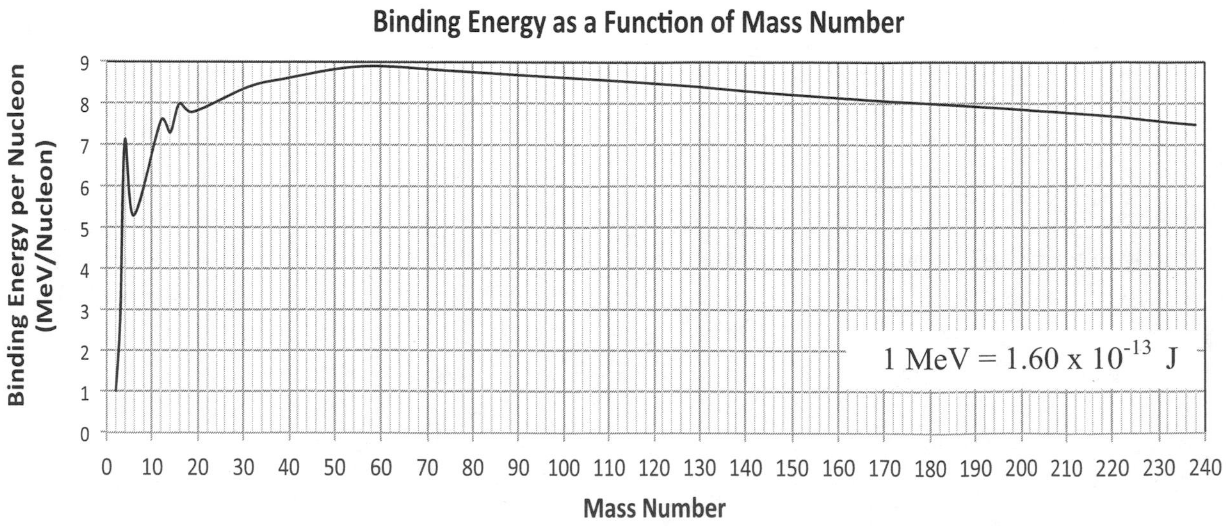

IX. Half-Life ($t_{1/2}$)

A *Half-Life* ($t_{1/2}$) is the time it takes for half of any radioactive to decay.

The following table provides an example of the decay of an 800 g sample of a radionuclide that has a half-life of 1,000 years. Note that after each half-life has passed (i.e., after 1,000 yr have passed) how half of the radioactive sample has decayed.

$t_{1/2}$ = 1,000 yr				
% and fraction of parent that is present after each half life ($t_{1/2}$) / % and fraction of parent that has decayed after each half-life ($t_{1/2}$)	100%	50% 50%	25% 75%	12.5% 87.5%
	1	$\frac{1}{2}$ $\frac{1}{2}$	$\frac{1}{4}$ $\frac{3}{4}$	$\frac{1}{8}$ $\frac{7}{8}$
amount present (g)	800	400	200	100
amount decayed (g)	0	400	600	700
time (yr)	0	1,000	2,000	3,000
# $t_{1/2}$	0	1	2	3

After 10 half-lives, 99.9% of the original radioactive element has been converted into its daughter.

All radionuclides' (R) mode of decay proceed via first-order kinetics: Rate = k $[R]^1$

The exponential form of the integrated rate equation is most often used, where we can calculate *the fraction of the radionuclide that remains* after a specified period of time. {NOTE: [R] and $[R]_o$ can be in any unit of amount as long as they are the same unit (i.e., g, mol, atoms).}

$$\frac{[R]}{[R]_o} = e^{-kt}$$

The following equation can be used to find the half-life: $t_{1/2} = \dfrac{0.693}{k}$

Instead of using one of the above equations to solve half-life problems involving radionuclides the following two equations are most often used. NOTE: n = # of half-lives that have elapsed.

$$\frac{[R]}{[R]_o} = \frac{1}{2^n} \qquad \text{or} \qquad n = \frac{t}{t_{1/2}}$$

$\dfrac{[R]}{[R]_o}$ } fraction of radionuclide (i.e., parent) that remains

Example Problems:

1. Answer the following questions regarding tritium ($t_{1/2}$ = 12.3 yr).

a) How many years will it take for 125 g of tritium to be reduced to 12.5?

$$\frac{[R]}{[R]_o} = \frac{1}{2^n} \Rightarrow \frac{12.5\ g}{125\ g} = \frac{1}{2^n} \Rightarrow \frac{1}{10} = \frac{1}{2^n} \Rightarrow n = \frac{\log 10}{\log 2} = 3.32$$

$$n = \frac{t}{t_{1/2}} \Rightarrow 3.32 = \frac{t}{12.3\ yr} \Rightarrow t = 3.32 \bullet 12.3\ yr = 40.9\ yr$$

b) How many half-lives will it take for 100 g of tritium to be reduced to 6.25 g?

$$\frac{[R]}{[R]_o} = \frac{1}{2^n} \Rightarrow \frac{6.25\ g}{100\ g} = \frac{1}{2^n} \Rightarrow 0.0625 = \frac{1}{2^n} \Rightarrow 2^n = \frac{1}{0.625} \Rightarrow 2^n = 16 \Rightarrow n = \frac{\log 16}{\log 2} = 4$$

c) After 49.2 yr, what percent of tritium has decayed?

$$n = \frac{t}{t_{1/2}} \Rightarrow n = \frac{49.2\ yr}{12.3\ yr} = 4$$

$$\frac{[R]}{[R]_o} = \frac{1}{2^4} \Rightarrow \frac{[R]}{[R]_o} = 0.0625$$ *fraction of tritium that remains (i.e., that has not decayed)*

$0.0625 \bullet 100 = 6.25\%$ ***remains*** $\Rightarrow 93.75\%$ ***has decayed***

2. The determination of the amount of C-14 ($t_{1/2}$ = 5,730 yr) that is still present relative to that which is present in current day organic (i.e., carbon containing) materials can be used to determine the age of organic materials via a technique called C-14 dating. How old in a piece of cotton in which 60% C-14 has been lost?

   If 60% of radioactivity has been lost, 40% of C-14 is still present (i.e., $\frac{[R]}{[R]_0} = 0.40$)

$$\frac{[R]}{[R]_o} = \frac{1}{2^n} \Rightarrow 0.40 = \frac{1}{2^n} \Rightarrow n = \frac{\log\left(\frac{1}{0.40}\right)}{(\log 2)} = 1.32$$

$$n = \frac{t}{5730\ yr} \Rightarrow 1.32 = \frac{t}{12.3\ yr} \Rightarrow t = 1.32 \bullet 5730\ yr = 7575\ yr$$

3. What is the half-life (in hr) of Na-24 given that it takes 60.0 hr of it to decay from 208 g to 13.0 g?

$$\frac{[R]}{[R]_o} = \frac{1}{2^n} \Rightarrow \frac{13.0}{208} = \frac{1}{2^n} \Rightarrow 0.0625 = \frac{1}{2^n} \Rightarrow n = \frac{\log\left(\frac{1}{0.0625}\right)}{(\log 2)} = 4$$

$$n = \frac{t}{t_{1/2}} \Rightarrow 4 = \frac{60\ hr}{t_{1/2}} \Rightarrow t_{1/2} = \frac{60\ hr}{4} = 15\ hr$$

The table below gives just but a few examples of radioisotopes, their half-life and use.

Radioisotope	Half-Life	Use	Radioisotope	Half-Life	Use
carbon-14	5,730 yr	archeological dating	cobalt-60	5.26 yr	radiation therapy
uranium-235	710,000,000 yr	nuclear reactors	iodine-131	8.07 days	thyroid therapy
uranium-238	4.5 billion yr	archeological dating	technetium-99m	6 hr	diagnostic imaging
plutonium-239	24,360 yr	atomic weapons	phosphorous-32	14 days	leukemia therapy

EXERCISES

1. Fill in the missing isotope in each of the following nuclear reactions.

a) ${}^{210}_{84}Po \rightarrow$ ________ $+ \ \alpha$

b) ________ $\rightarrow {}^{222}_{86}Rn + \alpha$

c) ${}^{63}Ni \rightarrow$ ________ $+ \ \beta^-$

d) ________ $\rightarrow {}^{133}I + \alpha$

e) ${}^{11m}B \rightarrow$ ________ $+ \ \gamma$

f) ________ $\rightarrow {}^{214}Po + \beta^- + \gamma$

g) ${}^{236}Pu \rightarrow$ ________ $+ \ \alpha$

h) ________ $\rightarrow {}^{242}Cm + \beta^-$

i) ${}^{13}N \rightarrow$ ________ $+ \ \beta^+$

j) ________ $\rightarrow {}^{54}Fe + \beta^+$

2. *Before you can answer this question, find each of the following parent radioisotopes in problem 1.* a) How would you protect/shield yourself from each? b) What minimum distance should be kept? c) Has this parent undergone a transmutation?

	A. Pu-236	B. Ni-63	C. Boron-11m
a)			
b)			
c)			

3. Explain whether or not each of the following is expected to be radioactive, if radioactive explain the most likely mode of decay?

a) ${}^{3}_{1}H$ b) ${}^{222}_{86}Rn$ c) ${}^{37}_{19}K$ d) ${}^{26}_{13}Al$

4. Given the following information about each radioisotope and the type of radiation that each emits, fill in the table.

	Radioisotope	Emits	Nuclear Equation	Information about Daughter: Atomic No.	Mass No.	# of p^+	# of n
a)	Americium-241 (Z = 95)	alpha and gamma					
b)	Phosphorus-33 (Z = 15)	beta					
c)	Carbon 14 (Z = 6)	beta					
d)	Hafnium-174 (Z = 72)	alpha					
e)	Silicon-27 (Z = 14)	positron					

5. Solve the following half-life problems.

A. Palladium-103 ($t_{1/2}$ = 17 days) is used in brachytherapy to treat prostate cancer. Assuming that Pd-103 doesn't get eliminated from the body after administered, if 2,400 mg of ${}^{103}Pd$ was given to a patient, then:

a) How many mg of palladium-103 will remain in the patient after 68 days?

b) After 68 days how many mg of palladium-103 would have decayed?

c) How many mg of palladium-103 will be remain in the patient after 6 half-lives?

d) How many weeks will it take for 600 mg of palladium-103 to remain in the patient?

B. If the amount of calcium-47 ($t_{1/2}$ = 4.5 days) needed to study cellular functions and bone formation is 1000 mg and if the time it takes for the hospital to receive a shipment of this radioisotope is 18 days, what is the minimum amount of calcium-47 that should be ordered?

C. Cobalt-60 emits both gamma rays and beta particles - it is thus radioactive. It is the gamma radiation given off by Co-60 that is used in Gamma Knife® radiosurgery to treat tumors and other abnormalities in the brain. Ten years ago, a hospital received a shipment of 200 g of Co-60. Today, 50 g are still present. ASSUMING that during this period of time none has been used in any diagnostic procedure, what is the half-life (in years) of Co-60?

6. Po-210, one of several polonium isotopes, is radioactive and emits a particle that can be stopped by a piece of paper. The half-life of ^{210}Po is 1.99 x 10^5 min. In 2006, within 22 days of being poisoned with Po-210, a former Soviet spy (Alexander Litvinenko) died of acute radiation poisoning (all his hair fell out and he developed pancytopenia). This goes to show that while the radiation being emitted by Po-210 can be stopped by a piece of paper and intact skin provides a good barrier, either inhalation or ingestion of Po-210 itself is lethal. Estimates suggest that one gram of Po-210 could kill 50 million individuals.

   a) What is the nuclear equation for the radioactive decay of Po-210?

   b) What is half-life (in days) of Po-210?

   c) Would 0.5 μg of Po-210, placed in a cup of tea, have been enough to kill Alexander Litvinenko if he ingested all of the tea? EXPLAIN.

7. A positron emission tomography (PET) scan is a type of imaging test that uses a radioactive substance, called a radiotracer, to show how organs and tissues are working. Radiotracers used in a PET scan are given intravenously, have short half-lives, won't remain in the body for long and won't cause you from avoiding contact with people. Carbon-11 ($t_{1/2}$ = 20 min) is a radiotracer used in PET scans.

   a) How many minutes will it take for one-eighth ($^1/_8$ or 12.5%) of C-11 to still be present in the patient?

   b) Given that C-11 is a positron emitter, write down the nuclear equation for its radioactive decay.

8. Metastable technitium-99 (^{99m}Tc) is the most commonly used radioisotope in nuclear medicine. Approximately 85% of diagnostic imaging procedures in nuclear medicine use this radionuclide. Worldwide within the span of a year, Tc-99m is used in approximately 40 - 45 million nuclear medicine procedures. The fact that both its physical half-life (6 hr) and biological half-life (1 day) is very short leads to very fast clearing of Tc-99m from the body after an imaging procedure. Typically the ^{99m}Tc used in nuclear medicine is administered with a syringe.

   Bombarding ^{98}Mo with neutrons (^1n) results in the formation of ^{99}Mo. ^{99}Mo then decays to form ^{99m}Tc. Tc-99m then decays via gamma emission. The gamma rays emitted by ^{99m}Tc can be detected during the diagnostic procedure using a gamma or Anger camera to create two-dimensional images.

   a) Write all three nuclear equations involved in the eventual formation of ^{99m}Tc from ^{98}Mo to its eventual decay via γ-emission.

   b) When it decays, does ^{99m}Tc undergo a transmutation?

   c) Why should the clinician or radiological technician administering ^{99m}Tc to a patient use a shielded syringe? What would serve as a good shielding material for the syringe?

   d) Is ^{99}Mo radioactive? Explain.

   e) If you underwent a diagnostic test that used ^{99m}Tc, would it be prudent for you to hold your baby at a very close range 2 hr after this test? Explain.

   f) After 24 hours, what percent of ^{99m}Tc has decayed? What % is still present?

   g) When a hospital received a shipment of ^{99}Mo, 1000 g of it were present. If after 10.8 days, only 75 g remained, what is the half-life of ^{99}Mo (in days)? Assume that during this period of time none has been used in any diagnostic procedure.

MULTIPLE CHOICE PRACTICE EXAM FOR MODULE 12

Radioactivity

1. Which of the following statements is/are true?

   a) An alpha particle, which has a positive charge, is the most penetrating type of nuclear radiation.

   b) A gamma ray has no mass and charge and as a consequence tends to travel a very short distance and thus is not very penetrating.

   c) A beta particle is an electron emitted from the nucleus of a radionuclide that is thought to be produced as a consequence of a neutron transforming itself into a proton and electron.

   d) A radionuclide that emits an alpha particle is emitting 2 protons and 2 neutrons from its nucleus which is analogous to a He nucleus being emitted from the radionuclide.

   e) A positron is expected to be emitted from the nucleus of an unstable nuclide if its $^{N}/_{Z} > 1.5$.

   1. only a and b 2. only c and d 3. only b and c 4. only d and e 5. only c

2. Which of the following would you expect to be radioactive?

   1. oxygen-20 2. U-235 3. ^{40}K 4. All of the isotopes listed.
   5. There is no way of predicting which isotopes would be radioactive.

3. Which of the following is/are true?

   1. $^{211}_{87}Fr$ is radioactive and in an attempt to stabilize itself it will emit an alpha particle.
   2. Gold-201 is expected to be radioactive and in attempt to stabilize itself it will either emit a positron or capture an electron close to its nucleus.
   3. Pb-210 is not expected to be radioactive.
   4. More than one of the above is true.
   5. None of the above is true.

4. *Once inside the body*, which of the following types of ionizing radiation is the most harmful?

   1. alpha particles 2. beta particles 3. gamma rays 4. All are equally harmful.

Nuclear Equations

5. Complete the following nuclear equation: $^{85}Br \rightarrow \beta^{-} + \gamma + $ _____

   1. ^{85}Kr 2. ^{86}Br 3. ^{81}As 4. ^{86}Kr 5. ^{86}Se

6. Who is the parent in the following nuclear reaction? ________ $\rightarrow {}^{218}Rn + \alpha + \beta^{-} + \gamma$

   1. ^{222}Ac 2. ^{223}Ra 3. ^{222}Fr 4. ^{223}Fr 5. ^{220}Th

7. Which of the following is not a correctly balanced nuclear reaction?

   1. $^{24}Mg + {}^{4}He \rightarrow {}^{27}Al + {}^{1}H$
   2. $^{56}Mn + {}^{1}n \rightarrow {}^{55}Mn + {}^{2}H$
   3. $^{237}Pa + {}^{19}N \rightarrow {}^{250}Cf + 6\ {}^{1}n$
   4. Only two of the above.
   5. All of the above.

8. Boron-13 (Z = 5) is a beta and gamma emitter. Given this information, which of the following is/are true?

   1. The daughter is carbon.
   2. The daughter has 6 protons.
   3. The daughter has 7 neutrons.
   4. Only two of the above.
   5. All of the above.

9. ^{214}Bi (Z = 83) is an alpha, beta, and gamma emitter. Given this information, which of the following is/are true?
   1. The daughter is lead-210.
   2. The daughter has 83 protons.
   3. The daughter has 127 neutrons.
   4. Only two of the above.
   5. All of the above.

10. A radioactive isotope emits a beta particle while giving birth to an isotope having 29 protons and 37 neutrons. Given this information, which of the following is/are true?
    1. The parent radioactive isotope has an atomic number of 30.
    2. The parent radioactive isotope is zinc-66.
    3. The parent radioactive isotope has a mass number of 66.
    4. Only two of the above.
    5. All of the above.

11. Which of the following is an example of a transmutation?
    1. $^{131}I \rightarrow {}^{131}Xe + \beta^- + \gamma$
    2. $^{201m}Tl \rightarrow {}^{201}Tl + \gamma$
    3. $Na_3PO_4 + Ba(OH)_2 \rightarrow NaOH + Ba_3(PO_4)_2$
    4. Only two of the above.
    5. All of the above.

12. Which of the following provides an example of a nuclear fission reaction?
    1. ${}^{235}_{92}U + {}^{1}_{0}n \rightarrow {}^{140}_{56}Ba + {}^{93}_{36}Kr + 3\ {}^{1}_{0}n + ENERGY$
    2. $^{201m}Tl \rightarrow {}^{201}Tl + \gamma$
    3. ${}^{2}_{1}H + {}^{3}_{1}H \rightarrow {}^{4}_{2}He + {}^{1}_{0}n + ENERGY$
    4. Only two of the above.
    5. All of the above.

Half-Life Problems

13. If 20.0 mg of fresh iodine-131 ($t_{1/2}$ = 8 days) is administered to a patient, how many milligrams will be left in the body after 24 days? [Assume that none of the iodine escaped/left the body by other means.]
    1. 5.00 2. 1.25 3. 4.00 4. 2.50 5. 2.00

14. Phosphorus-32 ($t_{1/2}$ = 14 days) is used in the detection of eye tumors. How many half-lives will it take for 100 mg of sample to be reduced to 6.25 mg?
    1. 16 2. 3 3. 4 4. 56 5. 42

15. How many years will it take for $^7/_8$ of tritium (H-3, $t_{1/2}$ = 12.3 yr) to decay?
    1. 49.2 2. 36.9 3. 24.6 4. 98.4 5. 356

16. Initially there were 400 mg of radon-222 present. After 16 days 25 mg remained. Given this information, what is the half-life (in days) of radon-222?
    1. 4 2. 23.7 3. 5.3 4. 8 5. 1.2

17. 800 mg of a radioactive isotope ($t_{1/2}$ = 4 days) is needed for a patient study. If the time it takes for the hospital to receive a shipment of this radioisotope is 12 days, what is the minimum amount (in mg) of it that should be ordered?
    1. 12,800 2. 3,200 3. 6,400 4. 2,400 5. 9,600

MODULE 12 - ANSWERS

1. a) $^{208}_{82}Pb$ b) $^{226}_{88}Ra$ c) $^{63}_{29}Cu$ d) $^{137}_{55}Cs$ e) $^{11}_{5}B$ f) $^{214}_{83}Bi$ g) $^{232}_{92}U$ h) $^{242}_{95}Am$ i) $^{13}_{6}C$ j) $^{54}_{27}Co$

2.

	A. Pu-236 (α emitter)	B. Ni-63 (β emitter)	C. Boron-11m (γ emitter)
a)	paper, heavy clothing	heavy clothing	lead or concrete
b)	2 - 4 cm	2 - 3 m	500 m
c)	Yes	Yes	No

3. a) Since $\frac{N}{Z} = \frac{2}{1} = 2 > 1.5$ this nuclide is radioactive and in an attempt to stabilize itself it would be expected to emit a beta particle.

   b) Since Z > 83 this nuclide is radioactive. In an attempt to stabilize itself it would be expected to emit an alpha particle.

   c) Since $\frac{N}{Z} = \frac{18}{17} = 1.1 < 1.5$ this nuclide is expected to be radioactive and in an attempt to stabilize itself it would be expected to emit a either a positron or to capture an electron close to the nucleus.

   d) Since Z < 21 and $\frac{N}{Z} = \frac{13}{13} = 1$ this nuclide is not expected to be radioactive.

4. a) $^{241}_{95}Am \rightarrow ^{237}_{93}Np + ^{4}_{2}\alpha + ^{0}_{0}\gamma$ Atomic No. = 93 Mass No. = 237 #p$^+$ = 93 # n = 144

   b) $^{33}_{15}P \rightarrow ^{33}_{16}S + ^{0}_{-1}\beta^-$ Atomic No. = 16 Mass No. = 33 #p$^+$ =16 # n = 17

   c) $^{14}_{12}C \rightarrow ^{14}_{7}N + ^{0}_{-1}\beta^-$ Atomic No. = 7 Mass No. = 14 #p$^+$ = 7 # n = 7

   d) $^{174}_{72}Hf \rightarrow ^{170}_{70}Yb + ^{4}_{2}\alpha$ Atomic No. = 72 Mass No. = 170 #p$^+$ = 70 # n = 100

   e) $^{27}_{14}Si \rightarrow ^{27}_{13}Al + ^{0}_{+1}\beta^+$ Atomic No. = 13 Mass No. = 27 #p$^+$ = 13 # n = 14

5. A. a) 150 mg b) 2400 - 150 = 2,250 mg c) 37.5 mg d) 4.9 wks (34 days)

   B. 16,000 mg (after 18 days 1000 mg must be present)

   C. 5 yr (to get from 200 g to 50 g, 2 half-lives have passed which is equal to 10 yr)

6. a) $^{210}_{84}Po \rightarrow ^{206}_{82}Pb + ^{4}_{2}\alpha$ (It states in the problem that the particle emitted by radioactive Po-210 can be stopped by a piece of paper. While there are other particles that can be emitted from a radioisotope, the only ones discussed in this module are alpha and beta particles and gamma rays. Of these, alpha particles are the ones that can be stopped by a piece of paper.)

   b) 138 days (given $t_{1/2} = 1.99 \times 10^5$ min, this you must convert from min to days)

   c) Yes because an estimate of 0.02 μg would kill 1 person. $? \frac{\mu g}{person} = \frac{1\ g}{50{,}000{,}000\ people}\left(\frac{1{,}000{,}000\ \mu g}{1\ g}\right) = 0.02 \frac{\mu g}{person}$

7. a) 60 min (After 3 half lives have passed, 1/8 is still present and 7/8 or 87.5% has decayed)

   b) $^{11}_{6}C \rightarrow ^{11}_{5}B + ^{0}_{+1}\beta^+$

8. a) 1. $^{98}_{42}Mo + ^{1}_{0}n \rightarrow ^{99}_{42}Mo$ 2. $^{99}_{42}Mo \rightarrow ^{99m}_{43}Tc + ^{0}_{-1}\beta^-$ 3. $^{99m}_{43}Tc \rightarrow ^{99}_{43}Tc + ^{0}_{0}\gamma$

   b) No. A transmutation involves the conversion of one element into another as a result of a nuclear reaction. Radioisotopes, such as ^{99m}Tc, that are only gamma emitters don't undergo a transmutation when they decay into their daughter.

   c) In the problem it states that ^{99m}Tc is a gamma emitter. Thus, as the clinician or radiological technician that would use ^{99m}Tc on a regular basis you would want to minimize your time and distance to the source of radiation, as well as, to use adequate shielding such as lead shielded syringe when working with a gamma emitter such as ^{99m}Tc.

   d) Yes. In the problem it states that ^{99}Mo decays into ^{99m}Tc. This involves a transmutation, in which ^{99}Mo emitted a beta particle when it decayed to form ^{99m}Tc. Any element that emits alpha particles, beta particles and/or gamma rays is radioactive.

   e) No. While doses that are administered for diagnostic tests are quite low, your clinician or radiation technician would give you the best advice. However, it would not be bad practice to keep your distance from others, especially babies who are quite sensitive to the effects of radiation because their cells are more rapidly growing and dividing. Cells that are rapidly growing and dividing are more prone to being disrupted by radiation. In 2 hours, one-half life has not even passed since $t_{1/2}$ for ^{99m}Tc is 6 hr. This means that more than 50% of ^{99m}Tc is still present in the body giving off gamma rays.

   f) After 24 hrs, 4 half-lives have passed. This means that $^{1}/_{16}$ or 6.25% of ^{99m}Tc is still present while $^{15}/_{16}$ or 93.75% has decayed.

   g) 2.7 hr

ANSWERS TO MULTIPLE CHOICE PRACTICE EXAM

1	2	3	4	5	6	7	8	9	10	11	12	13	14	15	16	17
2	4	1	1	1	3	5	5	1	3	1	1	4	3	2	1	3

Thermodynamic Data

A. Table of ΔH_f^o, ΔG_f^o, S^o Values at 25°C

Substance	$\Delta H_f^o \left(\frac{kJ}{mol}\right)$	$\Delta G_f^o \left(\frac{kJ}{mol}\right)$	$S^o \left(\frac{J}{mol \cdot K}\right)$
Ag^+ (aq)	105.9	77.1	73.9
Ag (g)	289.2	250.4	172.9
AgBr (s)	-99.5	-95.9	107.1
AgCl (s)	-127.0	-109.7	96.1
AgF (s)	-203	-185	84
AgI (s)	-62.4	-66.3	114
Al^{3+} (aq)	-524.7	-481.2	
Al_2O_3 (s)	-1669.8	-1576	50.99
Br (g)	111.9	82.4	174.9
Br^- (g)	-218.9		
Br^- (aq)	-120.9	102.8	80.7
Br_2 (g)	30.91	3.13	254.4
HBr (g)	-36.2	-53.2	198.5
C (diamond)	1.90	2.87	2.4
C (g)	715.0	669.6	158.0
CH_4 (g)	-74.87	-50.81	186.1
C_2H_2 (g)	227	209	200.8
C_2H_4 (g)	52.47	68.36	219.2
C_2H_6 (g)	-84.67	-32.89	229.5
C_6H_6 (l)	49.0	124.5	172.8
CH_3OH (g)	-201.2	-161.9	238
CH_3OH (l)	-238.6	-166.2	127
C_2H_5OH (l)	-277.6	-174.8	161
CCl_4 (g)	-96.0	-53.7	309.7
CCl_4 (l)	-139	-68.6	214.4
CN^- (aq)	151.0	166	118
HCN (aq)	105.4	112	129
HCN (g)	135	125	201.7
CO (g)	-110.5	-137.3	197.9
CO_2 (aq)	-412.9	-386.2	121.3
CO_2 (g)	-393.5	-394.4	213.6
CO_3^{2-} (aq)	-676.3	-528.1	
HCO_3^- (aq)	-691.1	-587.1	95
H_2CO_3 (aq)	-699.7	-623.2	187.4
CS_2 (g)	117.4	67.15	237.7

Substance	$\Delta H_f^o \left(\frac{kJ}{mol}\right)$	$\Delta G_f^o \left(\frac{kJ}{mol}\right)$	$S^o \left(\frac{J}{mol \cdot K}\right)$
Cl (g)	121.0	105.0	165.1
Cl^- (aq)	-167.2	-131.2	55.1
Cl^- (g)	-234	-240	153.2
HCl (aq)	-167.5	-131.2	55.1
HCl (g)	-92.3	-95.3	186.8
Cr^{2+} (aq)	-138.9		
CrO_4^{2-} (aq)	-863.2	-706.3	38
$Cr_2O_7^{2-}$ (aq)	-1461	-1257	214
Cu (g)	341.1	301.4	166.3
Cu^+ (aq)	51.9	50.2	
Cu^{2+} (aq)	64.4	65.0	
CuCl (s)	-134.7	-118.8	91.6
$CuCl_2$ (s)	-205.9	-175.7	108.1
CuO (s)	-155.2	-130	42.6
F (g)	78.9	61.8	158.6
F^- (aq)	-329.1	-276.5	
F^- (g)	-255.6	-262.5	145.5
HF (g)	-268.6	-275	173.7
H (g)	217.5	203.3	114.6
H^+ (aq)	0	0	0
OH^- (aq)	-229.9	-157.3	
H_2O (g)	-241.8	-228.6	188.7
H_2O (l)	-285.8	-237.2	69.4
I (g)	106.8	70.2	180.7
I^- (aq)	-55.9	-51.7	109.4
I^- (g)	-194.7		
I_2 (g)	62.4	19.4	260.6
HI (g)	25.9	1.3	206.3
K^+ (aq)	-251.2	-282.3	103
KBr (s)	-392.2	-380	95.9
KCl (s)	-435.9	-408.8	82.6
KI (s)	-327.7	-323	106.4

Substance	$\Delta H_f^o \left(\frac{kJ}{mol}\right)$	$\Delta G_f^o \left(\frac{kJ}{mol}\right)$	$S^o \left(\frac{J}{mol \cdot K}\right)$
KNO_3 (s)	-492.7	-393.1	132.9
KOH (s)	-424.7	-378.9	78.9
Li^+ (aq)	-278.5	-293.8	14
LiBr (s)	-351	-342	74.1
LiCl (s)	-408	-384	59.3
LiI (s)	-270	-270	85.8
LiOH (s)	-487.2	-443.9	50.2
N (g)	473	456	153.2
NH_3 (g)	-46.3	-16	193
NH_3 (aq)	-80.8	26.7	110
NH_4^+ (aq)	-132.8	-79.5	112.8
NH_4Cl (s)	-315.4	-203.9	94.6
NO_2 (g)	33.9	51	239.9
NO_3^- (aq)	-206.6	-110.5	146.4
HNO_3 (aq)	-206.6	-110.5	146
HNO_3 (l)	-174.1	-80.8	155.6
Na^+ (aq)	-239.7	-261.9	60.2
NaBr (s)	-361	-349	86.8
NaCl (s)	-411.0	-384.0	72.4
NaI (s)	-288	-285	98.5
Na_2CO_3 (s)	-1130.9	-1047.7	136.
$NaHCO_3$ (s)	-947.7	-851.9	102.1
NaOH (s)	-425.6	-379.5	64.5
O (g)	249.2	230.1	161.
O_3 (aq)	-12.1	16.3	110.9
O_3 (g)	142.2	163.4	237.6
S (g)	279	238.3	167.8
S_8 (monoclinic)	0.30	0.10	32.6
SO_2 (g)	-296.1	-300.4	248.5
SO_3 (g)	-395.2	-370.4	256.2
SO_4^{2-} (aq)	-907.5	-741.9	17.2
H_2S (g)	-20.2	-33.0	205.6
H_2SO_4 (aq)	-907.5	-742.0	17

B. Bond Energies

Average Single Bond Energies in kJ

H	C	N	O	F	Si	P	S	Cl	Br	I	
435	414	389	464	569	293	318	339	431	368	297	H
	347	293	351	439	289	264	259	330	276	238	C
		159	201	272	-	209	-	201	243?	-	N
			138	184	368	351	-	205	-	201	O
				159	540	490	327	255	197?	-	F
					176	213	226	360	289	213	Si
						213	230	331	272	213	P
							213	251	213	-	S
								243	218	209	Cl
									192	180	Br
										151	I

Average Multiple Bond Energies in kJ

N=N	418
N≡N	946
C=N	615
C≡N	891
C=C	611
C≡C	837
C=O*	741
C≡O	1070
O=O	498

* ***Exception: C=O bond energy for CO_2 is 799 kJ***

Common Mathematical Operations Used in this Course

A. Roots and Exponentials

$x^3 = 64$

to solve for x,
the cube root of both sides must be taken.

$\sqrt[3]{x^3} = \sqrt[3]{64} \rightarrow x = 4$

$\sqrt[3]{x} = 3 \rightarrow x^{1/3} = 3$

to solve for x,
both sides need to be cubed

$x^{(1/3)3} = 3^3 \rightarrow x = 27$

B. Logarithms (log or ln)

The log of a number is the power to which a base must be raised to obtain a number. Two types of logs are encountered frequently in this course: common log (log) and natural log (ln).

- log (base 10)
- ln (base e = 2.71828)

Relationship between log and ln $\rightarrow$ $\ln x = 2.303 \log x$

Relationships among logs:

$\log xy = \log x + \log y$ or $\ln xy = \ln x + \ln y$

$\log \frac{x}{y} = \log x - \log y$ or $\ln \frac{x}{y} = \ln x - \ln y$

$\log x^y = y \log x$ or $\ln x^y = y \ln x$

$\log \sqrt[y]{x} = \log x^{1/y} = \frac{1}{y} \log x$ or $\ln \sqrt[y]{x} = \ln x^{1/y} = \frac{1}{y} \ln x$

C. Antilogarithms (Antilogs)

An antilog is the number for which a given logarithm stands for (i.e., log x = y; x is the antilog of y).

$\log x = 7.10 \rightarrow x = 10^{7.10} = 1.25 \times 10^7$

$\ln x = 7.10 \rightarrow x = e^{7.10} = 1.21 \times 10^3$

<u>Example of how to solve for a variable (x)</u>

$\log 2.4x = 17.00$

$\log 2.4 + \log x = 17.00$

$0.38 + \log x = 17.00$

$\log x = 17.00 - 0.38$

$\log x = 16.62$

$x = 10^{16.62} = 4.17 \times 10^{16}$

D. Quadratic Equations

Quadratic equations are algebraic expressions in the following form: $\mathbf{a}x^2 + \mathbf{b}x + \mathbf{c} = 0$. To solve for x, the quadratic formula is used:

$$x = \frac{-b \pm \sqrt{b^2 - 4ac}}{2a}$$

You will get 2 values for x. One of its values has a physical significance and the other will not.

Solving for x

The following is an example of how to solve for a variable, x, using the quadratic formula. The following quadratic equation (i.e., an equation in which the highest term is squared) needs to be manipulated so that it has the form: $\mathbf{a}x^2 + \mathbf{b}x + \mathbf{c} = 0$

$$49.7 = \frac{(2x)^2}{(1.00 - x)(2.00 - x)}$$

$$49.7 = \frac{4x^2}{2.00 - 3.00\,x + x^2}$$

$$99.4 - 149.1\,x + 49.7\,x^2 = 4x^2$$

$$45.7\,x^2 - 149.1\,x + 99.4 = 0$$

Now quadratic formula can be used to solve for x.

$$x = \frac{-(-149.1) \pm \sqrt{(-149.1)^2 - 4(45.7)(99.4)}}{2(45.7)} \qquad x = 0.934 \text{ or } 2.33$$

Practice Final Exam Questions

MODULE 1 - Liquids and Solids

Intermolecular Forces and Their Effects (bp, fp, mp, vapor pressure, ΔH_{vap} etc.)

1. Which of the following is the strongest force (interaction)?
   1) hydrogen bond 2) covalent bond 3) London dispersion force
   4) dipole-dipole 5) dipole-induced dipole

2. What is the strongest intermolecular force existing in CH_4?
   1) hydrogen bond 2) ion-induced dipole 3) London dispersion force
   4) dipole-dipole 5) dipole-induced dipole

3. Which of the following exhibits hydrogen bonding?
   a. HI b. CH_3NH_2 c. AsH_3
   1) only b 2) only b & c 3) only a & c 4) a, b, & c
   5) none of the above

4. Which of the following has the largest London dispersion force?
   1) F_2 2) Cl_2 3) Br_2 4) I_2
   5) All have equally "sized" London dispersion forces

5. Which of the following is expected to have the highest boiling point?
   1) Cl_2 2) Ar 3) CH_3CH_3 4) CH_3CH_2OH 5) H_2S

6. Which of the following is expected to have the highest melting point?
   1) H_2O 2) Rn 3) H_2Se 4) HCl 5) SiO_2

7. Which of the following is expected to have the lowest vapor pressure?
   1) H_2O 2) Rn 3) H_2Se 4) HCl 5) H_2

8. Which of the following is expected to have the largest ΔH_{vap} (heat of vaporization)?
   1) CH_3NH_2 2) Rn 3) H_2Se 4) HCl 5) H_2

9. Arrange the following in order of increasing boiling point.

   LiCl, He, CH_3CH_2OH, H_2Se, CH_4

   1) LiCl < CH_4 < CH_3CH_2OH < He < H_2Se 2) He < CH_4 < H_2Se < CH_3CH_2OH < LiCl
   3) CH_4 < He < H_2Se < CH_3CH_2OH < LiCl 4) CH_4 < H_2Se < He < CH_3CH_2OH < LiCl
   5) He < CH_4 < CH_3CH_2OH < H_2Se < LiCl

10. On a relative basis, the stronger the intermolecular forces in a substance are,
    1) the smaller its heat of vaporization will be.
    2) the higher its molar heat of fusion will be.
    3) the higher its vapor presure.
    4) the more closely it will follow the ideal gas laws.
    5) Two of the above statements are correct.

Heat Transfer

11. The molar heat of fusion for C_6H_6 (MM = 78.1) is 10.9 kJ/mol at its freezing point of 5.5°C. How much heat (in J) is released by 25.0 g of C_6H_6 at 5.5°C when it is converted into a solid?

1) 3.49×10^3 2) 2.72×10^5 3) 2.13×10^4 4) 29.4 5) 3.49×10^{-3}

Consider the following information when answering questions 12 - 13

$$s_{steam} = 2.03\ \frac{J}{g \cdot °C},\quad s_{water} = 4.18\ \frac{J}{g \cdot °C},\quad s_{ice} = 2.09\ \frac{J}{g \cdot °C},\quad q_{vap} = 2260\ \frac{J}{g},\quad q_{fus} = 333\ \frac{J}{g}$$

12. Calculate the amount of heat (**in kJ**) that is released when 25.0 g of water at 40.0°C is cooled to 25.0°C.

1) 1.57×10^3 2) 4180. 3) 4.18 4) 1.57 5) 2.09×10^3

13. Calculate the amount of heat (in J) that is required when 10.0 g of water at 35.0°C is converted to steam at 125.°C.

1) 3.22×10^3 2) 3.76×10^4 3) 2.82×10^4 4) 5.12×10^4 5) 2.58×10^4

Phase Diagrams

Consider the phase diagram to the right in order to answer questions 14 - 17.

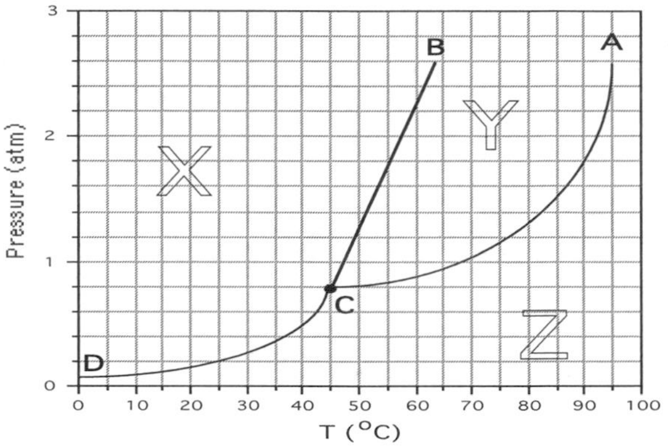

14. How many phases and/or phase mixtures can occur at 1 atm?

1) 1 2) 3 3) 3 4) 4 5) 5

15. What is the boiling point of the substance at a pressure of 1.4 atm?

1) 83°C 2) 52°C 3) 45°C 4) 0°C 5) This substance does not boil at this pressure.

16. If the unknown substance is at a pressure of 0.2 atm and a temperature of 50°C, which of the following statements would be correct?
   1) At a constant pressure if the temperature is lowered to 30°C a solid will deposit.
   2) At a constant temperature if the pressure is increased to 760 torr the substance will solidify.
   3) If the temperature is decreased to 45°C and the pressure is increased to 0.8 atm, all three phases will be in equilibrium with each other.
   4) Two or more of the above statements are correct.
   5) None of the above statements are correct.

17. Which of the following statements is correct?
   a. Line CA is the vapor pressure curve which indicates the temperatures and pressures where the liquid and vapor are in equilibrium.
   b. Point C is called the critical point and indicates the temperature and pressure where the solid, liquid, and vapor are in equilibrium.
   c. At temperatures above 95°C, the substance only exists as a liquid.
   d. At pressures below 0.8 atm, the subtance will never exist as a liquid.
   e. The melting point of the substance increases with an increase in pressure.

1) only a, c, d, e 2) only a, d, e 3) only b and c 4) only b, c, d 5) only a and e

MODULE 2 - Solutions

Solubility

1. Which of the following solute/solvent pairs have a high solubility in each other?

   a. SiH_4 in CCl_4 b. CH_3OH in H_2O c. BCl_3 in CCl_4

   1) only b 2) only c 3) only b & c 4) only a & c 5) a, b, & c

2. Which of the following are water soluble?

   1) SiH_4 2) CH_3NH_2 3) $Ba_3(PO_4)_2$ 4) $KMnO_4$

   5) More than one of the above

Concentration Calculations and Interconversions

Consider the following information when answering Questions 3 - 4. When 28.0 g of Br_2 (MM = 160) is dissolved in 150. g of CCl_4 (MM = 154), then

3. What is the molality of the solution?

   1) 0.0348 2) 0.432 3) 1.17 4) 1.41 5) 34.8

4. What is the mole fraction of Br_2?

   1) 1.17×10^{-3} 2) 0.152 3) 0.157 4) 0.181 5) 0.848

5. What is the molality of a 20.0% by weight $(NH_4)_2SO_4$ (MM = 132) solution (d = 1.117 g/mL)?

   1) 1.69 2) 0.150 3) 1.51 4) 2.10 5) 1.89

6. What is the molarity of a 20.0% by weight $(NH_4)_2SO_4$ (MM = 132)solution (d = 1.117 g/mL)?

   1) 1.69 2) 0.150 3) 1.51 4) 2.10 5) 1.89

7. Calculate the molarity of a 7.98 m H_2SO_4 (MM = 98.1) solution (d = 1.34 g/mL).

   1) 14.2 2) 4.44 3) 6.0 4) 5.96 5) 0.168

8. What is the mole fraction of H_3PO_4 (MM = 98.0) in a 14.7 M H_3PO_4 solution whose density is 1.70 g/mL?

   1) 0.505 2) 0.495 3) 0.116 4) 0.884 5) 0.255

Colligative Properties

9. As the concentration of a non-volatile solute in a solution is increased, ________.

   1) the vapor pressure of the solution increases.
   2) the freezing point of the solution increases.
   3) the osmotic pressure that is generated increases.
   4) Two of the above choices.
   5) None of the above choices.

Colligative Property of Vapor Pressure Lowering

10. If 28.2 g of $C_{20}H_{42}$ (MM = 282) are dissolved in 500. g of C_6H_6 (MM = 78.0, $P^{o}_{25.0°C}$ = 93.4 torr), then what is the vapor pressure (in torr) of the solution at 25.0°C? (Assume that the solute is a nonvolatile-nonelectrolyte.)

    1) 0.00 2) 92.0 3) 93.4 4) 94.8 5) 760

Colligative Property of Boiling Point Elevation

11. Which of the following has the highest boiling point? (The solvent is water.)

    1) 0.5 m $ZnCl_2$ 2) 1 m $C_3H_6O_3$ 3) 0.5 m $NaNO_3$ 4) 0.2 m Na_3PO_4 5) pure H_2O

12. If 1.00 mol of substance A (MM = 200) is dissolved in 500. g of CCl_4 (MM = 157, K_b = 5.03 °C/m, bp = 76.5°C), then what is the boiling point (in °C) of the solution? (Assume that the solute is a nonvolatile-nonelectrolyte.)

    1) 71.5 2) 81.5 3) 66.4 4) 86.6 5) 76.6

13. The boiling point for a solution prepared by dissolving 9.81 g of compound D into 90.0 g of water (MM = 18, K_b = 0.51 °C/m, bp = 100°C) was found to be 100.37°C. Given this information, what is the molar mass of compound D? (Assume that the solute is a nonvolatile-nonelectrolyte.)

    1) 175 2) 34 3) 150 4) 240 5) 79

Colligative Property of Freezing Point Lowering

14. Which of the following has the lowest freezing point? (The solvent is water.)

    1) 0.5 m $ZnCl_2$ 2) 1 m $C_3H_6O_3$ 3) 0.5 m $NaNO_3$ 4) 0.2 m Na_3PO_4 5) pure H_2O

15. What is the molality of an aqueous solution whose freezing point is -0.093°C? (Assume that the solute is a nonvolatile-nonelectrolyte.) For water, K_f = 1.86 °C/m & fp = 0.00°C

    1) 0.093 2) 0.17 3) 1.86 4) 20 5) 0.050

16. Calculate K_f (in °C/m) for the solvent bromoform (MM = 253, fp = 8.3°C, d = 2.89 g/mL) given the following information: When 28.2 g of $C_{20}H_{42}$ (MM = 282) are dissolved in 173. mL of bromoform, the freezing point of the solution is 5.4°C. (Assume that the solute is a nonvolatile-nonelectrolyte.)

    1) 17.8 2) 0.069 3) 5.0 4) 14.5 5) 2.9

Colligative Property of Osmotic Pressure Generation

17. Which of the following generates he highest osmotic pressure? (The solvent is water.)

    1) 0.5 M $ZnCl_2$ 2) 1 M $C_3H_6O_3$ 3) 0.5 M $NaNO_3$ 4) 0.2 M Na_3PO_4 5) pure H_2O

18. If 0.20 g of an unknown compound, dissolved in enough water so as to produce 100. mL of solution (MM = 18.0, d = 1.00 g/mL) at 25.°C, generates an osmotic pressure of 9.8 torr, then calculate the molar mass of this unknown compound. (Assume that the solute is a nonvolatile-nonelectrolyte.)

    1) 3.5×10^3 2) 3.8×10^3 3) 4.0×10^4 4) 4.5×10^4 5) 40.

19. What is the molarity of a solution that generates an osmotic pressure of 2000. mm Hg at 20.0°C? (Assume that the solute is a nonvolatile-nonelectrolyte.)

    1) 0.109 2) 1.60 3) 83.1 4) 0.624 5) 9.17

MODULE 3 - Chemical Thermodynamics

Thermochemical Equations

1. From the following thermochemical equation, $2\ Al_{(s)} + 1.5\ O_{2\ (g)} \rightarrow Al_2O_{3\ (s)}$ $\Delta H = -400$ kcal,
determine ΔH for the reaction: $2\ Al_2O_{3\ (s)} \rightarrow 4\ Al_{(s)} + 3\ O_{2\ (g)}$.

   1) -400 2) 400 3) 200 4) -200 5) 800

Stoichiometry of Reaction Heats

2. How much heat (in kJ) is released when 60.0 g of $SO_{2\ (g)}$ (MM = 64.1) is reacted with excess O_2?

$$2\ SO_{2\ (g)} + O_{2\ (g)} \rightarrow 2\ SO_{3\ (g)} \qquad \Delta H = -198\ kJ$$

   1) 0.546 2) 186 3) 5940 4) 92.7 5) 371

First Law of Thermodynamics (Heat, Work, and Internal Energy)

3. Calculate the internal energy change (in kJ) for a system that releases 200. kJ of heat as it does 300. kJ of work on its surroundings.

   1) 500 2) -100 3) 100 4) -500 5) 300

4. For which of the following chemical or physical processes carried out at constant pressure will there be work done on the system.

   a. $H_2O_{(s)} \rightarrow H_2O_{(l)}$
   b. $2\ SO_{3\ (g)} \rightarrow 2\ SO_{2\ (g)} + O_{2\ (g)}$
   c. $CH_{4\ (g)} + 2\ Cl_{2\ (g)} \rightarrow CH_2Cl_{2\ (l)} + 2\ HCl_{(g)}$
   d. $P_{4\ (s,\ white)} + 6\ Cl_{2\ (g)} \rightarrow 4\ PCl_{3\ (l)}$

   1) only a 2) only b 3) only c 4) only b, c, & d 5) only c & d

Internal Energy and Enthalpy

5. For the decomposition reaction: $2\ SO_{3\ (g)} \rightarrow 2\ SO_{2\ (g)} + O_{2\ (g)}$
$\Delta E = 196$ kJ and $\Delta H = 198$ kJ. If 1.00 mol of $SO_{2\ (g)}$ were to undergo a combination reaction with excess oxygen to yield $SO_{3\ (g)}$ in a bomb calorimeter, then what would be the expected heat transfer (in kJ)?

   1) -196 2) 99 3) -198 4) -98 5) 198

6. When the following reaction: $2\ SO_{2\ (g)} + O_{2\ (g)} \rightarrow 2\ SO_{3\ (g)}$, was carried out at a pressure of 760 torr and 25.0°C it released 198 kJ of heat. Given this information, calculate ΔE (in kJ).

   1) -200 2) 200 3) -198 4) -196 5) 198

7. The change in enthalpy for the combustion of $C_3H_{6\ (g)}$ (i.e., the reaction of $C_3H_{6\ (g)}$ with $O_{2\ (g)}$ to produce $CO_{2\ (g)}$ and $H_2O_{(l)}$) at 25°C is -2061 kJ/mol. Given this information, what is the change in internal energy for the combustion of $C_3H_{6\ (g)}$ (in kJ/mol) at 25°C.

   1) -2055 2) -2067 3) -2061 4) -2060 5) -2062

Hess's Law (Manipulating Thermochemical Equations)

8. Calculate the heat of reaction (in kJ) for the following reaction

$$2\ SO_2\ (g) + O_2\ (g) + 2\ H_2O\ (l) \rightarrow 2\ H_2SO_4\ (l)$$

given the following thermochemical equations:

$$2\ SO_2\ (g) + O_2\ (g) \rightarrow 2\ SO_3\ (g) \qquad \Delta H = -196.7\ kJ$$

$$SO_3\ (g) + H_2O\ (l) \rightarrow H_2SO_4\ (l) \qquad \Delta H = -130.1\ kJ$$

1) 326.7 2) 66.6 3) -456.9 4) -326.7 5) 456.9

Entropy

9. For which of the following chemical or physical processes carried out at constant pressure will ΔS be for sure positive.

a. $H_2O\ (s) \rightarrow H_2O\ (l)$

b. $2\ SO_3\ (g) \rightarrow 2\ SO_2\ (g) + O_2\ (g)$

c. $CH_4\ (g) + 2\ Cl_2\ (g) \rightarrow CH_2Cl_2\ (l) + 2\ HCl\ (g)$

d. $P_4\ (s, white) + 6\ Cl_2\ (g) \rightarrow 4\ PCl_3\ (l)$

1) only a 2) only b 3) only c 4) only c and d 5) only a & b

10. If ΔS for a reaction is negative, then:
   1) the products are more ordered than the reactants.
   2) the reactants are more ordered than the products.
   3) the reaction will always be spontaneous.
   4) $T\Delta S$ will be positive.
   5) More than one of the above statements is correct.

11. Given that the absolute entropy (at 25°C) for $N_2\ (g)$ = 198.6 J/K, $O_2\ (g)$ = 205.0 J/K, $NO_2\ (g)$ = 240.1 J/K, calculate the change in entropy (in J/K) for the reaction: $N_2\ (g) + 2\ O_2\ (g) \rightarrow 2\ NO_2\ (g)$.

1) 1088.8 2) -128.4 3) 691.6 4) 128.4 5) -691.6

Gibbs Free Energy and Spontaneity

For questions 12 - 14, consider the following information:

For the fictious reaction: 5 A (g) → 1 B (s) + 4 C (g), occurring at 59.0°C, the enthalpy change is -143.0 kJ and the Gibbs free energy change is -93.5 kJ.

12. What is the change in entropy (in kJ/K) for this reaction at 59.0°C?

1) -143.0 2) -192.5 3) -0.149 4) -8.79 5) -49.5

13. What is the Gibbs free energy change (in kJ) for this reaction at 25°C? (Assume that ΔH and ΔS are temperature independent and no change in state is occuring.)

1) -146.7 2) -139.2 3) -93.5 4) -187.4 5) -98.6

14. At what temperature (in K) would this reaction be at equilibrium? (Assume that ΔH and ΔS are temperature independent and no change in state is occuring.)

1) 960 2) 687 3) 1233 4) 143 5) 59.0

15. For a process, the enthalpy change is 100.0 kJ and the entropy change is 0.4770 kJ/K. Assuming that the change in enthalpy and entropy are temperature independent and that no change in state is occuring, this process is ___________.
    1) spontaneous at all temperatures
    2) spontaneous only if the temperature is less than 209.6 K
    3) spontaneous only if the temperature is equal to 209.6 K
    4) spontaneous only if the temperature is greater than 209.6 K
    5) non-spontaneous at all temperatures

For questions 16 - 17, consider the following information:

Compound	ΔG_f^o (kcal/mol)	ΔH_f^o (kcal/mol)
$NO_2(g)$	12.3	7.9
NO (g)	20.7	21.6
CO_2 (g)	-94.5	-94.1
CO (g)	-32.8	-26.4

16. Calculate the change in free energy (in kcal) for the reaction: $N_{2\,(g)} + 2\,O_{2\,(g)} \rightarrow 2\,NO_{2\,(g)}$.
    1) 12.3 2) 24.6 3) 15.8 4) 7.9
    5) There is not enough information to answer this question.

17. Which of the following reactions would be spontaneous under standard conditions?
    1) $N_{2\,(g)} + 2\,O_{2\,(g)} \rightarrow 2\,NO_{2\,(g)}$
    2) $C_{(s,\,graphite)} + O_{2\,(g)} \rightarrow CO_{2\,(g)}$
    3) $NO_{2\,(g)} + CO_{(g)} \rightarrow NO_{(g)} + CO_{2\,(g)}$
    4) Two of the above reactions are spontaneous.
    5) There is not enough information to answer the question.

18. For a reaction which occurs at 27.0°C, the enthalpy change is 14.5 kJ and the entropy change is 0.0784 kJ/K. Which of the following statements would be true?
    1) If the reaction is allowed to occur under constant pressure, heat would be evolved.
    2) The products are more ordered than the reactants.
    3) The reaction is not spontaneous.
    4) More than one of the above statements is correct.
    5) None of the above statements is correct.

19. A chemical reaction will always be spontaneous if:
    1) The sign of ΔH is positive and that of ΔS is negative.
    2) The sign of ΔG is positive.
    3) The sign of ΔH is negative and that of ΔS is positive.4) More than one of the above statements is correct.
    5) None of the above statements is correct.

MODULE 4 - Kinetics

Reaction Rates, Rate Laws, Reaction Order, Rate Constant

1. Which of the following would cause a change in the *rate constant* for the one-step reaction of: $A \rightarrow B$.
   1) Performing the reaction at a different temperature.
   2) The continuous passage of time causes it to change.
   3) An increase in the concentration of A.
   4) Two of the above statements are correct.
   5) None of the above statements are correct.

Consider the following information when answering questions 2 - 4.

The reaction ---- A + 2 B → C ---- was found to be second order in A and third order overall.

2. What is the rate law?
   1) rate = k $[A]^2$ 2) rate = k $[A]^2$ [B] 3) rate = k [A] $[B]^2$
   4) rate = k $[A]^2$ [B] [C] 5) rate = k $[A]^2$ [B] / [C]

3. Which of the following could be units for the rate constant in this case?
   1) $M^{-2} \bullet s^{-1}$ 2) $\frac{1}{M^2 \bullet s^1}$ 3) $\frac{L^2}{mol^2 \bullet s^1}$
   4) Only two of above units are correct.
   5) All of above units are correct.

4. If the concentration of A is tripled and that of B is doubled, then the rate would increase by a factor of:
   1) 6 2) 18 3) 12 4) 5 5) 72

5. For the reaction --- A + B → C, the reaction goes three times as fast when the concentration of A is tripled and not affected when the concentration of B is doubled. Given this information, what is the overall order for the reaction.
   1) 1 2) 2 3) 3 4) 4 5) 0

Consider the following balanced equation and data when answering questions 6 - 9.

A + B → C

[A], M	[B], M	Initial Rate, M/s
0.30	**0.35**	**2.05×10^{-3}**
0.52	**0.35**	**6.17×10^{-3}**
0.10	**0.50**	**3.26×10^{-4}**

6. What is the order with respect to **A**?
   1) 1 2) 1.5 3) 2 4) 2.5 5) 3

7. What is the order with respect to **B**?
   1) 1 2) 1.5 3) 2 4) 2.5 5) 3

8. What is the rate law?
   1) k $[A]^2$ [B] 2) k [A] $[B]^3$ 3) k [A] [B] 4) k [A] $[B]^2$ 5) k $[A]^3$ [B]

9. What is the rate constant (in $M^{-2} \bullet s^{-1}$)?
   1) 2.05×10^{-3} 2) 6.51×10^{-2} 3) 1.95×10^{-2} 4) 1.05×10^{-1} 5) 1.54×10^{1}

Integrated Rate Equation and Half-Life

Zero Order Reactions

Consider the following information when answering questions 10 - 11.

The following gas phase reaction ---- 2 A → 3 B + C ----- was conducted in a 1-L container with an initial concentration of A of 0.400 M. This reaction was found to be zero order in A and to have a half-life of 2 hr.

10. What is the rate constant with the correct units (if any)?
   1) 0.100 hr^{-1} 2) 0.100   3) 10.0 $M^{-1} \bullet hr^{-1}$ 4) 10.0   5) 0.100 M/hr

11. How many hours will it take for the reaction to reach a concentration of A which is 0.133 M?
   1) 0.333   2) 5.33   3) 3.00   4) 2.67   5) 0.266

First Order Reactions

Consider the following information when answering questions 12 - 13.

The following gas phase reaction ---- M → 2 E + G ----- was conducted in a 1-L container with an initial concentration of M of 0.400 M. This reaction was found to be first order in M and to have a half-life of 947 min.

12. What is the rate constant with the correct units (if any)?
   1) 7.32×10^{-4} min^{-1} 2) 2.64×10^{-3} $M^{-1} \bullet min^{1}$ 3) 7.32×10^{-4} M/min
   4) 2.11×10^{-4} min^{-1} 5) 2.11×10^{-4} M/min

13. What fraction of the initial amount of M remains after 1500 min?
   1) 1/2   2) 1/3   3) 1/8   4) 1/16   5) 1/32

Second Order Reactions

Consider the following information when answering questions 14 - 16.

The following gas phase reaction ---- D → 2 B + C ----- was conducted in a 1-L container with an initial concentration of D of 0.840 M. This reaction was found to be second order in D and to have a rate constant of 0.0729 $M^{-1} \bullet min^{-1}$.

14. What is the molarity of D after 19 min?
   1) 0.388   2) 0.0612   3) 0.0681   4) 0.0868   5) 2.58

15. What is the half-life (in min) of the reaction?
   1) 0.0612   2) 5.76   3) 9.51   4) 16.3   5) 0.105

16. What is the reaction rate (in M/min) when the concentration of D reaches 0.400 M?
   1) 1.41×10^{-2} 2) 1.17×10^{-2} 3) 2.99×10^{-3} 4) 1.16×10^{-1} 5) 1.46×10^{-2}

Temperature, Reaction Rates, and Energy of Activation

17. If a first order reaction has a frequency factor of 3.98×10^{13} s^{-} and an energy of activation of 160 kJ, then calculate the rate constant (in s^{-}) at 25°C?

    1) 3.98×10^{-1} 2) 3.47×10^{-15} 3) 8.18×10^{88} 4) 1.17×10^{93} 5) 3.23×10^{13}

18. For a reaction, the rate constant at 20°C is 7.50×10^{-5} min^{-1} and that at 50°C is 6.00×10^{-4} min^{-1}. What is the energy of activation (in kJ/mol)?

    1) 0.576 2) 54.5 3) 57.6 4) 0.125 5) 21.7

Potential Energy Diagrams

19. The one-step reaction of A $\rightarrow$ B has an activation energy of 350 kJ/mol. The reverse reaction, has an energy of activation of 260 kJ/mol. Given this information, which of the following statements is/are true?

    1) ΔH for the reaction is -90 kJ/mol.
    2) The reaction A $\rightarrow$ B is endothermic.
    3) The energy of the transition state is 90 kJ/mol.
    4) Two of the above statements are correct.
    5) None of the above statements are correct.

Catalysis

20. Which of the following statements is/are true about catalysts?

    1) Catalysts alter the reaction mechanism.
    2) Catalysts raise the energy of activation.
    3) Catalysts are not consumed during the overall reaction.
    4) Two of the above statements are correct.
    5) All of the above statements are correct.

MODULE 5 - Gas Phase and Heterogenous Chemical Equilibria

Equilibrium Constant Concepts and Calculations

1. Which of the following statements is (are) correct?
   1) The equilibrium constant (K) is dependent on initial reactant concentrations.
   2) If K < 1 this means that reactant formation is favored.
   3) If the K < Q, then the reverse reaction predominates.
   4) Two of the above statements are correct.
   5) None of the above statements are correct.

2. Which of the following equilibrium constants would favor the forward reaction (i.e., the formation of products) the most?

   1) 0.0791 2) 0.000941 3) 421 4) 1.00 5) 4.49

3. Consider the following reaction run at a particular temperature: $2\ A_{(g)} \rightleftharpoons A_{2\,(\ell)}$
   If the equilibrium partial pressure of A is 250 torr, then what is K_P for the reaction?

   1) 9.2 2) 4.0×10^{-3} 3) 6.3×10^{4} 4) 1.6×10^{-5} 5) 3.0

Consider the following gas phase reaction and information when answering questions 4 - 7.

$$3\ A_{(g)} + 2\ B_{(g)} \rightleftharpoons A_3B_{2\,(g)} \qquad K_C = 6.60\ (@\ 77°C)\ \text{and}\ \Delta H = -47.0\ kJ$$

4. What is the equilibrium concentration (**in M**) of B given that at equilibrium 0.450 mol of A and 0.970 mol of A_3B_2 were present in a 10.0-L reaction vessel at 77°C?

   1) 1.50 2) 12.7 3) 1.22 4) 150. 5) 6.68×10^{-3}

5. What is K_C at 77°C for the following reaction?

$$4\ A_3B_{2\,(g)} \rightleftharpoons 12\ A_{(g)} + 8\ B_{(g)}$$

   1) 1.90×10^{3} 2) 2.64×10^{1} 3) 5.27×10^{-4} 4) 3.79×10^{-2} 5) 1.65

Interconversion Between K_c and K_p

6. Calculate K_P at 77°C for the reaction.

   1) 1.52×10^{-6} 2) 4.13×10^{-3} 3) 2.90×10^{-17} 4) 7.71×10^{-10} 5) 9.68×10^{-6}

Thermodynamics and the Equilibrium Constant

7. Calculate ΔG° (in kJ) at 77°C for the reaction.

   1) -2.4 2) -0.29 3) -1.3 4) 33.6 5) -5.5

8. Calculate K_P for the following reaction at 25.0°C: $2\ CO_{2\,(g)} \rightleftharpoons 2\ CO_{(g)} + O_{2\,(g)}$

Compound	ΔG_f^o (kJ/mol)
CO_2 (g)	-394.4
CO (g)	-137.3

   1) 1.4×10^{90} 2) 1.2×10^{45} 3) 7.3×10^{-91} 4) 8.6×10^{-46} 5) e^{-2474}

Le Chatelier Principle

9. Given that ΔH for the following reaction at equilibrium is -92.6 kJ,

$$A_{(g)} + B_{(s)} \rightleftharpoons 2\,L_{(g)} + D_{(\ell)}$$

which of the following conditions will shift the equilibrium to produce more B?

a) increase the temperature b) increase [A] c) decrease the pressure
d) decrease [D] e) add some L f) add some He

1) only b, c, d, & g 2) only b, e & f 3) only c and e
4) only a & e 5) none of the choices

Predicting a Shift in Equilibrium Using Reaction Quotients

10. Consider the following reaction: $A_{(g)} \rightleftharpoons 2\,B_{(g)}$

For which of the following reaction conditions will the reaction proceed from left -> right.

	[A], M	[B], M	K_c	T, °C
1)	1	2	6×10^{-2}	25
2)	0.4	0.6	0.9	35
3)	0.9	0.6	1.0	40

4) Two of the above reaction conditions cause the reaction to proceed from left -> right.
5) None of the above reaction conditions cause the reaction to proceed from left -> right.

Equilibrium Calculations (Finding Equilibrium Constants / Concentrations)

11. Consider the following reaction: $A_{(g)} + B_{(s)} \rightleftharpoons 2\,D_{(g)}$

When 3.00 mol of A and 2.00 mol of B are placed in a 2.50-L reaction vessel and allowed to come to equilibrium, 2.65 mol of D was found to be present. Given this information, what is K_c?

1) 2.34 2) 1.58 3) 1.67 4) 8.03 5) 6.95

12. For the following reaction: $A_{(g)} + B_{(g)} \rightleftharpoons D_{(g)} + E_{(g)}$

K_c = 144 at 200°C. If 0.400 mol of both A and B are placed in a 2.00-L vessel at 200°C, then what will the concentration (**in M**) of D be at equilibrium?

1) 1.13 2) 0.185 3) 0.200 4) 1.64 5) 0.015

13. For the following reaction: $2\,A_{(g)} \rightleftharpoons 2\,D_{(g)} + E_{(g)}$ $K_c = 5.7 \times 10^{-6}$ at 37°C

If 0.400 mol of A were placed in a 4.00-L vessel, then what will the molarity of D be at equilibrium?

1) 0.100 2) 4.8×10^{-3} 3) 2.4×10^{-3} 4) 5.7×10^{-7} 5) 2.0×10^{-2}

MODULE 6 - Acid-Base Equilibria

Relationship between $[H^+]$, $[OH^-]$, pH, pOH, and K_w

1. In a sample of pure water, which of the following is always true at all temperatures and pressures?
   1) $[H^+] = 1.0 \times 10^{-7}$ M 2) pH = 7.00 3) $[H^+] = [OH^-]$
   4) $[OH^-] = 1.0 \times 10^{-7}$ M
   5) More than one of the above is correct.

2. An aqueous solution having a pH of 0 would:
   1) not be acidic 2) have an $[H^+] = 1.0$ M 3) have an $[OH^-] = 14$ M
   4) Two of the above choices are correct.
   5) None of the above choices are correct.

Calculations Involving Strong Acids and Strong Bases

3. What is the molarity of an HCl solution whose pH is 2.80?
   1) 1.6×10^{-3} 2) 6.3×10^{-3} 3) 4.2×10^{-3} 4) 6.3×10^{-2} 5) 4.2×10^{-2}

4. What is the pOH of a 0.175 M LiOH solution?
   1) 0.17 2) 1.50 3) 0.76 4) 13.24 5) 0.18

5. What is the pH of a 500. mL solution containing 0.0124 g of $Ca(OH)_2$ (MM = 74.1)?
   1) 3.17 2) 9.68 3) 11.04 4) 10.82 5) 2.96

Calculations Involving Weak Monoprotic Acids and Weak Monobasic Bases

Consider the following information when answering questions 6 - 7.

Given that the pH of a 0.500 M solution of an acid HX was 4.00, then:

6. What is thc $[H^+]$ (in molarity) of the solution?
   1) 10^{-4} 2) -4.00 3) 3.50 4) 2.00 5) 0.50

7. What is the pOH of the solution?
   1) 0.5 2) 13.50 3) 12.00 4) 2.00 5) 10.00

8. Calculate the pH of 0.350 M HF ($K_a = 7.2 \times 10^{-4}$).
   1) 1.80 2) 0.46 3) 0.016 4) 2.25 5) 3.50

9. Calculate the $[H^+]$ (in molarity) of 0.100 M NH_3 ($K_b = 1.8 \times 10^{-5}$).
   1) 10^{-12} 2) 4.4×10^{-10} 3) 7.5×10^{-12} 4) 1.3×10^{-3} 5) 11.11

10. Calculate the % ionization of a 0.100 M HNO_2 ($K_a = 4.5 \times 10^{-4}$) solution.
    1) 1.9 2) 6.7×10^{-2} 3) 4.5 4) 2.3 5) 6.7

11. Calculate the % ionization of a 0.300 M $C_6H_5NH_2$ ($K_b = 4.2 \times 10^{-10}$) solution.
    1) 0.89 2) 6.7×10^{-4} 3) 0.37 4) 0.0037 5) 0.0030

12. What is the initial molarity of a $CH_3COO\underline{H}$ ($K_a = 1.8 \times 10^{-5}$) solution that is 2.0% ionized?
   1) 0.044 2) 0.011 3) 0.022 4) 0.055 5) 0.0020

Trends

Consider the following information when answering questions 13 - 14.

Given the following K_a's: HNO_2 ($K_a = 4.5 \times 10^{-4}$) and HCN ($K_a = 4.9 \times 10^{-10}$)

13. Which has the lowest % ionization?
   1) 0.5 M HCN 2) 0.5 M HNO_2 3) 0.5 M HNO_3 4) 1.0 M HCN 5) 0.4 M HNO_3

14. Which has the highest pH?
   1) 0.5 M HCN 2) 0.5 M HNO_2 3) 0.5 M HNO_3 4) 1.0 M HCN 5) 0.4 M HNO_3

15. Which of the following 0.10 M aqueous solutions will have the lowest pH?
   1) HA ($pK_a = 3.79$) 2) HX ($pK_a = 4.79$) 3) HZ ($pK_a = 5.78$)
   4) $:NX_3$ ($pK_b = 1.89$) 5) $:NR_3$ ($pK_b = 6.89$)

16. Which of the following 0.10 M aqueous solutions will have the lowest pH?
   1) HCl 2) HBr 3) HI
   4) It is impossible to say since their K_a is not given in the problem.
   5) All have the same pH.

17. Which of the following has the smallest pK_a?
   1) HA ($K_a = 1.79 \times 10^{-8}$) 2) HX ($K_a = 3.72 \times 10^{-8}$) 3) HZ ($K_a = 5.66 \times 10^{-4}$)
   4) HL ($pK_a = 3.23$) 5) HJ ($K_a = 5.75 \times 10^{-4}$)

18. Which of the following statements is true?
   1) A 0.10 M aqueous HX solution ($pK_a = 3.79$) has a lower pH than a 0.10 M aqueous HA ($pK_a = 2.79$) solution.
   2) A 0.10 M aqueous $:NX_3$ solution ($pK_b = 3.79$) has a higher pH than a 0.10 M aqueous $:NZ_3$ ($pK_b = 4.79$) solution.
   3) A 0.10 M aqueous HCN solution has the same pH as a 0.10 M aqueous HCl solution.
   4) Two of the above statements are true.
   5) None of the above statements is true.

19. Which of the following statements is true?
   1) The pH of a 0.10 M HF solution is 1.00.
   2) The pOH of a 0.10 M aqueous NH_3 solution is 1.00.
   3) The pH of a 0.10 M HCl solution is 1.00.
   4) All of the above statements are true.
   5) None of the above statements is true.

20. Which of the following statements is true?
    1) A 0.10 M NH_3 solution is more alkaline than a 0.20 M NH_3 solution.
    2) The pH of a 0.10 M HF solution is greater than 1.00
    3) The pH of a 0.10 M HCl solution is less than the pH of a 0.20 M HCl solution.
    4) The pH of a 0.10 M NH_3 solution is greater than 13.00.
    5) More than one of the above statements are true.

21. Which of the following statements is true?
    1) A solution having a pH = 2.00 is five times more acidic than a solution having a pH = 10.00.
    2) A solution having a pH = 1.00 has two times $[H^+]$ as a solution having a pH = 2.00.
    3) The pOH of a 1.00×10^{-9} M LiOH solution is 9.00.
    4) A solution having pH = 6.00 is one-thousand times less basic than a solution having a pH = 9.00.
    5) More than one of the above statements are true.

MODULE 7 - Buffers

Common Ion Effect

1. The addition of NaF to an aqueous solution of HF will:
   1) decrease the pH of the solution.
   2) increase the pH of the solution.
   3) not affect the pH of the solution.
   4) increase the % ionization of HF.
   5) Two of the above choices are correct.

Buffer Problems (Weak Acid / Common Ion Salt and Weak Base / Common Ion Salt)

2. A solution composed of which of the following would act as a buffer.
   1) $HClO_4$ and $LiClO_4$
   2) $C_6H_5NH_2$ and $C_6H_5NH_3^+Cl^-$
   3) HBrO and NaOH
   4) Two of the above choices are correct.
   5) All of the above choices are correct.

3. What is the pH of a solution that is 0.10 M $HC_2H_3O_2$ ($K_a = 1.8 \times 10^{-5}$) and 0.30 M $NaC_2H_3O_2$?

   1) 4.87 2) 5.22 3) 4.74 4) 4.92 5) 5.06

4. What is the $[OH^-]$ (in M) of a solution that is 0.20 M NH_3 ($K_b = 1.8 \times 10^{-5}$) and 0.30 M $NH_4^+Cl^-$?

   1) 2.4×10^{-7} 2) 6.4×10^{-4} 3) 4.5×10^{-6} 4) 1.2×10^{-5} 5) 2.7×10^{-5}

5. Calculate the ratio of $[HC_2H_3O_2]/[NaC_2H_3O_2]$ that would yield a solution with a pH of 5.00. K_a ($HC_2H_3O_2$) = 1.8×10^{-5}

   1) 0.56 2) 0.63/1 3) 0.36 4) 0.44 5) 0.28

Consider the following information when answering questions 6 - 8.

Given that a buffer solution is 4.2 M $(CH_3)_3N$ ($K_b = 7.4 \times 10^{-5}$) and 2.7 M $(CH_3)_3NH^+Cl^-$, then:

6. What is the $[H^+]$ (in mol/L) in the buffer?

   1) 8.69×10^3 2) 3.94 3) 7.4×10^{-5} 4) 1.15×10^{-4} 5) 8.70×10^{-11}

7. If 120. mL of the buffer solution are mixed with 22. mL of 3.4 M NaOH, then what will be the resulting pH?

   1) 9.87 2) 9.97 3) 10.24 4) 10.06 5) 10.57

8. If 120. mL of the buffer solution are mixed with 25. mL of 3.0 M HCl, then what will be the resulting pH?

   1) 10.24 2) 9.50 3) 4.13 4) 9.90 5) 0.286

Consider the following information when answering questions 9 - 11.

A solution contains 3.6 M $C_6H_5COO\underline{H}$ ($K_a = 6.6 \times 10^{-5}$) and 2.4 M C_6H_5COOK.

9. What is the $[OH^-]$ (in molarity) in this solution?

   1) 4.4×10^{-5} 2) 2.3×10^{-10} 3) 1.5×10^{-2} 4) 1.0×10^{-10} 5) 9.9×10^{-5}

10. If 200. mL of the above solution are mixed with 13.0 mL of 3.60 M HBr, then what will be the resulting pH?

    1) 4.43 2) 4.00 3) 3.93 4) 3.82 5) 5.14

11. What is the pH after 0.200 mol of KOH are added to 500. mL of the above solution? Assume that there is no change in volume.

    1) 4.06 2) 3.89 3) 5.14 4) 4.24 5) 4.12

MODULE 8 - Hydrolysis (Salts Derived from Weak Acids and Bases)

1. Which of the following salts yields a neutral aqueous solution?
   1) CsI 2) $Ca(NO_3)_2$ 3) KF
   4) Two of the above.
   5) All of the above.

2. Which of the following aqueous salt solutions could not possibly have the pH (@ 25°C) that is indicated?
   1) KCN (pH = 6.48) 2) NaF (pH = 7.00) 3) $(CH_3)_3NH^+ I^-$ (pH = 8.16)
   4) Two of the above.
   5) All of the above.

3. Which response includes all of the following salts that hydrolyze to yield a solution whose pH > 7 at 25°C?
   a. $Fe(NO)_3$ b. $Ba(C_2H_3O_2)_2$ c. NaF d. NH_4NO_3 e. Li_2S
   1) b, e 2) b, c, e 3) d 4) a, c, e 5) c, e

4. The hydrolysis reaction that occurs when $NH_4^+Cl^-$ dissolves in water is:
   1) $NH_4^+Cl^- \xrightleftharpoons{\text{H-OH}} NH_4^+ + OH^- + Cl^+ + H^+$
   2) $Cl^- \xrightleftharpoons{\text{H-OH}} HCl + OH^-$
   3) $NH_4^+ \xrightleftharpoons{\text{H-OH}} NH_3 + H_3O^+$
   4) $NH_4^+ \xrightleftharpoons{\text{H-OH}} NH_5^+ + OH^-$
   5) $NH_4^+Cl^- \xrightleftharpoons{\text{H-OH}} NH_4^+ + Cl^-$

5. The hydrolysis reaction that occurs when $RbNO_2$ is placed in water is __________ and the pH of this solution would be _________.
   1) $RbNO_2 \xrightleftharpoons{\text{H-OH}} Rb^+ + OH^- + NO_2^- + H^+$; neutral
   2) $NO_2^- \xrightleftharpoons{\text{H-OH}} HNO_2 + OH^-$; basic
   3) $Rb^+ \xrightleftharpoons{\text{H-OH}} RbOH + H^+$; acidic
   4) $RbNO_2 \xrightleftharpoons{\text{H-OH}} Rb^+ + NO_2^-$; neutral
   5) This salt does not hydrolyze in water.

The following K_a's and K_b's will be useful in solving the following problems.

Substance	K_a	Substance	K_b
HCN	4.0×10^{-10}	NH_3	1.8×10^{-5}
HNO_2	4.5×10^{-4}	$(CH_3)_2NH$	7.4×10^{-4}
HClO	3.5×10^{-8}	C_5H_5N	1.5×10^{-9}

6. What is the base hydrolysis constant (K_b) for CN^-?

   1) 2.5×10^{-5} 2) 4.0×10^{-24} 3) 5.6×10^{-10} 4) 4.0×10^{-10} 5) 4.0×10^{4}

7. What is the acid hydrolysis constant for $(CH_3)_2NH_2^+$?

   1) 7.4×10^{-18} 2) 1.4×10^{-11} 3) 7.4×10^{10} 4) 7.4×10^{-4}
   5) It is undefined.

8. Which of the following hydrolyze to produce an <u>acidic</u> solution?

   1) $NH_4^+ ClO^-$ 2) $C_5H_5NH^+ CN^-$ 3) $(CH_3)_2NH_2^+ NO_2^-$
   4) Two of the above.
   5) None of the above.

9. Calculate the pOH of a 0.10 M KClO solution.

   1) 3.77 2) 1.00 3) 7.00 4) 5.92 5) 4.35

10. What is the pH of a 0.050 M $NH_4^+ I^-$ solution?

    1) 5.16 2) 4.62 3) 5.28 4) 4.84 5) 5.04

MODULE 9 - Acid-Base Titrations

1. How many mL of 0.4067 M NaOH are required to neutralize 1.673 g of CH_3COOH? (MM = 60.0, $K_a = 1.8 \times 10^{-5}$)

   1) 0.06856 2) 11.34 3) 26.37 4) 14.59 5) 68.56

2. What is the pH at the start of the titration of 45.00 mL of 0.3967 M LiOH with 0.4670 M HCl?

   1) 0.40 2) 13.60 3) 0.33 4) 13.67 5) 12.25

3. If 25.00 mL of 0.1005 M HNO_3 are titrated with 0.2010 M LiOH, then what is the pH after the addition of 12.50 mL of LiOH?

   1) 4.60 2) 5.70 3) 7.00 4) 10.10 5) 9.40

4. What is the pH at the equivalence point of the titration of 50.00 mL of 0.2311 M $HC_2H_3O_2$ ($K_a = 1.8 \times 10^{-5}$) with 0.2311 M KOH?

   1) 5.10 2) 5.60 3) 7.00 4) 8.90 5) 8.40

5. If 50.00 mL of 0.2311 M $HC_2H_3O_2$ ($K_a = 1.8 \times 10^{-5}$) are titrated with 0.2311 M CsOH, then what is the pH after the addition of 50.00 mL of CsOH?

   1) 5.10 2) 5.60 3) 7.00 4) 8.90 5) 8.40

6. What is the $[OH^-]$, in M, of a solution in which 22.00 mL of 0.3673 M NH_3 ($K_b = 1.8 \times 10^{-5}$) has been reacted with 13.67 mL of 0.2596 M HCl?

   1) 2.30×10^{-5} 2) 4.35×10^{-10} 3) 1.41×10^{-8} 4) 2.55×10^{-5} 5) 1.27×10^{-5}

7. What is the pH of a solution in which 50.00 mL of 0.1234 M HNO_2 ($K_a = 4.5 \times 10^{-8}$) has been titrated with 50.00 mL of 0.1399 M LiOH?

   1) 2.08 2) 11.92 3) 3.08 4) 10.92 5) 7.40

8. What is the pH of a solution resulting from the addition of 20.0 mL of 0.100 M NaOH to 30.0 mL of 0.100 M $HC_2H_3O_2$ ($K_a = 1.8 \times 10^{-5}$)?

   1) 4.88 2) 4.96 3) 5.05 4) 4.73 5) 4.56

9. What is the pH of a solution resulting from the addition of 15.0 mL of 0.250 M HBr to 25.0 mL of 0.150 M weak base (B:) whose base ionization constant is 3.00×10^{-5}?

   1) 7.00 2) 5.95 3) 5.43 4) 4.73 5) 5.25

10. What is the $[H^+]$, in M, of a solution resulting from the addition of 46.0 mL of 0.137 M LiOH with 47.0 mL of 0.137 M HI?

    1) 1.50×10^{-3} 2) 1.00×10^{-7} 3) 2.97×10^{-6} 4) 1.40×10^{-4} 5) 8.63×10^{-1}

11. In which of the following titrations is the pH at the equivalence point correctly identified?

    1) HClO + CsOH ($pH_{eq\ pt}$ - basic)
    2) NH_3 + HCl ($pH_{eq\ pt}$ - acidic)
    3) NaOH + $HClO_4$ ($pH_{eq\ pt}$ - basic)
    4) Two of the above choices.
    5) All of the above choices.

12. Which of the following titrations could the following curve describe?

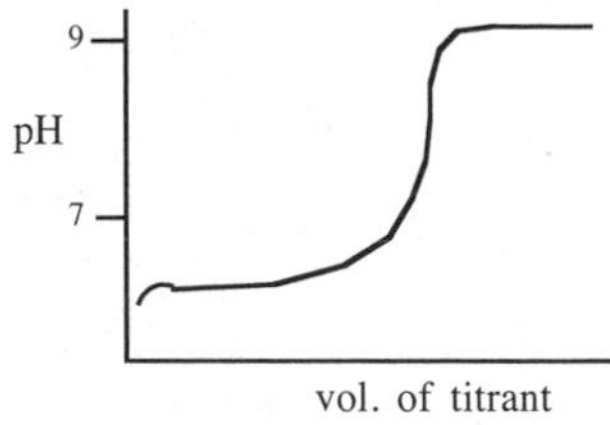

1) Titration of $HClO_2$ *with* KOH
2) Titration of HNO_3 *with* CsOH
3) Titration of $HC_2H_3O_2$ *with* NaOH
4) Two of the above choices.
5) All of the above choices.

Consider the following titration curve of HA with NaOH (titrant), as well as, the table of indicators when answering questions 13 - 17.

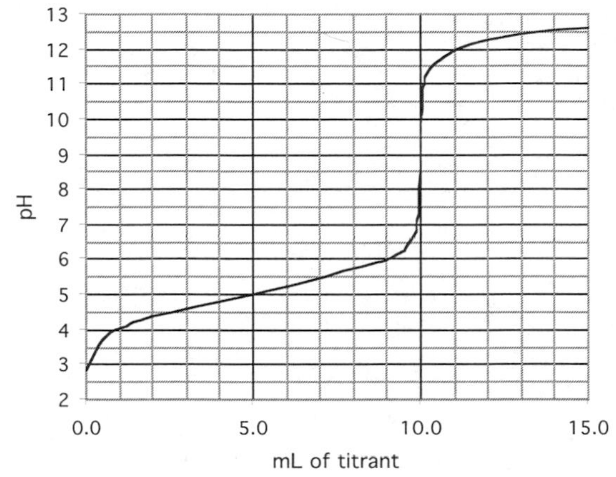

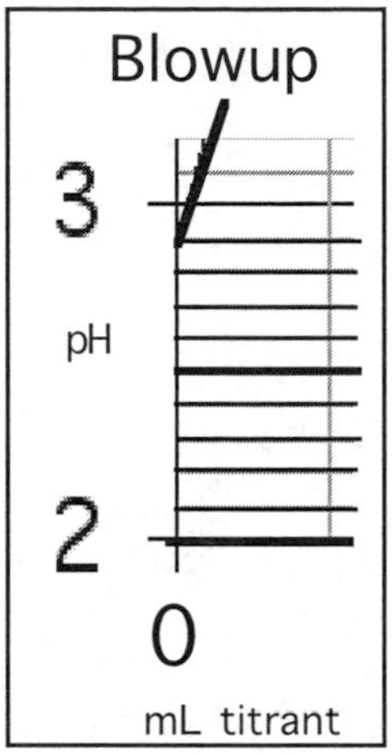

Indicator	Color In acid	Color In base	pH range*
methyl violet	yellow	blue	0.0 - 1.6
thymol blue‡	red	yellow	1.2 - 2.8
methyl orange	red	yellow	3.2 - 4.4
methyl red	red	yellow	4.2 - 6.3
bromocresol purple	yellow	purple	5.2 - 6.8
bromothymol blue	yellow	blue	6.2 - 7.6
litmus	red	blue	4.7 - 8.3
cresol red	yellow	red	7.0 - 8.8
thymol blue ‡	yellow	blue	8.0 - 9.6
phenolphthalein	colorless	pink	8.2 - 10.0
thymolphthalein	colorless	blue	9.4 - 10.6
alizarin yellow R	yellow	red	10.5 - 12.3

13. Which of the following best approximates what the pK_a of the acid, HA, being used in this titration is?
1) 3. 2) 7. 3) 4. 4) 5.
5) There is not enough information to be able to answer this question.

14. Which of the following statements is/are correct?
1) If thymolphthalein was used as an indicator, it would start to turn blue at the half-way point in the titration.
2) The approximate $[H^+]$ at the start of the titration is equal to 1.3×10^{-3} M.
3) The weak acid used in the titration could be HCN whose acid ionization constant is 4.9×10^{-10}.
4) Two of the above statements are correct.
5) None of the above statements are correct.

15. Which of the following best approximates what the pH after 10.0 mL of titrant have been added is?
1) 9. 2) 7. 3) 11. 4) 8. 5) 10.

16. Which of the following would be a suitable indicator to use?
1) cresol red 2) bromocresol purple 3) litmus
4) Two of the above. 5) None of the above.

17. Which of the following statements is/are **false** in regard to the titration curve of the weak acid H_2A with NaOH shown to your right?
A. Point D is where $[HA^-] = [A^{2-}]$.

B. An indicator whose pKa is10.2 would be a suitable indicator to signal when the second equivalence point has been reached.
C. At Point B and beyond of the titration, the $[H_2A]$ is equal to zero.
D. $K_{a1} \approx 4.1$
E. Point B is where the first equivalence point has been reached.
F. pK_{a2} $(H_2A) \approx 8.6$
G. Point A is where $[H_2A] = [HA^-]$.

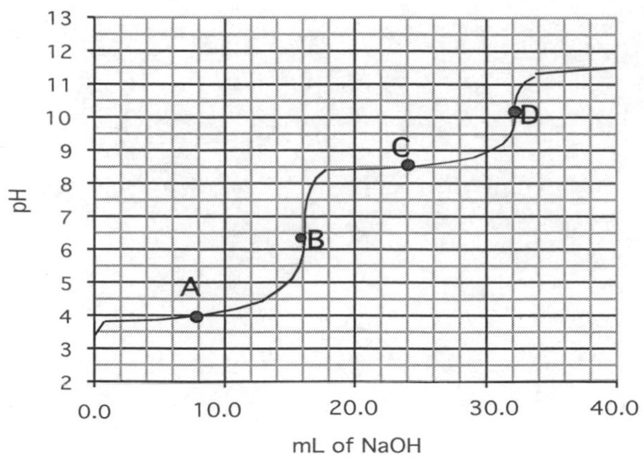

1) only D
2) only A and D
3) only D and G
4) only B and D
5) None of the above is false.

MODULE 10 - Solubility Product of Slightly Soluble and Insoluble Salts

K_{sp} and Water Solubility

1. Which of the following will be the most water soluble?
   1) $AgBrO_3$ ($K_{sp} = 9.3 \times 10^{-10}$) 2) $BaSO_4$ ($K_{sp} = 1.1 \times 10^{-10}$) 3) AgBr ($K_{sp} = 5.0 \times 10^{-13}$)
   4) $La(IO_3)_3$ ($K_{sp} = 6.4 \times 10^{-12}$) 5) Ag_2CO_3 ($K_{sp} = 8.1 \times 10^{-12}$)

Solubility Product and Solubility Calculations

2. The solubility product for $Ag_2C_2O_4$ is 1.10×10^{-11}. Given this information, what is its molar solubility?
   1) 2.22×10^{-4} 2) 1.10×10^{-11} 3) 1.66×10^{-6} 4) 1.40×10^{-4} 5) 3.32×10^{-6}

3. What is the maximum number of grams of $Cu(IO_3)_2$ ($K_{sp} = 1.44 \times 10^{-7}$, MM = 413.) that will dissolve in an aqueous solution whose volume is 205. mL?
   1) 0.279 2) 321 3) 0.0321 4) 0.388 5) 2.79×10^{-3}

4. Given that 8.30×10^{-3} g of $Ag_2Cr_2O_7$ (MM = 438.) dissolve in 100 mL of water, then what is its solubility product? (Assume that the total volume is 100. mL)
   1) 3.59×10^{-8} 2) 2.73×10^{-11} 3) 6.82×10^{-12} 4) 1.90×10^{-4} 5) 7.18×10^{-8}

5. Calculate the pH of a saturated aqueous solution of $Co(OH)_2$ ($K_{sp} = 2.5 \times 10^{-16}$).
   1) 8.60 2) 9.10 3) 8.90 4) 9.40 5) 9.20

6. What is the largest [Ca^{2+}] (in M) that will not cause precipitation of CaF_2 ($K_{sp} = 3.6 \times 10^{-11}$) in a solution that is 4.0×10^{-4} M NaF?
   1) 2.2×10^{-4} 2) 1.1×10^{-7} 3) 5.6×10^{-5} 4) 9.0×10^{-8} 5) 4.5×10^{-3}

Common Ion Effect in Solubility Predictions

7. In which of the following will $Mg(OH)_2$ ($K_{sp} = 1.5 \times 10^{-11}$) be the least soluble in?
   1) pure water 2) 0.015 M $Ba(OH)_2$ 3) 0.015 M $MgCl_2$
   4) 0.020 M $MgBr_2$ 5) In two of the above choices.

Relationship Between K_{sp} and Q_{sp} in Predicting Solubility

8. In which of the following is the outcome and explantation for the mixing of the following concentrations of [Ba^{2+}] with [F^-] correctly identified? K_{sp} (BaF_2) = 1.0×10^{-6}

	[Ba^{2+}]	[F^-]	Outcome	Explanation
1)	0.0250	0.0100	no precipitation occurs	$K_{sp} < Q_{sp}$
2)	0.0250	0.00633	solution is just saturated	$K_{sp} = Q_{sp}$
3)	0.0250	0.00525	solution is unsaturated	$K_{sp} > Q_{sp}$

   4) Two of the above outcomes and explanations are correct.
   5) None of the above outcomes are correct.

MODULE 11 - Electrochemistry

Electrolytic Cells

1. Which of the following statements is (are) correct about electrolytic cells?
   1) An electrolytic cell uses chemical energy to cause a spontaneous reaction to occur.
   2) The cathode is the positive electrode in an electrolytic cell.
   3) In an electrolytic cell the electrons travel from the cathode to the anode.
   4) Two of the above choices are correct.
   5) None of the above choices are correct.

2. Which of the following statements is/are true about the electrolysis of aqueous $MgBr_2$:
   1) The pH of the solution near the cathode will increase as the electrolysis reaction proceeds.
   2) Mg will form in the cathode.
   3) Mg^{2+} is getting reduced at anode.
   4) Br^- is getting reduced at the cathode.
   5) None of the above statements is correct.

3. The half-reaction that occurs at the anode in the electrolyis of molten NaBr is:
   1) $2\,H_2O + 2\,e^- \rightarrow H_2 + 2\,OH^-$
   2) $H_2O \rightarrow 2\,H^+ + \frac{1}{2}\,O_2 + 2\,e^-$
   3) $Br^- \rightarrow \frac{1}{2}\,Br_2 + e^-$
   4) $Na^+ + e^- \rightarrow Na$
   5) $Na \rightarrow Na^+ + e^-$

4. Which of the following is <u>not</u> a likely product that would be obtained during the electrolysis of aqueous $BaCl_2$?
   1) H_2
   2) Ba
   3) Cl_2
   4) Two of the above choices are correct.
   5) All of the above choices are correct.

5. Which of the following statements is (are) true about the electrolysis of aqueous $CuSO_4$?
   1) Cu plates onto the anode.
   2) The pH around the anode increases.
   3) O_2 is produced at the positive electrode.
   4) Two of the above choices are correct.
   5) None of the above choices are correct.

6. Which of the following is (are) **<u>false</u>** about the electrolytic cell to the right?

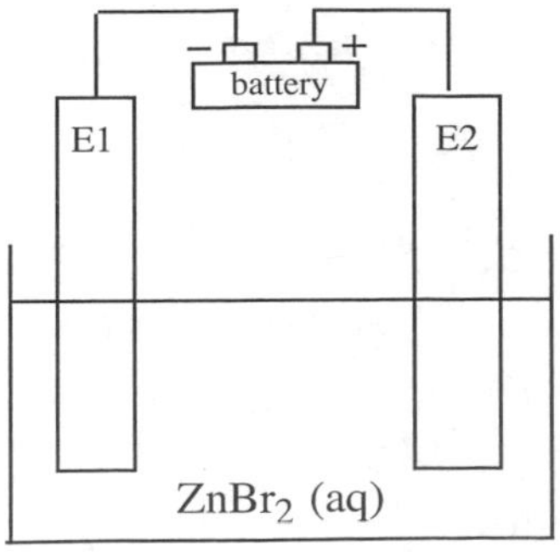

   1) The mass of the electrode labelled E1 will increase as metallic Zn plates onto it.
   2) E1 is the anode.
   3) As the bromide ion gets oxidized at the surface of the electrode labelled E2, it gets converted into molecular bromine.
   4) Electrons travel from the electrode labelled E2 to E1.
   5) More than one of the above statments is false.

Calculations Involving Electrolytic Reactions (Faraday's Law)

7. How many grams of metallic copper (MM = 63.5) can be obtained when a 2.00 A current is applied for 10 min to an aqueous $CuSO_4$ solution?

   1) 0.10 2) 0.18 3) 0.58 4) 0.79 5) 0.39

8. How many liters of chlorine gas could be theoretically obtained at STP during the electrolysis of molten NaCl if a current of 350 mA is applied for 100 min?

   1) 0.244 2) 0.487 3) 0.122 4) 487 5) 244

Voltaic (Galvanic) Cells

9. Which of the following statements is (are) true about a voltaic cell with the following cell notation?

   $$Cu \mid Cu^{2+}\ (1.0\ M) \parallel Au^{3+}\ (1.0\ M) \mid Au$$

   1) Gold(III) ions move toward the cathode to produce metallic gold.
   2) Oxidation of Cu^{2+} occurs at the anode.
   3) The copper anode is the positive electrode.
   4) Two of the above choices are correct.
   5) None of the above choices are correct.

10. The standard electrode potential for the following cell, $Mn \mid Mn^{2+}\ (1.0\ M) \parallel Fe^{3+}\ (1.0M) \mid Fe$, is 0.99 V. Knowing that the standard reduction potential for the half-reaction: $Mn^{2+} + 2\ e^- \rightarrow Mn$ is -1.03 V, then what is the standard reduction potential (in V) for the $Fe^{3+} + 3\ e^- \rightarrow Fe$ half reaction.

    1) -2.02 2) -0.10 3) 2.02 4) 0.04 5) -0.04

Use the following standard reduction potentials to answer questions 11 - 15.

	$\mathcal{E}°$ (volts)
$Ni^{2+} + 2\ e^- \rightarrow Ni$	**-0.25**
$Sn^{2+} + 2\ e^- \rightarrow Sn$	**-0.14**
$2\ H^+ + 2\ e^- \rightarrow H_2$	**0.00**
$Cu^{2+} + 2\ e^- \rightarrow Cu$	**0.337**
$Fe^{3+} + e^- \rightarrow Fe^{2+}$	**0.77**

11. Which of the following reactions *as written*, could be used to construct a voltaic cell under standard conditions?

    1) $Ni^{2+} + Sn \rightarrow Ni + Sn^{2+}$
    2) $2\ H^+ + 2\ Fe^{3+} \rightarrow H_2 + 2\ Fe^{2+}$
    3) $2\ H^+ + Cu \rightarrow H_2 + Cu^{2+}$
    4) $Cu^{2+} + Sn \rightarrow Cu + Sn^{2+}$
    5) Two of the above choices.

12. Which of the following is (are) true about the voltaic cell to the right?

    1) Sn is the negative electrode.
    2) Oxidation occurs at the Cu electrode.
    3) Electrons travel from the Sn cathode to the Cu anode.
    4) The Cu electrode starts to lose weight as the reaction progresses.
    5) None of the above choices.

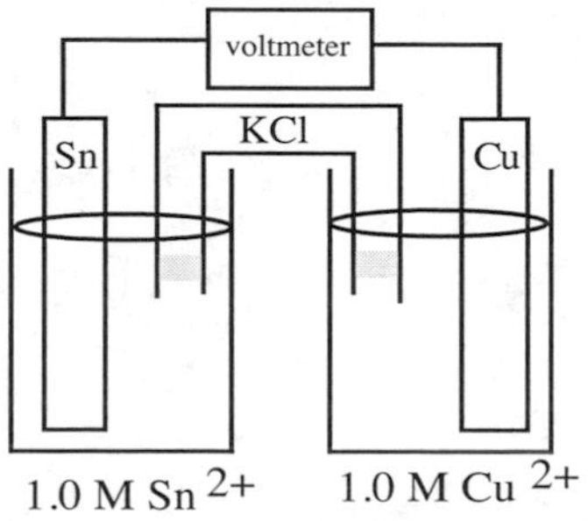

13. Which of the following is (are) true about the above voltaic cell diagram?
    1) K^+ moves into the Sn half-cell as the reaction progresses.
    2) The mass of the Sn in the Sn half-cell is increasing as the reaction progresses.
    3) The concentration of Cu^{2+} in the Cu half-cell increases as the reaction progresses.
    4) Two of the above statements are correct.
    5) None of the above statements are correct.

14. Which of the following is the correct reaction and standard cell voltage for the above voltaic cell diagram?
    1) $Cu + Sn \rightarrow Cu^{2+} + Sn^{2+}$ $\mathcal{E}° = 0.477$ V
    2) $Cu + Sn^{2+} \rightarrow Cu^{2+} + Sn$ $\mathcal{E}° = 0.477$ V
    3) $Cu^{2+} + Sn \rightarrow Cu + Sn^{2+}$ $\mathcal{E}° = 0.477$ V
    4) $Cu^{2+} + Sn \rightarrow Cu + Sn^{2+}$ $\mathcal{E}° = 0.197$ V
    5) $Cu + Sn^{2+} \rightarrow Cu^{2+} + Sn$ $\mathcal{E}° = 0.197$ V

Using Reduction Potentials to Predict Best Reducing or Oxidizing Agents

15. With the aid of the standard reduction potentials given in the previous page, which of the following would be the best reducing agent?
    1) Ni^{2+} 2) Sn 3) H_2 4) Fe^{3+} 5) Cu

Relationship Between Electrochemistry ($\mathcal{E}°$), Equilibrium (K), & Thermodynamics ($\Delta G°$)

16. What is $\Delta G°$ (in kcal) for a voltaic cell involving the following reaction?

$$2\,Fe^{3+} + 3\,Mn \rightarrow 2\,Fe + 3\,Mn^{2+} \qquad \mathcal{E}° = 0.99\text{ V}$$

    1) -137 2) 45.7 3) 114 4) 5.73×10^5 5) 23.1

17. What is the equilibrium constant (at 25°C) for the following reaction?

$$2\,Fe^{3+} + 3\,Mn \rightarrow 2\,Fe + 3\,Mn^{2+} \qquad \mathcal{E}° = 0.99\text{ V}$$

    1) 100 2) 10^{84} 3) 10^{100} 4) 2.00 5) 10^{2754}

The Nernst Equation

18. The galvanic cell, $Ni^{2+} + Zn \rightarrow Ni + Zn^{2+}$, has a standard cell potential of 0.51 V. What is the cell potential under the following conditions: $[Ni^{2+}] = 0.200$ M and $[Zn^{2+}] = 0.0300$ M?
    1) 0.53 2) 0.51 3) 0.49 4) 0.55 5) 0.47

19. Consider the following reduction potentials.

Reduction Half-Reaction	$\mathcal{E}°$ (volts)
$Mg^{2+} + 2\,e^- \rightarrow Mg$	-2.37
$Cr_2O_7^{2-} + 14H^+ + 6\,e^- \rightarrow 2Cr^{3+} + 7\,H_2O$	1.33

Calculate the potential (in V) for the following voltaic cell.

$$Mg \mid Mg^{2+}\ (0.49\text{ M}) \parallel Cr_2O_7^{2-}\ (2.6\text{ M}),\ Cr^{3+}\ (0.61\text{ M}),\ H^+\ (0.040\text{ M}) \mid Pt$$

    1) 3.10 2) 3.52 3) 3.70 4) 2.90 5) 3.90

MODULE 12 - Nuclear Chemistry

Radioactivity

1. Which of the following statements is/are true?

   a) An alpha particle, which has a positive charge, is the most penetrating type of nuclear radiation.

   b) A gamma ray has no mass and charge and as a consequence tends to travel a very short distance and thus is not very penetrating.

   c) A beta particle is an electron emitted from the nucleus of a radionuclide that is thought to be produced as a consequence of a neutron transforming itself into a proton and electron.

   d) A radionuclide that emits an alpha particle is emitting 2 protons and 2 neutrons from its nucleus which is analogous to a He nucleus being emitted from the radionuclide.

   e) A positron is expected to be emitted from the nucleus of an unstable nuclide if its $^{N}/_{Z} > 1.5$.

   1. only a and b 2. only c and d 3. only b and c 4. only d and e 5. only c

2. Which of the following would you expect to be radioactive?

   1. oxygen-20 2. U-235 3. ^{40}K 4. All of the isotopes listed.
   5. There is no way of predicting which isotopes would be radioactive.

3. Which of the following is/are true?

   1. $^{211}_{87}Fr$ is radioactive and in an attempt to stabilize itself it will emit an alpha particle.
   2. Gold-201 is expected to be radioactive and in attempt to stabilize itself it will either emit a positron or capture an electron close to its nucleus.
   3. Pb-210 is not expected to be radioactive.
   4. More than one of the above is true.
   5. None of the above is true.

4. *Once inside the body*, which of the following types of ionizing radiation is the most harmful?

   1. alpha particles 2. beta particles 3. gamma rays 4. All are equally harmful.

Nuclear Equations

5. Complete the following nuclear equation: $^{85}Br \rightarrow \beta^{-} + \gamma +$ ________

   1. ^{85}Kr 2. ^{86}Br 3. ^{81}As 4. ^{86}Kr 5. ^{86}Se

6. Who is the parent in the following nuclear reaction? ________ $\rightarrow$ $^{218}Rn + \alpha + \beta^{-} + \gamma$

   1. ^{222}Ac 2. ^{223}Ra 3. ^{222}Fr 4. ^{223}Fr 5. ^{220}Th

7. Which of the following is not a correctly balanced nuclear reaction?

   1. $^{24}Mg + {}^{4}He \rightarrow {}^{27}Al + {}^{1}H$ 2. $^{56}Mn + {}^{1}n \rightarrow {}^{55}Mn + {}^{2}H$
   3. $^{237}Pa + {}^{19}N \rightarrow {}^{250}Cf + 6\ {}^{1}n$ 4. Only two of the above.
   5. All of the above.

8. Boron-13 (Z = 5) is a beta and gamma emitter. Given this information, which of the following is/are true?

   1. The daughter is carbon. 2. The daughter has 6 protons.
   3. The daughter has 7 neutrons. 4. Only two of the above.
   5. All of the above.

9. ^{214}Bi (Z = 83) is an alpha, beta, and gamma emitter. Given this information, which of the following is/are true?
   1. The daughter is lead-210.
   2. The daughter has 83 protons.
   3. The daughter has 127 neutrons.
   4. Only two of the above.
   5. All of the above.

10. A radioactive isotope emits a beta particle while giving birth to an isotope having 29 protons and 37 neutrons. Given this information, which of the following is/are true?
    1. The parent radioactive isotope has an atomic number of 30.
    2. The parent radioactive isotope is zinc-66.
    3. The parent radioactive isotope has a mass number of 66.
    4. Only two of the above.
    5. All of the above.

11. Which of the following is an example of a transmutation?
    1. $^{131}I \rightarrow {}^{131}Xe + \beta^{-} + \gamma$
    2. $^{201m}Tl \rightarrow {}^{201}Tl + \gamma$
    3. $Na_3PO_4 + Ba(OH)_2 \rightarrow NaOH + Ba_3(PO_4)_2$
    4. Only two of the above.
    5. All of the above.

12. Which of the following provides an example of a nuclear fission reaction?
    1. $^{235}_{92}U + {}^{1}_{0}n \rightarrow {}^{140}_{56}Ba + {}^{93}_{36}Kr + 3\ {}^{1}_{0}n + ENERGY$
    2. $^{201m}Tl \rightarrow {}^{201}Tl + \gamma$
    3. $^{2}_{1}H + {}^{3}_{1}H \rightarrow {}^{4}_{2}He + {}^{1}_{0}n + ENERGY$
    4. Only two of the above.
    5. All of the above.

Half-Life Problems

13. If 20.0 mg of fresh iodine-131 ($t_{1/2}$ = 8 days) is administered to a patient, how many milligrams will be left in the body after 24 days? [Assume that none of the iodine escaped/left the body by other means.]
    1. 5.00 2. 1.25 3. 4.00 4. 2.50 5. 2.00

14. Phosphorus-32 ($t_{1/2}$ = 14 days) is used in the detection of eye tumors. How many half-lives will it take for 100 mg of sample to be reduced to 6.25 mg?
    1. 16 2. 3 3. 4 4. 56 5. 42

15. How many years will it take for $^{7}/_{8}$ of tritium (H-3, $t_{1/2}$ = 12.3 yr) to decay?
    1. 49.2 2. 36.9 3. 24.6 4. 98.4 5. 356

16. Initially there were 400 mg of radon-222 present. After 16 days 25 mg remained. Given this information, what is the half-life (in days) of radon-222?
    1. 4 2. 23.7 3. 5.3 4. 8 5. 1.2

17. 800 mg of a radioactive isotope ($t_{1/2}$ = 4 days) is needed for a patient study. If the time it takes for the hospital to receive a shipment of this radioisotope is 12 days, what is the minimum amount (in mg) of it that should be ordered?
    1. 12,800 2. 3,200 3. 6,400 4. 2,400 5. 9,600

Answers to Practice Final Exam

Question Number	Module 1	2	3	4	5	6	7	8	9	10	11	12
1	2	5	5	1	3	3	2	4	5	4	5	2
2	3	5	4	2	3	2	2	5	2	4	1	4
3	1	3	4	5	1	1	2	2	3	1	3	1
4	4	2	5	2	2	3	4	3	4	2	2	1
5	4	5	4	1	3	4	1	2	4	3	3	1
6	5	1	4	3	5	1	5	1	1	1	2	3
7	1	3	1	1	4	5	3	2	2	2	5	5
8	1	1	3	1	3	1	4	5	3	4	1	5
9	2	3	5	2	4	3	4	1	5		1	1
10	2	2	1	5	3	5	3	3	1		5	3
11	1	1	2	4	3	4	5		4		4	1
12	4	4	3	1	2	1			4		1	1
13	5	3	5	2	2	4			5		5	4
14	5	1	1	1		1			2		3	3
15	1	5	4	4		1			1		2	2
16	3	4	2	2		5			1		1	1
17	2	1	4	2		4			2		3	3
18		2	5	2		2					1	
19		1	3	2		3					2	
20				4		2						
21						4						

Constants, Conversions, Definitions, Formulas, Concepts and Equations that are Used in the Final Exam

Constants and Conversions

$$R = 0.0821 \frac{L \cdot atm}{mol \cdot K} = 1.99 \times 10^{-3} \frac{kcal}{mol \cdot K} = 1.99 \frac{cal}{mol \cdot K} = 8.31 \times 10^{-3} \frac{kJ}{mol \cdot K} = 8.31 \frac{J}{mol \cdot K}$$

$$F = 96{,}500 \frac{J}{mol\ e^- \cdot V} = 23.1 \frac{kcal}{mol\ e^- \cdot V}$$

1 mol electrons = 6.02×10^{23} electrons = 1 F = 96,500 C

$K_w = 1.0 \times 10^{-14}$ (@25°C) 1 cal = 4.184 J 1 mol gas @ STP = 22.4 L

Concentration Definitions

$$wt\ \% = \frac{g\ solute}{g\ soln} \times 100$$

$$M = \frac{mol\ solute}{L\ soln} = \frac{\left(\frac{g_{solute}}{MM_{solute}}\right)}{L_{soln}}$$

$$m = \frac{moles\ of\ solute}{kg\ of\ solvent} = \frac{\left(\frac{g_{solute}}{MM_{solute}}\right)}{kg_{solvent}}$$

$$X_A = \frac{moles\ of\ A}{moles\ A + moles\ B}$$

Module 1 - Equations

$$q = m \times s \times \Delta T$$

Module 2 - Equations

$$\Delta T_f = K_f m \qquad \Delta T_b = K_b m$$

$$P_A = X_A P^o_A \qquad P_{soln} = X_{solute} P^o_{solute} + X_{solvent} P^o_{solvent}$$

$$\Delta P_{solvent} = P^o_{solvent} - X_{solvent} P^o_{solvent}$$

$$\pi V = nRT \qquad \pi V = \left(\frac{g}{MM}\right) RT \qquad \pi = MRT$$

Module 3 - Equations

$$\Delta E = q + w \qquad \Delta H = \Delta E + P\Delta V = \Delta E + \Delta nRT$$

$$\Delta G = \Delta H - T\Delta S \qquad w = -P\Delta V = -(\Delta n)RT$$

Module 3 - Sign Conventions for q and w

	Sign	Process
heat (q)	+	heat absorbed by the system from the surroundings (endothermic process)
	-	heat released by the system to the surroundings (exothermic process)
work (w)	+	work done on the system by the surroundings
	-	work done by the system on the surroundings

Module 4 - Equations

$[A] = -kt + [A]_o$ $\ln[A] = -kt + \ln[A]_o$ $\frac{1}{[A]} = kt + \frac{1}{[A]_o}$

$t_{1/2} = \frac{[A]_o}{2k}$ $t_{1/2} = \frac{0.693}{k}$ $t_{1/2} = \frac{1}{k[A]_o}$

$k = A e^{-Ea/RT}$ $\ln\frac{k_2}{k_1} = \frac{E_a}{R}\left(\frac{1}{T_1} - \frac{1}{T_2}\right)$

Module 5 - Equations

$K_P = K_c(RT)^{\Delta n}$ $\left(R = 0.0821 \frac{L\cdot atm}{mol\cdot K}\right)$ $\Delta G = -RT\ln K$ $k = A e^{-E_a/RT}$

$\ln\frac{K_2}{K_1} = \frac{\Delta H^\circ}{R}\left(\frac{1}{T_1} - \frac{1}{T_2}\right)$

Module 6 - Definitions

$pH = -\log[H^+]$ $pOH = -\log[OH^-]$ $K_w = [H^+][OH^-]$

$\%\text{ ionization} = \frac{[H^+]_{equil}}{[Acid]_i} \times 100$ $\%\text{ ionization} = \frac{[OH^-]_{equil}}{[Base]_i} \times 100$

Module 7 - Formulas

Weak Acid Buffer Formula

$[H^+] = \frac{a}{s} K_a$

where $a = [HA]$ or mol HA
$s = [A^-]$ or mol A^-

Weak Base Buffer Formula

$[OH^-] = \frac{b}{s} K_b$

where $b = [B:]$ or mol B:
$s = [BH^+]$ or mol BH^+

NOTE: $[A^-]$ = [salt] and $[BH^+]$ = [salt] in cases where there is a 1 :1 mole ratio between A^- and a salt derived from A^- or BH^+ and a salt derived from BH^+.

Module 8 - Definitions

$K_w = K_a K_b$

Module 9 - Equations

$eq = N \times V = (n \times M) \times V = \frac{g}{EW}$ $EW = \frac{MM}{n}$

Module 11 - Equations

$\Delta G^\circ = -nF\mathcal{E}^\circ$ $\mathcal{E}^\circ = \frac{0.0592}{n}\log K$ $\mathcal{E} = \mathcal{E}^\circ - \frac{0.0592}{n}\log Q$

Module 11 - Electrolysis of Aqueous Salt Solutions

- *In an aqueous salt solution, there are two possibilities for reduction at the cathode:*

a) $M^{n+} + n e^- \rightarrow M$ (All metal ions get reduced except: IA^+, IIA^{2+}, or Al^{3+})

b) $2 H_2O + 2 e^- \rightarrow H_2 + 2 OH^-$ (If metal ion is IA^+, IIA^{2+}, or Al^{3+}, then water gets reduced)

- *In an aqueous salt solution, there are two possibilities for oxidation at the anode:*

a) $X^- \rightarrow \frac{1}{2}\ X_2 + e^-$ (Of the common anions only Cl^-, Br^-, or I^- get oxidized)

b) $H_2O \rightarrow 2\ H^+ + \frac{1}{2}\ O_2 + 2\ e^-$ (If anion is <u>not</u> Cl^-, Br^-, or I^-, then water gets oxidized)

Module 12 - Definitions

alpha	beta	positron	gamma
α *or* ${}^{4}_{2}\alpha$ *or* $\left[{}^{4}_{2}He^{2+}\right]$	β^+ *or* ${}^{0}_{+1}\beta^+$ *or* $\left[{}^{0}_{+1}e^+\right]$	β^+ *or* ${}^{0}_{+1}\beta^+$ *or* $\left[{}^{0}_{+1}e^+\right]$	γ *or* ${}^{0}_{0}\gamma$

Module 12 - Equations

$$\frac{[R]}{[R]_o} = \frac{1}{2^n}$$

$$n = \frac{t}{t_{1/2}}$$

n = # of half-lives that have elapsed

$\frac{[R]}{[R]_o}$ } fraction of radionuclide (i.e., parent) that remains